DIFFERENTIAL

EQUATIONS

MAX MORRIS *and* **ORLEY E. BROWN**

Professors of Mathematics
Case Institute of Technology

Third Edition

PRENTICE-HALL INCORPORATED · NEW YORK

1952

Preface to Third Edition

THE PRESENT revision embodies the experience that resulted from our own use of the book. No less important were the friendly and helpful suggestions that came to us from other users of the book. To all of these we extend our thanks.

As to the revision itself, our aim was, while retaining the general organization and scope, to simplify the exposition, to omit a topic here and there where the omission would make the text more readable, and to insert such items as we believed should have been originally present in the book.

The introduction of the lineal element at the beginning of the course, as well as of a couple of interesting types of equations in Chapter IV, should be welcome.

Chapter III has been recast considerably, while Chapter V has undergone a most thoroughgoing revision. The troublesome cases in solution in series have been greatly simplified in Chapter VI, while the treatment of the Laplace Equation, later in the book, has been enlarged. Throughout, the problems have been improved in character as well as in number, particularly those of an applied nature dealing with geometry, mechanics, and electric circuits.

M. M.
O. E. B.

Preface to Revised Edition

IN REVISING this book, the authors have dealt lightly with the text, except where the interests of clarity or elegance have dictated a modification. Such is the case with the chapter on Linear Differential Equations, which has been considerably recast. Elsewhere, the text has been altered only occasionally and sparingly.

The main feature of the revised edition is an improved and augmented list of problems. Particularly, a void has been filled in the matter of problems exploiting the use of initial conditions.

A section has been added to treat the Laplace Equation, with exercises to follow it. Also the chapter on Numerical Approximation has been enlarged by the inclusion of the Runge-Kutta method and Milne's method.

In the interest of completeness, brief tables of integrals and natural logarithms have been appended to the book.

M. M.
O. E. B.

Preface to First Edition

THE course in Differential Equations for which this text has been prepared is given, as a rule, in our colleges and engineering schools, to a class of student who brings to it the background of only a first year course in the Calculus. The teacher must make his terms with the limitations imposed by that background, implying as it does that the student has mastered only the merely manipulative aspects of the Calculus. Under such conditions, a searching and serious study of the more theoretical aspects of the subject of Differential Equations must of necessity be left in abeyance. On the other hand, the opportunity, as the subject is developed, for implanting in the student something like a feeling for mathematical rigor, presents itself frequently enough—and should be improved when met with. A course in which a generous amount of drill in integrating the various standard types of differential equations is accompanied by an exposure of the student, on as wide a front as possible, to the more exacting and searching aspects of mathematics, is a desideratum with every teacher of the subject.

This text has been prepared with the aim of assisting the teacher to come measurably near that end.

In the first place, the exercise material has been chosen with the greatest care. The exercises are numerous—generously so. The teacher will be pleased to find exercises in sufficient abundance to enable him to assign separate problems to individual students or groups of students, and also to enable him to select material for examinations, if desired, or for use in succeeding semesters.

The exercises have far more to commend them, however, than mere profusion. The authors have built them up carefully, all the way from those that serve no more than to illustrate a definite formula or a specific method, to such as lead the student on to something like independent study and criticism. Throughout, the text has been restricted to only as much as must be included, consistent with clearness and completeness, in the way of definition, proof, or discussion. Further treatment and elaboration of the subject matter has been relegated to the exercises, which have been supplemented with adequate hints where necessary.

A student cannot be led very far into the subject of Differential Equations, or indeed into any serious doctrine in mathematics, without being confronted with certain central ideas, such as linear dependence, functional dependence, the notion of the rank of a matrix, and so forth. Where germane to the subject of the text, such notions are introduced by an adequate treatment, though this treatment is not developed to such length as to become a digression. By this means, statements which would otherwise be loose, or even incorrect, are replaced with statements that are both precise and correct and the opportunities alluded to above are used to advantage.

The so-called applications—*i. e.*, the portrayal, by differential equations, of definite states of affairs that arise in Geometry, Mechanics, Engineering, and so forth—are numerous throughout the book. Care has been taken, in presenting such problems, to avoid a blunt statement of the equation, accompanied merely by an explanation of the terms involved; instead, an attempt has consistently been made to state briefly but adequately the background of the problem. Thus presented, each problem becomes indeed what it purports to be—an "application," and not just another manipulative exercise.

So far as possible, references have been restricted to two books which are very generally available, *viz.*, Wilson's "Advanced Calculus" and Dickson's "First Course in the Theory of Equations."

The authors are under obligation, for helpful criticism and suggestions, to various members of the mathematical staff at Case School. A particular debt of gratitude is due to Professor Wood of Northwestern University, who carefully read a considerable portion of the manuscript, and whose criticism was highly beneficial. Needless to say, the responsibility for such faults as the book may be found to possess is solely the authors'.

We also wish to acknowledge the unfailing courtesy and coöperation accorded us by our publishers.

M. M.
O. E. B.

Table of Contents

PAGE

PREFACE TO THIRD EDITION................................. iii

PREFACE TO REVISED EDITION iv

PREFACE TO FIRST EDITION................................ v

CHAPTER
I. INTRODUCTION...................................... 1
    1. Definitions.. 1
    2. The point and the lineal element..................... 3
    3. Solutions of a differential equation.................. 5
    4. Primitives.. 6
    5. The general solution............................... 10
    6. Equations of higher order.......................... 14
    7. Miscellaneous exericises on Chapter I............... 15

II. DIFFERENTIAL EQUATIONS OF THE FIRST ORDER AND
    FIRST DEGREE................................. 21
    8. Variables separable................................ 21
    9. Exact differential equations........................ 23
    10. Integrating factors................................. 26
    11. Homogeneous equations............................ 30
    12. Equations reducible to homogeneous equations........ 34
    13. Linear equations of the first order.................. 36
    14. Equations reducible to linear equations.............. 38
    15. Riccati equation................................... 40
    16. Applications of differential equations................ 43
    17. Miscellaneous exercises on Chapter II............... 52

III. EQUATIONS OF THE FIRST ORDER, BUT NOT OF THE FIRST
    DEGREE....................................... 57
    18. Introduction....................................... 57
    19. Singular solutions.................................. 57
    20. Equations solvable for p or y....................... 60
    21. Clairaut's equation................................ 63
    22. Equations solvable for x........................... 63

IV. LINEAR DIFFERENTIAL EQUATIONS.................... 69
    23. Introduction....................................... 69
    24. Homogeneous, with constant coefficients.............. 69
    25. Real and distinct roots............................. 70

CHAPTER   PAGE
    26. Complex roots.. 75
    27. Repeated roots... 77
    28. Right-hand side not zero............................... 80
    29. Method of operators.................................... 86
    30. Method of variation of parameters..................... 90
    31. The linear equation with variable coefficients........ 93
    32. Cauchy's linear equation.............................. 94
    33. Exact linear equations................................ 96
    34. One variable absent................................... 100
    35. Simultaneous linear equations......................... 101
    36. Miscellaneous exercises on Chapter IV................. 110

  V. NUMERICAL APPROXIMATION TO SOLUTIONS............. 124

    37. Taylor's series.. 124
    38. Picard's method....................................... 125
    39. Milne's method.. 129
    40. Milne's method extended............................... 134
    41. Starting the solution................................. 135
    42. Halving the interval.................................. 140

 VI. INTEGRATION IN SERIES............................. 143

    43. Equations of the first order.......................... 143
    44. Linear equations of the second order.................. 147
    45. Roots of indicial equation equal...................... 153
    46. A coefficient in the series becoming infinite......... 154
    47. The particular integral............................... 156
    48. The Legendre equation................................. 159
    49. The Bessel equation................................... 166
    50. The Gauss equation.................................... 173
    51. Miscellaneous exercises on Chapter VI................. 177

VII. ORDINARY DIFFERENTIAL EQUATIONS IN MORE THAN
     TWO VARIABLES................................... 180

    52. Total differential equations; introductory remarks.... 180
    53. Condition for exactness............................... 181
    54. Conditions for integrability.......................... 182
    55. Total differential equations which are integrable..... 183
    56. Geometric significance................................ 187
    57. Pairs of total differential equations................. 187
    58. Solutions of a pair of total differential equations in three
        variables.. 188
    59. Non-integrable equations.............................. 195
    60. Dependence and functional determinants................ 196
    61. Determinate systems involving several variables....... 198
    62. Jacobi's multipliers.................................. 201
    63. Indeterminate systems................................. 206
    64. Exercises... 207

CHAPTER   PAGE

VIII. PARTIAL DIFFERENTIAL EQUATIONS OF THE FIRST ORDER 210

    65. Illustrations and definitions.......................... 210
    66. Lagrange's equations................................ 212
    67. Functions of several variables....................... 216
    68. Lagrange's equations; case of $n + 1$ variables........ 218
    69. Equations not of the first degree; Charpit's method.... 219
    70. Equations involving several variables; Jacobi's method 225

IX. LINEAR PARTIAL DIFFERENTIAL EQUATIONS WITH CONSTANT COEFFICIENTS........................... 231

    71. Homogeneous linear equations with constant coefficients 231
    72. Case of complex roots.............................. 233
    73. Case of multiple roots.............................. 234
    74. Right-hand member not zero......................... 237
    75. Special cases....................................... 237
    76. Inverse operators; factoring......................... 239
    77. Partial fractions.................................... 241
    78. Case of α_i not all different from zero................. 243
    79. Non-homogeneous equations........................ 245
    80. Right-hand member zero............................ 245
    81. Particular integrals................................. 246
    82. Other forms of $f(D_1, D_2)$............................ 249
    83. Equations reducible to linear equations with constant coefficients....................................... 250
    84. Laplace's equation.................................. 251

X. PARTIAL DIFFERENTIAL EQUATIONS OF ORDER TWO.... 259

    85. Introduction....................................... 259
    86. Intermediate integrals of a second order differential equation.. 260
    87. Monge's method for $Rr + Ss + Tt = V$.............. 261
    88. Integrability of $dz = p\,dx + q\,dy$.................... 264
    89. Monge's method for $Rr + Ss + Tt + U(rt - s)^2 = V$ 266
    90. Laplace's transformation............................ 275

TABLE OF INTEGRALS...................................... 281

TABLE OF NATURAL LOGARITHMS.......................... 289

ANSWERS TO EXERCISES................................... 293

INDEX... 339

CHAPTER I

Introduction

1. Definitions. Let a curve be defined by the property that the slope of the tangent at any of its points equals the sum of the coördinates at that point. The student will readily express this property by the equation

$$\frac{dy}{dx} = x + y, \tag{1}$$

where x and y have the usual meaning of abscissa and ordinate, respectively.

Again, let the motion of a particle on a straight line be defined by the condition that the acceleration of the particle at any instant exceeds its velocity at that instant by a quantity equal to the displacement. If we denote the displacement and time by s and t, respectively, the condition is embodied in the equation

$$\frac{d^2s}{dt^2} - \frac{ds}{dt} = s. \tag{2}$$

Relations (1) and (2) are examples of equations which involve derivatives (or differentials), and which are, on that account, called *differential equations*. It is readily seen that such equations will arise in a great variety of problems in geometry, mechanics, and elsewhere.

We now lay down the following:

DEFINITION. *A differential equation of order* n *is one that involves a derivative of order* n *and none of higher order.*

Thus, (1) is of the first order, and (2) is of the second. We distinguish differential equations, as to their *degree*, in the light of the following:

DEFINITION. *The degree of a differential equation is the degree to which the highest ordered derivative enters into the equation, after it has been made rational and integral in all the derivatives.*

1

Thus, (1) and (2) are both of the first degree, while

$$\left(\frac{d^2y}{dx^2}\right)^2 + 3\left(\frac{dy}{dx}\right)^3 - x = 0$$

is of the second, as is also

$$\frac{d^2y}{dx^2} = \sqrt{1 + \frac{dy}{dx}},$$

which, when rationalized, becomes

$$\left(\frac{d^2y}{dx^2}\right)^2 = 1 + \frac{dy}{dx}.$$

Lastly, we shall classify differential equations as *ordinary* or *partial* by means of the following:

DEFINITION. *If an equation involves more than one independent variable, and partial derivatives with respect to one or more of the independent variables, it is said to be partial; otherwise, ordinary.*

Hence, all the equations displayed above are ordinary, while

$$\frac{\partial^2 z}{\partial x^2} + \frac{\partial^2 z}{\partial y^2} = xy$$

is partial (of order two and degree one).

Exercises

Classify the following into ordinary and partial differential equations; also name the order and degree of each:

1. $x^2 \dfrac{dy}{dx} + \left(\dfrac{dy}{dx}\right)^2 = 0.$

2. $\dfrac{\partial z}{\partial y} + x \dfrac{\partial z}{\partial x} = y.$

3. $\dfrac{d^2y}{dx^2} = 3x \left[1 + \left(\dfrac{dy}{dx}\right)^2\right]^{3/2}.$

4. $\dfrac{d^3y}{dx^3} + \dfrac{2y}{\dfrac{d^3y}{dx^3}} = 2x.$

5. $\dfrac{\partial^4 z}{\partial x^4} - \left(\dfrac{\partial^2 z}{\partial x \partial y}\right)^2 = 0.$

6. $y \dfrac{d^2y}{dx^2} - x \dfrac{dy}{dx} = \sqrt{x}.$

7.* $e^{\frac{d^2y}{dx^2}} = x \dfrac{dy}{dx}.$

8. $\log\left(\dfrac{dy}{dx}\right) + \log x^2 = 2y.$

9. $x^2 \dfrac{d^2y}{dx^2} - x \dfrac{dy}{dx} + y = 3x^3.$

---

* Note that the idea of degree is not applicable to this equation, inasmuch as a derivative enters exponentially.

2. The point and the lineal element.   A first order equation has been defined as one of the form $f(x, y, y') = 0$.   If such an equation is solved for y', it yields one or more equations of the form

$$y' = F(x, y). \tag{3}$$

If we interpret x and y as the rectangular coordinates of a point and y' as a slope, we obtain, from Equation (3), a direction corresponding to each point (x, y) for which the function $F(x, y)$ is defined.

Thus, a differential equation like (3) gives an intuitive picture. The picture extends throughout the region R at each point of which the function $F(x, y)$ is defined.   In it we see the region R filled up with points, and at each point there is a piece of straight line or lineal element.   Upon this picture as a background we visualize the integral curves of (3).

DEFINITION.   *An integral curve of* (3) *is so constructed that at each of its points the tangent line has the direction called for by* (3) *at that point.*

The solution of a differential equation may be stated as the problem of finding its integral curves.

Table 1

y \ x	-3	-2	-1	0	1	2	3
3	-1	$-\frac{2}{3}$	$-\frac{1}{3}$	0	$\frac{1}{3}$	$\frac{2}{3}$	1
2	$-\frac{3}{2}$	-1	$-\frac{1}{2}$	0	$\frac{1}{2}$	1	$\frac{3}{2}$
1	-3	-2	-1	0	1	2	3
0	∞	∞	∞		∞	∞	∞
-1	3	2	1	0	-1	-2	-3
-2	$\frac{3}{2}$	1	$\frac{1}{2}$	0	$-\frac{1}{2}$	-1	$-\frac{3}{2}$
-3	1	$\frac{2}{3}$	$\frac{1}{3}$	0	$-\frac{1}{3}$	$-\frac{2}{3}$	-1

Example: Let us examine the differential equation

$$y' = \frac{x}{y}.$$

If we assign to each of x and y the seven values -3, -2, -1, 0, 1, 2, and 3 and compute y', we obtain the values listed in Table 1. It is to be noticed that there is no value determined for y' corresponding to $(0, 0)$. If we plot the 49 points and draw the

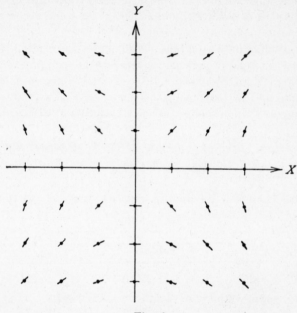

Fig. 1.

lineal elements for the 48 at which they are determined, we obtain Figure 1. The figure suggests two straight lines through the origin, *viz.*, $y = x$ and $y = -x$ and other integral curves apparently asymptotic to those lines. This leads us to try the equation $y^2 - x^2 = c$ as a possible solution. Verification that these equations do actually satisfy is left to the student.

Exercises

For each of the following differential equations, make up a table of values of x and y and compute the corresponding values of y'. Plot the points and draw the lineal elements. By observation of these points and lineal elements, write down a possible form for the equation of the integral curves. Finally, determine by differentiation and substitution whether or not the equations found by inspection do actually satisfy the given differential equation.

1. $\dfrac{dy}{dx} = \dfrac{y}{x},$

2. $\dfrac{dy}{dx} = -\dfrac{x}{y}.$

3. $\dfrac{dy}{dx} = \dfrac{y-2}{x+3},$

4. $\dfrac{dy}{dx} = -\dfrac{x-1}{y-2}.$

3. Solutions of a differential equation. By a *solution* of a differential equation is meant a relation between the variables involved, free of derivatives and satisfying the equation identically. In other words,

$$f(x, y, y', y'', \cdots) = 0*$$

is said to have

$$y = g(x)$$

as a solution if

$$f[x, g(x), g'(x), g''(x), \cdots] \equiv 0\dagger$$

For example,

$$y'(x + 3x^2) - y(1 + 6x) = 0$$

has as a solution

$$y = 2x + 6x^2,$$

for, when y and y' are substituted from the latter, the former becomes

$$(2 + 12x)(x + 3x^2) - (2x + 6x^2)(1 + 6x) \equiv 0.$$

In like manner, the partial differential equation

$$F[x, y, z, z_x, z_y, z_{xx}, \cdots] = 0$$

is said to have

$$z = h(x, y)$$

as a solution if

$$F[x, y, h(x, y), h_x(x, y), h_y(x, y), h_{xx}(x, y), \cdots] \equiv 0.$$

---

* We shall use freely the notation y', y'', $\cdots$ for $\dfrac{dy}{dx}$, $\dfrac{d^2y}{dx^2}$, $\cdots$, as well as $z_x, z_y, z_{xx}, z_{xy}, \cdots$ for $\dfrac{\partial z}{\partial x}, \dfrac{\partial z}{\partial y}, \dfrac{\partial^2 z}{\partial x^2}, \dfrac{\partial^2 z}{\partial y \partial x}, \cdots$.

† The notation $f(x) \equiv g(x)$ signifies that $f(x) = g(x)$ for every value of x for which f and g are defined, and it is read: "$f(x)$ equals $g(x)$, identically." The above, then, is read:

"$f[x, g(x), g'(x), g''(x), \cdots]$ equals zero, identically."

Thus,

$$z = 4x^2 + 3y$$

is a solution of

$$z - \tfrac{1}{2}x^2 z_{xx} - y z_y = 0,$$

for, when z, z_{xx}, and z_y are substituted from the former, the latter becomes

$$4x^2 + 3y - 4x^2 - 3y \equiv 0.$$

Exercises

Verify that the following are solutions of the corresponding differential equations.

1. $y = x + 3x^2$; $y'(x + 3x^2) - y(1 + 6x) = 0$.

2. $y = 0$; $y'(x + 3x^2) - y(1 + 6x) = 0$.

3.* $y = cx + 3cx^2$; $y'(x + 3x^2) - y(1 + 6x) = 0$.

4. $x^2 + y^2 = 5$; $yy' = -x$.

5.* $x^2 + y^2 = c$; $yy' = -x$.

6. $z = 3x^2 - y$; $z - \tfrac{1}{2}x^2 z_{xx} - y z_y = 0$.

7.† $z = ax^2 + by$; $z - \tfrac{1}{2}x^2 z_{xx} - y z_y = 0$.

8.† $y + ae^x + bx^2 = 0$; $y''(x^2 - 2x) + y'(2 - x^2)$
$$+ 2y(x - 1) = 0.$$

9.† $y = a \sin 2x + b \cos 2x$; $y'' + 4y = 0$.

10. $z = 2x^3 - xy$; $2xyz_{xy} + xz_x = 3z$.

11. $z = ax^3 + bxy$; $2xyz_{xy} + xz_x = 3z$.

12. $y = 1 + \dfrac{2}{x^2}$; $x^3 \dfrac{d^3y}{dx^3} + 2x^2 \dfrac{d^2y}{dx^2} - 6x \dfrac{dy}{dx} = 0$.

13.‡ $x^2 y - x + y \cos z - z^2 = c$; $(2xy - 1)\,dx$
$$+ (x^2 + \cos z)\,dy - (y \sin z + 2z)\,dz = 0.$$

4. Primitives. Let us now consider the following problem: to find the differential equation satisfied by all relations of the form

$$y = cx^2 + x, \tag{4}$$

---

* Where c is any constant.

† Where a and b are any constants.

‡ This is a so-called *total differential equation*. The term will be defined later.

where c is an arbitrary constant. By that we shall mean the differential equation of the lowest order satisfied by every one of the relations (4), regardless of the value assigned to c. If we differentiate (4), we obtain

$$y' = 2cx + 1, \tag{5}$$

a differential equation obviously satisfied by (4). But (5) is not yet the equation we set out to find, for it is satisfied by (4) only if the same value of c is employed in (4) and (5) [thus, $y = 4x^2 + x$ is not a solution of (5) unless we set $c = 4$ in (5)]. To obtain an equation free of c and satisfied by (4) identically for every c, we eliminate c between (4) and (5), say as follows:

$$c = \frac{y' - 1}{2x}$$

by (5), hence, by (4),

$$y = \frac{x^2(y' - 1)}{2x} + x,$$

or

$$y'x - 2y + x = 0. \tag{6}$$

From the mode of its derivation, (6) is satisfied by (4) for every c and is the equation we proposed to find.

More generally, if we set out with a relation of the form

$$f(x, y, c) = 0, \tag{7}$$

where c is an arbitrary constant, and propose the problem of forming the differential equation of the lowest order having (7) for its solutions, regardless of the value assigned to c, we differentiate (7), obtaining an equation which involves y' and which is certainly satisfied by (7). If that relation is free of c,* it is the differential equation desired; if it is not free of c, we eliminate c between it and (7), obtaining an equation of the form

$$F(x, y, y') = 0, \tag{8}$$

which is the equation we proposed to find.

We speak of (7) as the *primitive* of (8), and it is seen that a primitive involving one arbitrary constant gives rise to a differential equation of the first order.

---

* Thus, (A) $y = 2x^2 + c$ leads to the equation (B) $y' = 4x$, and (B) is the differential equation of lowest order satisfied by every relation (A), with c any constant whatsoever.

If, next, our problem should be to build the differential equation having

$$f(x, y, c_1, c_2) = 0 \tag{9}$$

for its primitive—*i. e.*, the differential equation of lowest order satisfied by every one of the relations (9), and free of c_1 and c_2—our procedure clearly would be to differentiate (9) twice in succession, and then to eliminate c_1 and c_2 between (9) and the two derived equations. This procedure would yield a differential equation of type

$$F(x, y, y', y'') = 0. \tag{10}$$

On account of the mode of its formation, (10) is clearly satisfied by (9), independently of the particular values assigned to c_1 and c_2 (since (10) is free of c_1 and c_2).

The elimination of c_1 and c_2 demanded three equations, and thus two successive differentiations of (9) were necessary. Hence, a primitive involving two arbitrary constants gives rise to a differential equation of the second order.

Illustration

Given

$$c_1 y + c_2 x - xy = 0 \tag{11}$$

as a primitive of a proposed differential equation, we adjoin to (11)

$$c_1 y' + c_2 - xy' - y = 0 \tag{12}$$

and

$$c_1 y'' - xy'' - 2y' = 0, \tag{13}$$

where (12) is the result of differentiating (11), and (13) the result of differentiating (12). The elimination of c_1 and c_2 may now be done, say, as follows. By (13),

$$c_1 = \frac{xy'' + 2y'}{y''};$$

hence, by (12),

$$c_2 = xy' + y - c_1 y' = xy' + y - \frac{xy'y'' + 2y'^2}{y''} = \frac{yy'' - 2y'^2}{y''}$$

Now (11) becomes

$$\frac{xyy'' + 2yy'}{y''} + \frac{xyy'' - 2xy'^2}{y''} - xy = 0,$$

or

$$xyy'' - 2xy'^2 + 2yy' = 0, \qquad (14)$$

which last is the differential equation having (11) for its primitive.*

It will be easy for the student to extend the argument to the case of a primitive involving n arbitrary constants, and to conclude that the differential equation of lowest order, free of those constants and satisfied by the given primitive for all values whatsoever of the arbitrary constants, will be of order n.

Exercises

1. In each of the following, form the differential equation having the given primitive:

(a) $y = x + cx^2$.

(b) $cx + 2cy = y$.

(c) $c^2 - cx = y$.

(d) $c_1 x + y = c_2$.

(e) $c_1 x^2 + c_2 y = x$.

(f) $c_1 y - x = c_2 xy$.

(g) $y = c_1 e^x + c_2 x e^x$.

(h) $y = c_1 \sin ax + c_2 \cos ax$, where a is a fixed constant.

(i) $y = e^x(c_2 \cos x + c_3 \sin x)$ $+ c_1 + \dfrac{x}{4}$

(j) $y = c_1 + c_2 e^x + c_3 x e^x + x^2$.

2. Form the differential equation representing all circles whose centers are at the origin. *Hint:* The differential equation is that having for its primitive $x^2 + y^2 = c^2$, where c is an arbitrary constant.

3. Form the differential equation representing all parabolas with vertices at the origin and foci on the x-axis.

4. Form the differential equation representing all straight lines in the xy-plane.

5. Form the differential equation representing all tangents to the parabola $y^2 = 4x$. Show that the equation of the parabola is a solution of the differential equation obtained. *Hint:* Derive the equa-

---

* A student familiar with the theory of eliminants, might have written directly as the eliminant of (11), (12), and (13):

$$\begin{vmatrix} y & x & -xy \\ y' & 1 & -xy' - y \\ y'' & 0 & -xy'' - 2y' \end{vmatrix} = 0,$$

which expands into (14). See Dickson's, *First Course in the Theory of Equations*, pp. 110–112.

tion of an arbitrary tangent as $yy_0 = 2(x + x_0)$, where (x_0, y_0) is an arbitrary point of tangency on the parabola. Since (x_0, y_0) is on the parabola, this equation may be written, $yy_0 = 2\left(x + \dfrac{y_0^2}{4}\right)$, and may be taken as the primitive, with y_0 as an arbitrary constant.

6. Form the differential equation representing all tangents to the parabola $x^2 = 3y + 1$. Show that the equation of the parabola is itself a solution of that differential equation.

5. The general solution.

In the preceding section we found it a direct and generally soluble problem to form a differential equation whose solutions were prescribed in advance. On the other hand, it is by no means a soluble problem, in general, to start with a given differential equation and to obtain its solutions, though in the succeeding chapters, methods of attack will be developed for a great variety of special types of differential equations.

What is of importance, however, is to have some assurance, to begin with, that a differential equation, at least under specified conditions, actually has solutions. Furthermore, where a differential equation is derived from a given primitive, it is of significance to inquire whether that primitive includes all the solutions that the equation may have.

The argument involved, in considering the above, demands greater rigor than the scope of this book permits of, and hence we shall content ourselves with merely stating, without proof, the theorem pertaining to the questions raised; namely, the so-called

EXISTENCE THEOREM. *If, in a given differential equation,*

$$y' = F(x, y), \tag{15}$$

$F(x, y)$ *is continuous and single-valued in a certain region of the* xy-*plane and if, for all values of* (x, y) *within that region,* F_y *exists and is continuous,* then the equation admits of a family of solutions,*

$$f(x, y, c) = 0, \tag{16}$$

such that an arbitrary pair of values (x_0, y_0) *within the region deter-*

---

* A condition actually sufficient is the so-called condition of Lipschitz, *viz.*:

$$| F(x, y_1) - F(x, y_2) | < M | y_1 - y_2 |$$

where x, y_1, and y_2 are in the range, M is some constant, and the symbol $|\ |$ denotes absolute value. This condition, however, is always realized when F_y exists and is continuous.

mines one and only one value of c. *Furthermore, all of the solutions of* (15) *within the region are included in the family* (16).

The result, (16), is called the *complete* or *general* solution of (15); any solution obtained by assigning to c a particular value is called a *particular solution.* The curves represented by (16) are called *integral curves* of (15).

The question raised above with regard to the primitive is now easily settled in the light of this theorem.

Let a primitive,

$$g(x, y, c) = 0, \tag{17}$$

give rise to the differential equation

$$y' = F(x, y), \tag{18}$$

satisfying the hypotheses of the above theorem and having the complete solution,

$$f(x, y, c) = 0. \tag{19}$$

Now all the equations (17), being solutions of (18), are to be found among the equations (19). On the other hand, should there be a curve (19) passing through a point (x_0, y_0) and not found among the curves (17), then through that point would be passing more than one integral curve, since there is a curve of (17) through (x_0, y_0) corresponding to the value of c determined by $g(x_0, y_0, c) = 0$. This would contradict the uniqueness statement of the Existence Theorem. The family of curves (17) is, then, identical with the family (19); in other words, the primitive is identical with the complete solution.

If a differential equation is of the first order and of the second degree, it defines y' in the form of two single-valued functions of x and y. For example,

$$y'^2 + y'(2x + 2y) + (y^2 + 2xy - 3x^2) = 0$$

yields

$$(y' + 3x + y)(y' - x + y) = 0,$$

whence,

$$y' = -3x - y$$

or

$$y' = x - y.$$

Each of these, within the range of values of x and y where it meets the requirements of the Existence Theorem, has a complete solution, so that through an arbitrary point (x_0, y_0), within both ranges, passes one integral curve of each. If both sets of solutions are embodied in a single equation involving one arbitrary constant c, it is evident that, in general, this equation must determine two values of c for an arbitrary point (x_0, y_0), corresponding to the two curves passing through it. Hence, such an equation will involve c to the second degree.

The student may now extend the argument to a differential equation of the first order and of any degree whatsoever, in order to conclude that the degree of the arbitrary constant in the complete solution will be the same as the degree of the differential equation.

A word should be added here about a type of solution called *singular*. In Exercise 5 of Section 4 the student built the differential equation representing all tangents to the parabola $y^2 = 4x$; in other words, the equation having for its primitive the one-parameter family of lines

$$yc = 2\left(x + \frac{c^2}{4}\right).$$

(The change in notation, from y_0 in the exercise to c, is immaterial.) The equation derived was

$$xy'^2 - yy' + 1 = 0,$$

and its complete solution would be expected to be the primitive with which we started. As a matter of fact, it is. However, as noticed in the exercise, the equation of the parabola, *viz.*, $y^2 = 4x$, is also a solution of the equation, and it is obviously not one included in the complete solution; *i. e.*, it is not a solution derivable from

$$yc = 2\left(x + \frac{c^2}{4}\right)$$

by assigning a fixed value to c.

We say that

$$y^2 = 4x$$

is a *singular solution* of

$$xy'^2 - yy' + 1 = 0,$$

and we define, in general, any solution of a differential equation which is not included in the general solution, as a *singular solution*.

The matter of singular solutions will be taken up in detail in Chapter III, but a brief remark at this point might be relevant. The above differential equation defines y' as a double-valued function of x and y; *viz.*,

$$y' = \frac{y \pm \sqrt{y^2 - 4x}}{2x},$$

so that through any point (x, y), not on the parabola $y^2 = 4x$, there are two integral curves with two distinct slopes. The points of the parabola are *singular*, *i. e.*, exceptional, in that for them the two values of y' are equal. The locus of these singular points is our singular solution.*

Exercises

1. (a) Verify that the complete solution of $y' = y - 2x$ is $y = 2x + 2 + ce^x$. Find the particular solution satisfied by $x = 0$, $y = 1$ [*i. e.*, find the equation of the integral curve through $(0, 1)$].

(b) Verify that the complete solution of $y'^2x^2 - y'(2xy + 1) + y^2 = 0$ is $y = c^2x + c$. Find the two integral curves through $(2, 1)$.

(c) Verify that the complete solution of $y'^3 + xy' - y = 0$ is $y = cx + c^3$. Find the three integral curves through $(-1, 0)$.

2. (a) In the illustration on page 12, obtain the singular solution $y^2 = 4x$ as the locus of points whose coördinates (x, y) determine one value of c instead of two distinct values, in the complete solution $yc = 2\left(x + \frac{c^2}{4}\right)$. *Hint:* Solve this equation for c.

(b) Verify that $4xy = -1$ is a solution in Exercise 1 (b). It is a singular solution. Why?

(c) Obtain the singular solution of Exercise 1 (b) by two methods: first as the locus of points (x, y) at which y' has only one value, instead of two distinct values; then as the locus of points whose coördinates (x, y) determine only one value of c in the complete solution, instead of two distinct values.

3. Verify that the complete solution of $y = xy' + 2(y')^2 - y'$ is $y = cx + 2c^2 - c$. Obtain the singular solution by two methods as in Exercise 2 (c).

4. Write down the complete solution of $y' = -\dfrac{x}{y}$ directly from

---

* Note that the function $F(x, y)$ of (15) in this case is $\dfrac{y \pm \sqrt{y^2 - 4x}}{2x}$ and $F_y = \dfrac{1}{2x}\left(1 \pm \dfrac{y}{\sqrt{y^2 - 4x}}\right)$, and F_y is not continuous for (x, y) satisfying $y^2 - 4x = 0$.

the fact that the tangent at any point (x, y) of an integral curve is perpendicular to the line joining (x, y) to the origin.

5. Using an argument similar to that in Exercise 4, write down directly the complete solution of $y'(3 - y) = x + 2$.

6. Equations of higher order. We have seen in Section 4 that a primitive representing an n-parameter family of curves, *i. e.*, one involving n arbitrary constants, gives rise to a differential equation of order n. Accordingly, we must expect the general solution of a differential equation of order n to involve n arbitrary constants. Otherwise, *i. e.*, if the general solution were to involve $m \neq n$ arbitrary constants, then, starting with that solution as primitive, we would derive an equation of order $m \neq n$—a contradiction.

It must be understood throughout that when we speak of an n-parameter family, the n arbitrary constants are meant to be essential, *i. e.*, that precisely n conditions are required to determine them. Thus,

$$y = c_1 x + c_2$$

is actually a two-parameter family, since two conditions, and only two, will serve to determine the constants c_1 and c_2. For example, the two conditions that a curve of the family pass through $(1, 3)$ and $(-1, 2)$ determine c_1 and c_2 by

$$3 = c_1 + c_2$$
$$2 = -c_1 + c_2$$

as $c_1 = \frac{1}{2}$ and $c_2 = \frac{5}{2}$, and the curve as

$$y = \tfrac{1}{2}x + \tfrac{5}{2}.$$

On the other hand,

$$y = c_1 x + c_2 x$$

is a one-parameter family involving only one essential constant, $c_1 + c_2$, which could be fixed only by imposing one condition. In fact, the equation of the family is essentially $y = cx$.

Exercises

1. (a) Verify that $y = c_1 e^x + c_2$ is the complete solution of $y'' - y' = 0$. Find the integral curve passing through $(0, 1)$ and $(1, e)$.

(b) Verify that $y = e^{2x}(c_1 \cos x + c_2 \sin x)$ is the complete solution of $y'' - 4y' + 5y = 0$. Find the integral curve passing through $(\pi, e^{2\pi})$ and $\left(\dfrac{\pi}{2}, 1\right)$.

(c) Verify that $y = e^{2x}(c_1 + c_2 x)$ is the complete solution of $y'' - 4y' + 4y = 0$. Find the integral curve passing through $(0, 0)$, with its slope equal to 1 at that point.

2. (a) Is $y = c_1 e^{x+c_2}$ a two-parameter family? If so, determine the curve of the family passing through $(0, 2)$ and $(1, -2)$. If not, write it as an equation with one arbitrary constant.

(b) Is $y = c_1 + \log (c_2 x)$ a two-parameter family? If not, write it as an equation with one arbitrary constant.

(c) Is $y = c_1 \sqrt{c_2 + x}$ a two-parameter family? If so, determine the curve of the family passing through $(0, 1)$, with slope equal to 2 at that point.

7. Miscellaneous exercises on Chapter I.

1. (a) Verify that the following are solutions of $xz_x + yz_y = 2z$:

$$z = x^2 e^{\frac{x}{y}}; \quad z = x^2 \log \frac{y}{x}; \quad z = x^2 f\left(\frac{y}{x}\right), \text{ where } f\left(\frac{y}{x}\right) \text{ is an arbitrary func-}$$

tion of $\dfrac{y}{x}$.

(b) Verify that the following are solutions of $y^2 z_x + xy z_y = xz$:

$z = y \sqrt{x^2 - y^2}$; $z = y \sin (x^2 - y^2)$; $z = y f(x^2 - y^2)$, where $f(x^2 - y^2)$ is an arbitrary function of $(x^2 - y^2)$.

2. (a) Obtain the partial differential equation of the first order having $z = ax + by^2$ as its primitive (a, b being arbitrary constants). *Hint:* Differentiate the primitive with respect to x, also with respect to y; then eliminate a and b from the three equations.

(b) Obtain the partial differential equation of the first order having $z = ax^2 + bxy + by^2$ as its primitive (a, b being arbitrary constants).

(c) Obtain the differential equation of the first order having $z^2 = c_1 x + c_2 y^2$ as its primitive.

(d) Obtain the differential equation of the first order having $z = x^2 f(x + y)$ as its primitive, $f(x + y)$ being an arbitrary function of the quantity $x + y$.

(e) Obtain the differential equation of the first order having $z = f(x + y^2 - y)$ as its primitive, f being an arbitrary function.

3. (a) Find the differential equation of the family of tangents to the parabola $x^2 = 2y$. Show that the equation of the parabola is a (singular) solution.

(b) Find the differential equation of all circles with centers on the y-axis. *Hint:* The primitive is $x^2 + (y - a)^2 = r^2$ (a, r arbitrary constants).

(c) Find the differential equation of the family of ellipses with foci at $(a, 0)$ and $(-a, 0)$.

(d) Derive the singular solution in Exercise 3 (a) by the two methods of Exercise 2 (c) of Section 5.

(e) Find the differential equation of all circles tangent to the line $y = 2$.

(f) Find the differential equation representing all lines whose y-intercepts are twice their x-intercepts.

4. (a) Find the equation of the line tangent at $(3, -1)$ to an integral curve of $y' = 2xy - y^2$.

(b) Find the equation of the line tangent at $(\pi/2, 0)$ to an integral curve of $y' - 3y + \sin x = 0$.

(c) Find the radius of curvature at $(0, 2)$ of the integral curve of $y' - 2y + e^{xy} = 0$ which passes through that point. *Hint:* The radius of curvature of a curve at (x, y) is given by $R = \dfrac{(1 + y'^2)^{3/2}}{|y''|}$.

(d) For each of the two integral curves of $y'^2 + y'(x - 2y) - xy + y^2 = 0$ which pass through $(1, -2)$, find the equation of the tangent at that point; also the radius of curvature at that point.

5. (a) Find the angle between the two integral curves passing through the point $(4, 3)$ of the equation $x = \left(\dfrac{dy}{dx}\right)^2 + y$.

(b) Show that the two integral curves passing through any point of the x-axis of the equation

$$y = 2\frac{dy}{dx} + 3\left(\frac{dy}{dx}\right)^2$$

meet at a constant angle.

6. Obtain, in the form of an infinite series, the particular solution of $y' = 2x - y$ which passes through $(2, 1)$. *Hint:* The equation defines the values of y' and of all the subsequent derivatives at $(2, 1)$ by

$$
\begin{aligned}
y' &= (2 \cdot 2) - 1 = 3 \\
y'' &= 2 - y' = -1 \\
y''' &= -y'' = 1 \\
y^{iv} &= -y''' = -1, \text{ etc.}
\end{aligned}
$$

Hence, by Taylor's Theorem, *viz.*,

$$y = y_0 + (x - x_0)y_0' + \frac{(x - x_0)^2}{2!} y_0'' + \frac{(x - x_0)^3}{3!} y_0''' + \cdots$$

with $x_0 = 2$, $y_0 = 1$, $y_0' = 3$, $y_0'' = -1$, $y_0''' = +1$, $\cdots$ we have

$$y = 1 + (x - 2)3 + \frac{(x - 2)^2}{2!} (-1) + \frac{(x - 2)^3}{3!} (1) + \cdots,$$

the series sought. That the series so obtained is actually a Taylor expansion, in the neighborhood of $(2, 1)$, of a function

$$y = f(x),$$

which is a solution of the given equation, is a matter vouched for by the Existence Theorem if $F(x, y)$ is assumed, in that theorem, to be a function capable of being developed into a power series

$$a_0 + a_1x + a_2y + a_3x^2 + a_4xy + a_5y^2 + \cdots,$$

as is $2x - y$ in the problem at hand.

Now verify that the above series is a Taylor expansion, about the point $(2, 1)$, of

$$y = 2x - 2 - e^{2-x}.$$

7. By the method of the previous exercise, obtain, in the form of an infinite series:

(a) The particular solution of $y' = 3x + 2y$ passing through $(0, 1)$.

(b) The particular solution of $y' = e^{-x} - y$ passing through $(0, -1)$.

(c) The particular solution of $y' = 2xe^{-x^2/2} - xy$ passing through $(0, 3)$.

8. Verify that the series obtained in Exercise 7(a) is a Taylor expansion, about $(0, 1)$, of $y = -\frac{3}{4}(2x + 1) + \frac{7}{4}e^{2x}$; that the series obtained in Exercise 7(b) is a Taylor expansion, about $(0, -1)$, of $y = (x - 1)e^{-x}$; and that the series obtained in Exercise 7(c) is a Taylor expansion, about $(0, 3)$, of $y = (x^2 + 3)e^{-\frac{x^2}{2}}$.

9. Find, in the form of an infinite series:

(a) The particular solution of $y'' = \dfrac{2x - y + xy'}{x^2}$ passing through $(1, 2)$ with its slope equal to zero.

(b) The particular solution of $y'' - y' + 2y = \log x$ passing through $(1, 3)$ with its slope equal to 1.

10. Obtain the general solution of $\dfrac{dy}{dx} = \dfrac{y}{x}$ directly from the fact that the tangent at any point (x, y) of an integral curve has the same slope as the line joining (x, y) to $(0, 0)$.

11. Given the equation $y' = xy - 1$, show:

(a) That the points on the branch of the curve $xy = 1$ which lies in the first quadrant are points of minimum ordinate for the integral curves through them.

(b) That the points on the other branch of $xy = 1$ are points of maximum ordinate for the integral curves through them.

(c) That the points of inflection of the integral curves lie on the locus $x^2y - x + y = 0$.

12. (a) Given the equation $y' = 2x - 3xy$, find the locus of the points which are points of maximum or minimum ordinate for the integral curves through them; also the locus of the points which are points of inflection for the integral curves through them.

(b) Obtain the same loci as described in (a) for the equation

$$y' = y + e^x.$$

13. Verify that $y = cx$ is the general solution of $y' = \dfrac{y}{x}$. Show that the origin is a singular point for this equation. *Hint:* Consider the number of integral curves through the origin. In what way does the behavior of the function $\dfrac{y}{x}$ at the origin fail to meet the requirements of the Existence Theorem?

14. Show that the system

$$\frac{dx}{dt} = -\frac{y}{t},$$

$$\frac{dy}{dt} = -\frac{x}{t},$$

is satisfied by

$$x = c_1 t + \frac{c_2}{t},$$

$$y = -c_1 t + \frac{c_2}{t}$$

where c_1 and c_2 are arbitrary constants.

Note. The above represents, in fact, the general solution, by the Existence Theorem, for a system of n simultaneous differential equations of the first order, with one independent variable and n dependent variables. We quote the

THEOREM. Given a system of n differential equations in one independent variable t and n dependent variables $x, y, z, \cdots viz.$,

$$
\begin{cases}
\dfrac{dx}{dt} = F_1(x, y, z, \cdots , t), \\[2mm]
\dfrac{dy}{dt} = F_2(x, y, z, \cdots , t), \\[2mm]
\dfrac{dz}{dt} = F_3(x, y, z, \cdots , t), \\[2mm]
\quad \cdots\cdots\cdots\cdots\cdots\cdots ,
\end{cases}
\tag{20}
$$

where each function F_i is continuous and single valued for a certain range of values of $t, x, y, z, \cdots$ and has, within that range, a continuous partial derivative with respect to each dependent variable, then the system admits of an infinity of solutions

$$
\begin{cases}
f_1(x, t, c_1, c_2, \cdots , c_n) = 0, \\
f_2(y, t, c_1, c_2, \cdots , c_n) = 0, \\
f_3(z, t, c_1, c_2, \cdots , c_n) = 0, \\
\quad \cdots\cdots\cdots\cdots\cdots\cdots ,
\end{cases}
\tag{21}
$$

(where the c's are arbitrary constants) such that an assigned set of values $(t_0, x_0, y_0, z_0, \cdots)$ within the range is satisfied by one, and only one, set of (21). (That is, $c_1, c_2, \cdots c_n$ are determined by the assigned set of values $t_0, x_0, y_0, z_0, \cdots .$)

15. Verify that the system

$$
\frac{dx}{dt} = 1 - \frac{2x}{t},
$$
$$
\frac{dy}{dt} = x + y + \frac{2x}{t} - 1,
$$

has for its general solution

$$
x = \frac{t}{3} + \frac{c_1}{t^2},
$$
$$
y = c_2 e^t - \frac{t}{3} - \frac{c_1}{t^2}.
$$

16. Derive the statement made in Section 6, *viz.*, that the general solution of a differential equation of order n contains n

arbitrary constants, as a corollary to the Existence Theorem stated in Exercise 14. *Hint:* Consider the equation

$$f(x, y, y', \cdots, y^{(n)}) = 0$$

as solved for $y^{(n)}$, *viz.*,

$$y^{(n)} = F(x, y, y', y'', \cdots, y^{(n-1)}).$$

Put the last equation in the form of a system of n simultaneous equations in one independent variable x and n dependent variables y, y', y'', $\cdots$, $y^{(n-1)}$; *viz.*,

$$\frac{dy}{dx} = y',$$

$$\frac{dy'}{dx} = y'',$$

$$\cdots \cdots \cdots \cdots$$

$$\cdots \cdots \cdots \cdots$$

$$\frac{dy^{(n-2)}}{dx} = y^{(n-1)},$$

$$\frac{dy^{(n-1)}}{dx} = F(x, y, y', \cdots, y^{(n-1)}).$$

17. Exhibit the equation $x^2 y''' + (1 - x)y'' - 2y' + xy = \sin x$ in the form of a system of equations of first order, as suggested in Exercise 16.

CHAPTER II

Differential Equations of the First Order and First Degree

8. Variables separable. A differential equation in x and y of the first order and first degree is an equation of the form

$$\frac{dy}{dx} = f(x, y),$$

or, what is the same thing,

$$M\,dx + N\,dy = 0, \tag{1}$$

where M and N are functions of x and y such that

$$f(x, y) \equiv -\frac{M}{N}.$$

It may happen that the function M contains x alone and that the function N contains y alone, or that the equation is reducible to one in which M and N have those properties. In such a case we may write the equation in the form

$$X(x)\,dx + Y(y)\,dy = 0. \tag{2}$$

The process of reducing an equation to the form (2) is called *separating the variables*. The resulting equation may be solved at once by an integration, giving

$$\int X(x)\,dx + \int Y(y)\,dy = c.^*$$

As an illustration, consider the equation

$$3x^3(1 + y^2)\,dx + x\,dy = 0.$$

Upon dividing through by $x(1 + y^2)$, we have

$$3x^2\,dx + \frac{dy}{1 + y^2} = 0,$$

---

* A differential equation is considered solved if it is reduced to quadratures.

whence, by integration,

$$x^3 + \text{arc tan } y = c.$$

Exercises

1. Solve the following by separating the variables:

(a) $dx - 2dy = 0.$

(b) $y(1 - x)\, dx + x^2(1 - y)\, dy = 0.$

(c) $5(1 - y)\, dx - xy(1 + x^2)\, dy = 0.$

(d) $2xy(4 - y^2)\, dx + (y - 1)(x^2 + 2)\, dy = 0.$

(e) $(1 + y)\, dx + \dfrac{dy}{x^2 - 2x} = 0.$

(f) $y \sqrt{y^2 - 1}\, dx - \sqrt{1 - x^2}\, dy = 0.$

(g) $\dfrac{ds}{dt} + \cos 2t = 0.$

(h) $e^{x^3 - v^2} + \dfrac{y}{x^2} \cdot \dfrac{dy}{dx} = 0.$

2. Find the system of all curves having the property that the normal at every point passes through the origin.

3. The acceleration of a particle moving in a straight line is the negative of its velocity. It starts from the origin with a velocity equal to 1. Find its position at the end of two units of time.

4. A ten-pound object, falling under the force of gravity, and with an initial velocity of 1 foot per second, is subject to a force of resistance which, in pounds, is equal to twice the velocity, in feet per second, of the object. Find the distance through which it falls in the first 5 seconds and its velocity at the end of t seconds. Also find out if its velocity approaches a limit as time goes on. *Hint:* The effective force is $m \dfrac{dv}{dt}$, where m is the mass, v the velocity of the particle, while t denotes time. Also $m = w/g$ is called mass, w being the weight and g the acceleration of gravity. The equation determining the motion is then

$$\frac{10}{g} \cdot \frac{dv}{dt} = 10 - 2v,$$

when $t = 0$, $v = 1$. To find the distance s, recall that $v = \dfrac{ds}{dt}$.

5. The acceleration of a falling particle is inversely proportional to the square of its distance from the center of the earth. Find its velocity when it is s miles from the center of the earth, if it falls from rest from a very great distance. Take the radius of the earth as R miles. *Hint:* Acceleration $= \dfrac{dv}{dt} = \dfrac{dv}{ds} \cdot \dfrac{ds}{dt} = v\dfrac{dv}{ds}$; when $s = \infty$, $v = 0$; and when $s = R$, $v\dfrac{dv}{ds} = -\dfrac{g}{5280}$ miles per sec^2.

9. Exact differential equations. If we take the differential of the relation $x^2y - x + 3y^2 = c$, where c is constant, we obtain the differential equation

$$(2xy - 1)\, dx + (x^2 + 6y)\, dy = 0.$$

We may identify this with the equation

$$M\, dx + N\, dy = 0 \tag{1}$$

by putting $M \equiv 2xy - 1$ and $N \equiv x^2 + 6y$. If we form the partial derivative of M with respect to y and the partial derivative of N with respect to x, we notice that each is equal to $2x$ and hence that

$$M_y \equiv N_x. \tag{3}$$

Similarly, any relation of the form $f(x, y) = c$ in which the partial derivatives f_x and f_y exist, gives a differential equation

$$f_x\, dx + f_y\, dy = 0.$$

This is of the form (1), with $M \equiv f_x$ and $N \equiv f_y$, and, from the mode of its derivation, it is said to be *exact*. An equation of the form (1) will evidently be exact if, and only if, there exists a function $f(x, y)$ such that $f_x \equiv M$ and $f_y \equiv N$. If this function $f(x, y)$ not only exists but has second partial derivatives, we may note that $M_y \equiv f_{xy}$ and $N_x \equiv f_{yx}$. If, further, these second partial derivatives are continuous, the order of differentiation is immaterial, and we have (3). In other words, if (1) is exact and is obtained from the primitive $f(x, y) = c$ such that $f(x, y)$ has continuous first and second partial derivatives, then (3) holds.

Let us now ask whether or not relation (3) is a sufficient condition for the exactness of (1), *i. e.*, whether or not there can be shown to exist a function $f(x, y)$ such that $f_x \equiv M$ and $f_y \equiv N$, whenever (3) holds. To prove that the answer is in the affirmative, we argue as follows. Set up the function $f(x, y) = \int M(x, y)\, dx = g(x, y)$

$+ h(y)$, where y is held constant in the integration and $h(y)$ is an arbitrary function. This function, $f(x, y)$, obviously satisfies the relation

$$f_x(x, y) = g_x(x, y) = M(x, y).$$

Again,

$$f_y(x, y) = g_y(x, y) + h'(y),$$

and the right-hand member will be identical with $N(x, y)$ if

$$h'(y) = N(x, y) - g_y(x, y).$$

Such a function, $h(y)$, can evidently be found if $N(x, y) - g_y(x, y)$ turns out to be a function of y alone.

That this is actually the case is shown by

$$\frac{\partial}{\partial x} [N(x, y) - g_y(x, y)] = N_x(x, y) - g_{yx}(x, y) = M_y(x, y)$$

$$- g_{xy}(x, y) = \frac{\partial}{\partial y} [M(x, y) - g_x(x, y)]$$

$$= \frac{\partial}{\partial y} [M(x, y) - M(x, y)] = 0.$$

Thus, we have established a function $f(x, y)$ satisfying both equalities

$$f_x(x, y) \equiv M(x, y),$$
$$f_y(x, y) \equiv N(x, y).$$

To illustrate, consider the equation

$$(2xy^2 - y \sin x + 2x - 1)\, dx + \left(2x^2 y + \cos x + \frac{1}{y}\right) dy = 0, \quad (4)$$

in which

$$M(x, y) = 2xy^2 - y \sin x + 2x - 1,$$
$$N(x, y) = 2x^2 y + \cos x + \frac{1}{y},$$
$$M_y = 4xy - \sin x = N_x.$$

Set up the function

$$f(x, y) = \int M(x, y)\, dx = \int (2xy^2 - y \sin x + 2x - 1)\, dx$$
$$= x^2 y^2 + y \cos x + x^2 - x + h(y),$$
$$[g(x, y) = x^2 y^2 + y \cos x + x^2 - x],$$

so that $f_y(x, y) = 2xy^2 + \cos x + h'(y)$ and

$$h'(y) = \frac{1}{y} = N(x, y) - g_y(x, y).$$

One value of $h(y)$ is, clearly, $\log y$, and

$$f(x, y) = x^2 y^2 + y \cos x + x^2 - x + \log y.$$

Then the solution of the equation is

$$x^2 y^2 + y \cos x + x^2 - x + \log y = C.$$

Note: A direct way of integrating the above would be to group the terms as follows:

$$2xy^2 \, dx + 2x^2 y \, dy + (-y \sin x \, dx + \cos x \, dy) + (2x - 1) \, dx$$
$$+ \frac{1}{y} \, dy = 0,$$

i. e.,

$$d(x^2 y^2) + d(y \cos x) + (2x - 1) \, dx + \frac{1}{y} \, dy = 0,$$

whence

$$x^2 y^2 + y \cos x + x^2 - x + \log y = C.$$

Exercises

1. Test the following for exactness, and solve those which are exact:

    (a) $(x + 3y) \, dx + (x - 2y) \, dy = 0.$
    (b) $(y + 3x) \, dx + x \, dy = 0.$
    (c) $(x^2 - 4xy + 4y^2) \, dx + (2y^2 + 8xy - 6x^2) \, dy = 0.$
    (d) $(ax^2 + 2bxy + cy^2) \, dx + (bx^2 + 2cxy + gy^2) \, dy = 0.$
    (e) $(x^3 + 5xy^2) \, dx + (5x^2 y + 2y^3) \, dy = 0.$
    (f) $(x^2 + xy + y^2) \, dx + (4x^2 - 2xy + 3y^2) \, dy = 0.$
    (g) $(7x - 3y + 2) \, dx + (4y - 3x - 5) \, dy = 0.$
    (h) $(5xy^4 + x) \, dx - (2 + 3y^2 - 10x^2 y^3) \, dy = 0.$

    (i) $x^{-2} y^{-1} (e^{-\frac{1}{xy}} - 1) \, dx + y^{-2} x^{-1} (e^{-\frac{1}{xy}} - 1) \, dy = 0.$
    (j) $\sec^2 x \tan y \, dx + \sec^2 y \tan x \, dy = 0.$
    (k) $(2xy - \cos x) \, dx + (x^2 - 1) \, dy = 0.$
    (l) $(\tan y - 3x^2) \, dx + x \sec^2 y \, dy = 0.$
  (m) $ye^x \, dx + e^x \, dy = 0.$
    (n) $\cosh x \cosh y \, dx - \sinh x \sinh y \, dy = 0.$
    (o) $\cosh x \, (\cosh y - 1) \, dx + \sinh y \, (\sinh x + 1) \, dy = 0.$
    (p) $2x \tan y + \sin 2y + (x^2 \sec^2 y + 2x \cos 2y - e^y) y' = 0.$

2. Determine b so that the equation $(3x - 5y + 7) \, dx + (bx + 6y + 10) \, dy = 0$ will be exact.

3. Show that for the exact equation $M\,dx + N\,dy = 0$, the solution can also be written in the form

$$f(x, y) = \int M(x, b)\,dx + \int_b^y N(x, y)\,dy = C.$$

Write the solution of Exercise 1(h) above by this method.

4. Find the equation of the curve passing through $(0, 1)$ for which

$$\frac{dy}{dx} = \frac{x + y - 1}{2y - x + 3}.$$

10. Integrating factors. As we saw in Chapter I, the general solution of a differential equation of the form

$$M\,dx + N\,dy = 0 \tag{1}$$

is a relation of the form

$$f(x, y, c) = 0,$$

where c is an arbitrary constant. If we solve this last equation for c, we may write it in the form

$$\varphi(x, y) = c.$$

Differentiated, this gives

$$\varphi_x\,dx + \varphi_y\,dy = 0. \tag{5}$$

In order that Equations (1) and (5) may be simultaneously satisfied by quantities dx and dy, not both zero, it is necessary and sufficient* that the determinant

$$\begin{vmatrix} M & N \\ \varphi_x & \varphi_y \end{vmatrix}$$

have the value zero. Then the elements in the second row are proportional to those in the first. The factor of proportionality being, in general, a function of x and y, we have

$$\varphi_x \equiv \mu(x, y) \cdot M,$$
$$\varphi_y \equiv \mu(x, y) \cdot N.$$

---

* See Dickson's *Theory of Equations*, p. 119.

If (1) is multiplied through by $\mu(x, y)$, the result is the exact differential equation (5). The function $\mu(x, y)$, as employed here, is called an *integrating factor* of Equation (1). The integrating factor μ is by no means unique. As a matter of fact, it can be shown that if an equation of form (1) satisfies the hypotheses of the Existence Theorem, and hence has a general solution, it has an infinite number of integrating factors. The demonstration is left to the student in an exercise at the close of this chapter.

No general rule may be given for finding integrating factors. For certain highly special forms of differential equations, it is possible to specify the form of an integrating factor. Some of the more useful of such cases are discussed in Exercises 3, 8, 10, 14, 17, 25, and 26 at the end of Section 10. It is very often possible to find an integrating factor by inspection.

Illustrations

If the differential equation

$$x \, dy - y \, dx = 0$$

is multiplied through by $\dfrac{1}{x^2}$, it becomes

$$\frac{dy}{x} - \frac{y}{x^2} \, dx = 0,$$

in which $N \equiv 1/x$, $M \equiv -y/x^2$, $M_y \equiv -1/x^2 \equiv N_x$, and hence (3) holds and the equation is exact. The student may readily show that $\dfrac{1}{y^2}$, $\dfrac{1}{xy}$, and $\dfrac{1}{x^2 \pm y^2}$ are other integrating factors of this equation. If we solve the equation by using each of these five integrating factors in turn, we obtain

$$\frac{y}{x} = c, \frac{x}{y} = c, \log \frac{y}{x} = c, \tan^{-1} \frac{y}{x} = c, \tfrac{1}{2} \log \frac{y + x}{y - x} = c$$

in the respective cases. These solutions may be seen to be essentially the same by observing that, when considered geometrically, each represents a family of straight lines through the origin.

The student's success in finding integrating factors by inspection will depend largely upon his experience and ingenuity, but he might do well to keep in mind the following differentials of common functions:

$$d(xy) = y\,dx + x\,dy;$$
$$d(x^2 \pm y^2) = 2x\,dx \pm 2y\,dy;$$
$$d\left(\frac{y}{x}\right) = \frac{x\,dy - y\,dx}{x^2};$$
$$d\left(\tan^{-1}\frac{y}{x}\right) = \frac{x\,dy - y\,dx}{x^2 + y^2};$$
$$d\left(\log\frac{y - x}{y + x}\right) = \frac{2x\,dy - 2y\,dx}{y^2 - x^2};$$
$$d\left(\frac{x + y}{x - y}\right) = \frac{2x\,dy - 2y\,dx}{(x - y)^2};$$
$$d\left(\frac{x - y}{x + y}\right) = \frac{2y\,dx - 2x\,dy}{(x + y)^2}.$$

The form of the algebraic expressions in the differential equation may suggest an integrating factor, as in the examples below.

Illustration 1

To find an integrating factor of

$$y\,dx - x\,dy + \log x\,dx = 0,$$

note that $\log x$ suggests $\dfrac{1}{x}$, while $y\,dx - x\,dy$ suggests $\dfrac{1}{x^2}$. Trying the latter, we obtain

$$\frac{y + \log x}{x^2}\,dx - \frac{1}{x}\,dy = 0,$$

which is exact.

Illustration 2

Given the equation

$$(x^2 + y^2)(x\,dx + y\,dy) + (1 + x^2 + y^2)^{\frac{1}{2}}(y\,dx - x\,dy) = 0,$$

the algebraic factor $x^2 + y^2$ in one term and the differential factor $y\,dx - x\,dy$ in the other both suggest $1/(x^2 + y^2)$, while the algebraic factor $(1 + x^2 + y^2)^{\frac{1}{2}}$ in one term and $x\,dx + y\,dy$ in the other both suggest $1/(1 + x^2 + y^2)^{\frac{1}{2}}$. Trying the product, we obtain

$$\frac{x\,dx + y\,dy}{(1 + x^2 + y^2)^{\frac{1}{2}}} + \frac{y\,dx - x\,dy}{x^2 + y^2} = 0,$$

the left member of which is the differential of

$$(1 + x^2 + y^2)^{\frac{1}{2}} + \tan^{-1}\frac{x}{y},$$

and the equation is therefore exact.

Exercises

1. In each of the following, find an integrating factor by inspection, and solve:

(a) $2y\,dx + (3y - 2x)\,dy = 0$.

(b) $(x + 2y)\,dx + (y - 2x)\,dy = 0$.

(c) $(y^2 - xy)\,dx + x^2\,dy = 0$.

(d) $\dfrac{1}{x}\,(2x - y^3)\,dx - 3y^2\,dy = 0$.

(e) $(x^2 + y^2)\,dx = x(x\,dy - y\,dx)$.

(f) $y\,dx + (x + x^2y^2)\,dy = 0$.

(g) $(2x^3y^3 - y)\,dx + (2x^3y^3 - x)\,dy = 0$.

(h) $2y\,dx + (1 - \log y - 2x)\,dy = 0$.

(i) $(x^2y + xy^2 - y^3)\,dx + (y^2x + yx^2 - x^3)\,dy = 0$.

(j) $a(3x\,dy + 2xy\,dx) + 3y\,dx = 0$.

(k) $(x^4 \cos x + 2py^2x)\,dx - 2px^2y\,dy = 0$.

(l) $ye^{x/y}\,dx + (y - xe^{x/y})\,dy = 0$.

(m) $(y + \sinh y\ \text{sech}\ x)\,dx + (x\ \text{sech}\ x \cosh y + \tanh x)$ $dy = 0$.

(n) $(xy - y)\,dx + (x^2 - 2x + y)\,dy = 0$.

(o) $\sqrt{x^2 + y^2} - x + (\sqrt{x^2 + y^2} - y)\,\dfrac{dy}{dx} = 0$.

2. Derive the partial differential equation which must be satisfied by an integrating factor $\mu(x, y)$ of the differential equation $M\,dx + N\,dy = 0$.

3. If $M \equiv yf(xy)$ and $N \equiv xg(xy)$ where f and g are functions of the product xy, show that $1/(Mx - Ny)$ is an integrating factor provided $Mx - Ny$ is not identically zero.

4. Solve $(y - xy^2)\,dx + (3x - x^2y)\,dy = 0$.

5. Solve $y(1 + 2xy - x^2y^2)\,dx + x(1 + 2xy)\,dy = 0$.

6. Solve $(y - xy^2 + x^{3/2}y^{5/2})\,dx + x(1 - xy - 2x^{3/2}y^{3/2})\,dy = 0$.

7. Solve $(y - xy^2 \sin xy)\,dx + (4x - x^2y \sin xy)\,dy = 0$.

8. If the functions M and N are of the form of Exercise 3 above, but $Mx - Ny$ is identically zero, find an integrating factor.

9. Solve $(xy^2 - y)\,dx + x(xy - 1)\,dy = 0$.

10. Show that the substitution $v = xy$ ($\therefore\ y = v/x$) will reduce the equation of Exercise 3 above to an equation in x and v in which the variables are separable.

11. Solve the equation of Exercise 5 by the substitution $v = xy$.

12. Solve $(2y - xy^2 - x^2y^3)\ dx + (2x - x^2y)\ dy = 0$ by the substitution $v = xy$.

13. Solve Exercise 7 by the substitution $v = xy$.

14. Show that an equation of the form $x^r y^s (my\ dx + nx\ dy) = 0$ has an infinite number of integrating factors of the form $x^a y^b$, and find expressions for a and b.

15. Solve $x^{-1}y^3(3y\ dx - 2x\ dy) = 0$.

16. Solve $5x^2y^6\ dx - x^3y^5\ dy = 0$.

17. Show that a differential equation of the form $x^r y^s (my\ dx + nx\ dy) + x^p y^\sigma (\mu y\ dx + vx\ dy) = 0$ has an integrating factor of the form $x^a y^b$, if the determinant $\begin{vmatrix} m & n \\ \mu & v \end{vmatrix}$ is not zero, and find the values of a and b.

18. Solve $x^4 y(3y\ dx + 2x\ dy) - x(y\ dx - 2x\ dy) = 0$.

19. Solve $y^2(3y\ dx - 6x\ dy) - x(y\ dx + x\ dy) = 0$.

20. Solve $(2x^3y - 2y)\ dx + (x - 2x^4)\ dy = 0$.

21. Solve $a(x\ dy - 3y\ dx) = bxy\ dx$.

22. Find an integrating factor for an equation of the form of Exercise 17 in case $\begin{vmatrix} m & n \\ \mu & v \end{vmatrix}$ vanishes.

23. Solve $x^2(4y\ dx + 3x\ dy) - y^2(8y\ dx + 6x\ dy) = 0$.

24. Solve $(2x^3 + 4xy^2)\ dy - (3x^2y + 6y^3)\ dx = 0$.

25. If $(M_y - N_x)/N \equiv f(x)$, a function of x alone, show that $e^{\int f(x)\,dx}$ is an integrating factor of $M\ dx + N\ dy = 0$.

26. Find an integrating factor of $M\ dx + N\ dy = 0$ in case $(N_x - M_y)/M \equiv g(y)$, a function of y alone.

27. Solve $(y^4 - 5y)\ dx + (7xy^3 - 5x + y)\ dy = 0$.

28. Solve $(3x^2 + 6xy + 3y^2)\ dx + (2x^2 + 3xy)\ dy = 0$.

29. Solve $(3xy - 8y + x^2)\ dx + (x^2 - 5x + 6)\ dy = 0$.

30. Solve $(4x^2y^3 + 2x^2y)\ dx + 4x^3y^2\ dy = 0$.

31. Solve $(3xy - x^2)\ dx + x^2\ dy = 0$.

11. Homogeneous equations. A differential equation of the form

$$\frac{dy}{dx} = f\left(\frac{y}{x}\right), \tag{6}$$

or one reducible to that form is called a *homogeneous* equation. Thus

$$(y^2 + xy)\,dx - x^2\,dy = 0, \tag{7}$$

when written as

$$\frac{dy}{dx} = \frac{y^2 + xy}{x^2} = \left(\frac{y}{x}\right)^2 + \left(\frac{y}{x}\right),$$

is evidently of such form and is, by definition, homogeneous.

For solving (6), the device suggests itself of introducing a new dependent variable v as $v = y/x$. Indeed, this makes $y = vx$, $\frac{dy}{dx} = v + x\frac{dv}{dx}$, and (6) takes the form $v + x\frac{dv}{dx} = f(v)$, or $x\frac{dv}{dx} = f(v) - v$. Separation of the variables gives

$$\frac{dv}{f(v) - v} = \frac{dx}{x}, \tag{8}$$

and the equation may be integrated.

Thus, in (7), setting $y = vx$, we get $v + x\frac{dv}{dx} = v^2 + v$, and $\frac{dv}{v^2} = \frac{dx}{x}$, leading to $-1/v = \log x + c$. If one wishes, the solution can be put in the form

$$x = e^{-\frac{x}{y} - c} = e^{-x/y}e^{-c} = \mathrm{K}e^{-x/y}.$$

Exercises

1. A function, $g(x, y)$, is defined as *homogeneous* and of *degree n* if it has the property that

$$g(tx, ty) \equiv t^n g(x, y).$$

Verify that

(a) $x^2 + y^2 - xy$ is homogeneous and of degree 2.

(b) $xe^{y/x} + \frac{y^2}{x}\log\left(\frac{x^2}{y^2}\right)$ is homogeneous and of degree 1.

(c) $\frac{(x^2 + y^2)^{\frac{1}{2}}}{x} + \cos\left(\frac{y}{x}\right)$ is homogeneous and of degree 0.

2. (a) Show that a homogeneous function, $g(x, y)$, of degree n can be put in the form $x^n h\left(\dfrac{y}{x}\right)$. For example, $x^2 + y^2 - xy = x^2\left[1 + \dfrac{y^2}{x^2} - \dfrac{y}{x}\right]$.

Hint: In $g(tx, ty) \equiv t^n g(x, y)$, put $t = 1/x$.

(b) Put the functions of Exercises 1(b) and 1(c) in the form $x^n h\left(\dfrac{y}{x}\right)$, also the function $x^3 - 3x^2 y + xy^2$.

3. (a) Show that if M and N are homogeneous functions of the same degree, the equation $M\, dx + N\, dy = 0$ is homogeneous.

Hint: By Exercise 2(a) above $M(x, y) = x^n h\left(\dfrac{y}{x}\right)$, $N(x, y) = x^n g\left(\dfrac{y}{x}\right)$.

(b) Show that Equation (7) in the text is homogeneous by the test in part (a) of this exercise.

4. Solve the following homogeneous differential equations:

(a) $(2x + y)\, dy = (x - 2y)\, dx$.

(b) $y' = \dfrac{4y^2 + xy - 3x^2}{x^2}$.

(c) $\dfrac{y}{x}\, dx = dy + \sec^2 \dfrac{y}{x}\, dx$.

(d) $(x^2 - y^2)\, dx - \dfrac{2y^3}{x}\, dy = 0$.

(e) $\dfrac{dy}{dx} = e^{y/x} + \dfrac{y}{x} + 1$.

(f) $x\, dy - y\, dx = \sqrt{x^2 + y^2}\, dx$.

5. Show that the substitution $x = vy$ will separate the variables in the homogeneous equation $M\, dx + N\, dy = 0$.

6. Solve Exercises 4(a), 4(c), and 4(f) by use of the substitution of Exercise 5.

7. Show that a straight line through the origin intersects at a constant angle all integral curves of a homogeneous equation.

8. Prove that $\dfrac{1}{Mx + Ny}$ is an integrating factor for the homogeneous equation $M\, dx + N\, dy = 0$ if $Mx + Ny$ is not identically zero.*

---

* In completing this exercise, the student may find it well to resort to an important theorem on homogeneous functions, due to Euler and bearing his

9. Solve the following by employing an integrating factor:

(a) $(y^4 - 2x^3y)\, dx + (x^4 - 2xy^3)\, dy = 0.$

(b) $\left(2x \sinh \dfrac{y}{x} - y \cosh \dfrac{y}{x}\right) dx + x \cosh \dfrac{y}{x}\, dy = 0.$

(c) $\dfrac{y - x}{x}\, dx = dy + \cos \dfrac{y}{x}\, dx.$

10. The method of Exercise 8 obviously does not apply if $Mx + Ny$ is identically zero. Find an integrating factor in that case.

11. *Prove:* If $M(x, y)$ and $N(x, y)$ are homogenous functions of the same degree $\neq -1$, while the equation $M\, dx + N\, dy = 0$ is exact, its solution is $Mx + Ny = C$. (Hence, the solution is written down at sight without a quadrature.)   *Hint:* See Exercises 1 and 3 and footnote to Exercise 8.

12. Apply the principle of Exercise 11 to the following:

(a) $(2x + y)\, dx + (x - 2y)\, dy = 0.$
(b) $(3x^2 - 2xy + y^2)\, dx - (x^2 - 2xy + y^2)\, dy = 0.$

13. *Prove:* If $M(x, y)$ and $N(x, y)$ are homogenous and of degree -1, while the equation $M\, dx + N\, dy = 0$ is exact, then $Mx + Ny$ is identically equal to some constant. Find that constant for the equation

$$\frac{1 + e^{x/y}}{x + ye^{x/y}}\, dx + \frac{(y - x)e^{x/y}}{xy + y^2e^{x/y}}\, dy = 0.$$

Note. This shows why the principle of Exercise 11 is subject to the exception stated.

14. (a) Discuss the equation of the text, $\dfrac{x\, dv + v\, dx}{dx} = F(v)$, for the case when $F(v)$ is identically equal to v.

(b) If α is a root of $F(v) = v$, show that $y = \alpha x$ is a solution of $y' = F(y/x)$.

(c) Solve $y' = \dfrac{y^2}{x^2} + \dfrac{y}{x} - 1.$

---

name; *viz.*, if $f(x, y, z, \cdots)$ is homogeneous and of degree n, then $xf_x + yf_y + zf_z + \cdots \equiv nf$. This theorem will be frequently used, and hence if the student is not already familiar with it, he should refer to any good book on the calculus for its proof and discussion.

15. Prove. If in a homogeneous equation a change is made to polar coordinates (*i. e.*, by $x = r \cos \theta$, $y = r \sin \theta$) the variables are separable in the resulting equation.

16. Prove that the non-homogeneous equation $\dfrac{dy}{dx} = \dfrac{y}{x} + x^m y^n f\left(\dfrac{y}{x}\right)$ can be solved by the substitution $y = vx$.

17. Use the method of Exercise 16 to solve the following non-homogeneous equations:

(a) $\dfrac{dy}{dx} = \dfrac{y}{x} + x^2 e^{\frac{-2y}{x}}$.   (b) $\dfrac{dy}{dx} = \dfrac{y}{x} + \dfrac{\sec^2 \frac{y}{x}}{y^2}$.

(c) $x \dfrac{dy}{dx} = y + y^2 \sqrt{\dfrac{3y - x}{x}}$.

18. At any point, P, of a curve, the inclination of OP, where O is the origin, is equal to the angle from OP to the tangent drawn at P to the curve. Find the equation of the curve.

12. Equations reducible to homogeneous equations. Consider the non-homogeneous equation

$$(2x - y + 3)\, dx + (x + y - 1)\, dy = 0. \tag{9}$$

If we introduce new variables defined by

$$\begin{aligned} u &= 2x - y + 3 \\ v &= x + y - 1 \end{aligned} \tag{10}$$

whence $du = 2dx - dy$, $dv = dx + dy$, and hence, $dx = \dfrac{du + dv}{3}$ and $dy = \dfrac{-du + 2dv}{3}$, the equation becomes

$$(u - v)\, du + (u + 2v)\, dv = 0,$$

which is homogeneous and may therefore be solved by the method of the preceding section. Its solution is

$$\log (u^2 + 2v^2)^{\frac{1}{2}} = c - \frac{1}{\sqrt{2}} \tan^{-1} \left(\frac{v}{u}\sqrt{2}\right),$$

or

$$e^{-\frac{\sqrt{2}}{2} \tan^{-1} \frac{v\sqrt{2}}{u}} = c(u^2 + 2v^2)^{\frac{1}{2}}.$$

(The student should solve the last differential equation and obtain this result.) We now replace u and v by their equivalents in (10), and obtain, as the solution of (9),

$$e^{-\frac{\sqrt{2}}{2}\tan^{-1}\frac{(x+y-1)\sqrt{2}}{2x-y+3}} = c[(2x-y+3)^2 + 2(x+y-1)^2]^{\frac{1}{2}}.$$

Evidently, this method is applicable to any equation of the form

$$(ax + by + c)\,dx + (\alpha x + \beta y + \gamma)\,dy = 0, \tag{11}$$

where $a, b, c, \alpha, \beta, \gamma$ are constants such that $\begin{vmatrix} a & b \\ \alpha & \beta \end{vmatrix} \neq 0.$

Exercises

1. Solve $(2x - 5y + 3)\,dx - (5x - 12y + 8)\,dy = 0.$

2. Solve $(8x + 25y - 62)\,dx + (-11x - 4y + 11)\,dy = 0.$

3. Solve $(x - y + 1)\,dx + (2x + y - 2)\,dy = 0.$

4. Solve $(2x + y + 7)\,dx + (x - 3y)\,dy = 0.$

5. Show that the method of this section is applicable to any equation of the form

$$\frac{dy}{dx} = f\left(\frac{ax + by + c}{\alpha x + \beta y + \gamma}\right)$$

in which the determinant $\begin{vmatrix} a & b \\ \alpha & \beta \end{vmatrix}$ is not zero.

6. Solve

$$\frac{dy}{dx} = \left(\frac{6x + 4y - 3}{3x + y - 1}\right)^2 - 2\left(\frac{6x + 4y - 3}{3x + y - 1}\right).$$

Note: The method here presented obviously fails for an equation of the form (11) in which $a\beta - b\alpha = 0$, since the substitutions $u = ax + by + c$, $v = \alpha x + \beta y + \gamma$, lead to $dx = \dfrac{\beta\,du - b\,dv}{a\beta - b\alpha}$, $dy = \dfrac{-\alpha\,du + a\,dv}{a\beta - b\alpha}$. But in that case, since $a\beta - b\alpha = 0$ implies $\dfrac{a}{\alpha} = \dfrac{b}{\beta} = k$, we have $ax + by = k(\alpha x + \beta y)$, and the substitution $z = \alpha x + \beta y$ will separate the variables. Indeed, (11) becomes

$$(kz + c)\,dx + (z + \gamma)\frac{dz - \alpha\,dx}{\beta} = 0,^*$$

---

* The case $\beta = 0$ now presents an apparent difficulty, but since $\dfrac{b}{\beta} = k$, then $b = 0$, and (11) has its variables immediately separable.

or

$$(\beta k z + \beta c - \alpha z - \alpha \gamma) \, dx + (z + \gamma) \, dz = 0,$$

or

$$dx + \frac{z + \gamma}{z(\beta k - \alpha) + (\beta c - \alpha \gamma)} \, dz = 0.$$

7. Solve $(x - 2y + 1) \, dx + (2x - 4y + 3) \, dy = 0$.

8. Solve $(3x - y + 2) \, dx - (6x - 2y) \, dy = 0$.

9. Solve $\dfrac{dy}{dx} = \dfrac{x + 2y - 1}{x + 2y + 1}$.

10. Show that the substitution $ax + by = z$ will separate the variables in any equation of the form $\dfrac{dy}{dx} = f\left(\dfrac{ax + by + c}{\alpha x + \beta y + \gamma}\right)$ if $a\beta = b\alpha$.

11. Solve $y' = \dfrac{(2x - y)^2}{(4x - 2y - 1)^2}$.

12. Solve $(x + 2y^3) \, dx + 6xy^2 \, dy = 0$.   *Hint:* Put $u = y^3$.

13. Solve $y' = \dfrac{3x + 2}{-2x + y - 1} + \dfrac{-2x + y - 1}{3x + 2} + 1$.

14. Solve $y' = \dfrac{3y - 2x - 3}{4x - 6y}$.

13. Linear equations of the first order.   An equation of the form

$$y' + yP(x) = Q(x), \tag{12}$$

in which the dependent variable and its derivative enter to the first degree, is called *linear*.   The notion of a linear differential equation extends to equations of all orders, and Chapter IV of this book is devoted to linear equations of higher orders.   Linear equations are important because of their frequent occurrence in applied mathematics.

Equation (12) may be solved by employing the integrating factor (see Exercise 25, Section 10)

$$e^{\int P(x) \, dx}.$$

Indeed, the introduction of this factor reduces the equation to

$$y' e^{\int P(x) \, dx} + yP(x) e^{\int P(x) \, dx} = Q(x) e^{\int P(x) \, dx},$$

and the left-hand member is the derivative with respect to x of

$$ye^{\int P(x) \, dx}. \tag{13}$$

The right-hand number, being a function of x alone, may be integrated and equated to the Expression (13) to give the general solution.

Illustration

Given the equation

$$y' - 2y = e^{3x}, \tag{14}$$

the integrating factor is seen to be

$$e^{\int P(x)dx} \equiv e^{\int -2dx} \equiv e^{-2x}.$$

By the use of this factor, (14) reduces to the exact differential equation

$$e^{-2x}y' - 2ye^{-2x} = e^{x},$$

whose solution is

$$ye^{-2x} = e^{x} + c,$$

or

$$y = e^{3x} + ce^{2x}.$$

Exercises

1. Solve the following:

(a) $y' + y \cos x = e^{-\sin x}$.

(b) $2x \, dy = (2x^3 - y) \, dx$.

(c) $3xy \, dx = \sin 2x \, dx - dy$.

(d) $2yy' - \dfrac{y^2}{x^2} = e^{\frac{x^2-1}{x}}$.   *Hint:* Put $u = y^2$.

(e) $y' \sec^2 y + \dfrac{x \tan y}{x^2 + 1} = x$.

(f) $y' + 2xy + x = e^{-x^2}$.

(g) $x^2y'' + 2xy' = 2$.   *Hint:* Set $p = y'$.

2. Adapt the methods of the text to the equation

$$\frac{dx}{dy} + xP(y) = Q(y),$$

and employ it to obtain a solution for the following equations:

(a) $dx - dy(x + \log y) = 0$.

(b) $\cos x \, dx - 4 \sin x \, dy = y^2 \, dy$.

(c) $\cos y + x \sin y \log x \cdot y' = x \cos^2 y$.

(d) $dx + \dfrac{x}{\sqrt{1 - y^2}} \, dy = e^{\cos^{-1}y} \, dy$.

3. Solve the following:

(a) $\cos y \dfrac{dy}{dx} + \dfrac{\sin y}{x} = \sin 2x.$

(b) $y \sec^2 x\, dx + 3 \tan x\, dy = y \cos^2 2y\, dy.$

4. Show that if $y = f(x)$ is a solution of $y' + yP(x) = 0$, then $y = c \cdot f(x)$ is also a solution, where c is any constant.

5. Show that if $y = f(x)$ is any solution of (12), then $y = f(x) + ce^{-\int P\,dx}$ is the general solution of (12); *i.e.*, that any solution of (10) added to the general solution of the corresponding homogeneous equation $y' + yP(x) = 0$ gives the general solution of (12).

6. If $y = f(x)$ and $y = g(x)$ are two distinct solutions of (12), show that the complete solution is given by

$$\frac{y - f(x)}{g(x) - f(x)} = c.$$

7. Assume $y = f(x)$ to be a known solution of $y' + y \cdot P(x) = 0$. To find the solution of $y' + y \cdot P(x) = Q(x)$, set $y = v \cdot f(x)$ and determine v. This provides another method of treating the linear equation.

8. Solve by the method of Exercise 7 the example worked out in the text.

14. Equations reducible to linear equations. An equation easily reducible to the linear form is the so-called *Bernoulli* equation*,

$$y' + yP(x) = y^n Q(x) \quad (n \neq 0,\ n \neq 1). \quad (15)$$

If we divide through by y^n, to obtain

$$y^{-n}y' + y^{-n+1}P(x) = Q(x),$$

an obvious change of variable is to set $y^{-n+1} = z$. From this we have $z' = (1 - n)y^{-n}y'$, leading to

$$\frac{1}{1 - n} z' + zP(x) = Q(x),$$

a linear equation.

To illustrate, consider the equation $y' - \dfrac{y}{3x} = y^4 \log x$. Divid-

---

* So named after James Bernoulli (1654–1705), a member of a family that contributed several illustrious names to the mathematics of the 17th and 18th centuries.

ing through by y^4, we have

$$y^{-4}y' - y^{-3} \cdot \frac{1}{3x} = \log x.$$

Setting $y^{-3} = z$, and hence $z' = -3y^{-4}y'$, we have the new equation

$$-\frac{1}{3} z' - \frac{1}{3x} \cdot z = \log x, \qquad (16)$$

which is linear. Let us solve this by the method of Exercise 7 of the preceding section. (The other methods would apply as well, of course.) The solution of the corresponding homogeneous equation, *i. e.*, of

$$-\frac{1}{3} z' - \frac{1}{3x} \cdot z = 0,$$

is $z = c/x$. (For simplicity, a particular solution may be taken, say $z = 1/x$.) Now let $z = \frac{1}{x} \cdot v$, hence $z' = \frac{v'}{x} - \frac{v}{x^2}$; then substitute in (16), to obtain

$$-\frac{1}{3x} \cdot v' + \frac{v}{3x^2} - \frac{v}{3x^2} = \log x,$$

or

$$dv = -3x \log x \, dx,$$

whence,

$$v = \int -3x \log x \, dx + c \equiv -3x^2 \left(\frac{\log x}{2} - \frac{1}{4} \right) + c.$$

From this we have

$$z = \frac{v}{x} = -\frac{3x}{4} (2 \log x - 1) + \frac{c}{x} = y^{-3},$$

and hence

$$y = \left[-\frac{3x}{4} (2 \log x - 1) + \frac{c}{x} \right]^{-\frac{1}{3}}.$$

Exercises

1. Solve the following:

(a) $dy = (xy^2 + 3xy) \, dx$.

(b) $t \, dx \, (2xt^2 \log x + 1) = 2x \, dt$.

(c) $(2y + 1) \, dx = (2y^3x^2 + x^2y^2 - 2x) \, dy$.

(d) $yy' + y^2 \cdot \cot x = \csc^2 x$.

(e) $(4 - x^2)y' + 4y = (2 + x)y^2$.

(f) $x \, dy + y \, dx = xy^2 \, dx$.

2. Solve $y' \cos y - \sin y = \cos x \cdot \sin^2 y$.   *Hint:* Put $u = \sin y$.

3. Solve $\sec^2 u \, du - \tan^3 u \, dx = -x \tan u \, dx$.

4. Discuss Equation (15) of the text for the cases $n = 0$ and $n = 1$.

15. Riccati equation. The student may have noted that up to this point the differential equations presented as illustrations and exercises have usually had solutions expressible in terms of elementary functions.* He should guard against any tendency to suppose that all functions may be so expressed, and should be prepared to accept as solutions of a differential equation functions which are not so expressible. Suppose, for example, we consider the problem of determining the length of arc of the ellipse

$$x = a \cos \theta$$
$$y = b \sin \theta$$

from the point $\theta = \dfrac{\pi}{2}$ to a variable point θ. From the relation $ds^2 = dx^2 + dy^2$ we have

$$ds = (a^2 \sin^2 \theta + b^2 \cos^2 \theta)^{1/2} \, d\theta.$$

It is not possible to solve this equation in terms of elementary functions, although the nature of the problem indicates that s is a perfectly definite function of θ and is, furthermore, a continuous function having a derivative. We may indicate the solution of the above equation in the form

$$s = \int_{\pi/2}^{\theta} (a^2 \sin^2 \theta + b^2 \cos^2 \theta)^{1/2} \, d\theta.$$

The integral is known as an elliptic integral, in terms of which elliptic functions may be defined. The subject of elliptic integrals and elliptic functions occurs in many branches of mathematics, and many volumes have been written on its exposition.

One differential equation of the first order and first degree which is not always solvable in terms of elementary functions is

$$y' + Py^2 + Qy + R = 0, \tag{17}$$

where P, Q, and R are functions of x alone. This is usually called

---

* By an *elementary function* we mean a function defined in a finite formula involving algebraic, trigonometric, exponential, and logarithmic functions.

a *Riccati equation*, after Count Riccati (1676–1754), an Italian mathematician who studied the special case $y' + by^2 = cx^m$. While (17) cannot always be solved in terms of elementary functions, we easily establish the following properties of the equation and its solutions:

PROPERTY 1. *If a particular solution, $y = y_1(x)$, is known, we may reduce the equation to a linear equation of the first order.*

To establish this property, let $y = y_1 + u$. Then $y' = y_1' + u'$, and the equation becomes

$$u' + u(Q + 2Py_1) + u^2P = 0.$$

This is recognized as a Bernoulli equation and, after the manner of Section 14, we put $v = \dfrac{1}{u}$, to obtain

$$v' - v(Q + 2Py_1) - P = 0,$$

which is linear.

PROPERTY 2. *If three distinct particular solutions $y = y_1(x)$, $y = y_2(x)$, and $y = y_3(x)$ are known, we may write down the complete solution without a quadrature.*

To show this, let us first substitute $y = y_3(x) + \dfrac{1}{v}$, and thus derive the linear equation

$$v' - v(Q + 2Py_3) - P = 0, \qquad (18)$$

as in Property 1. The other two solutions $y = y_1(x)$ and $y = y_2(x)$ of (17) furnish two solutions of (18); *viz.*,

$$v = v_1(x) \equiv \frac{1}{y_1(x) - y_3(x)}$$

and

$$v = v_2(x) \equiv \frac{1}{y_2(x) - y_3(x)},$$

whence, by Exercise 6, Section 13, the complete solution of (18) is given by

$$\frac{v - v_1}{v_2 - v_1} = c.$$

Replacing v by $\dfrac{1}{y - y_3}$, and v_1 and v_2 by their values, we have

$$\frac{\dfrac{1}{y - y_3} - \dfrac{1}{y_1 - y_3}}{\dfrac{1}{y_2 - y_3} - \dfrac{1}{y_1 - y_3}} = c,$$

which is easily reduced to

$$\frac{y - y_1}{y - y_3} \cdot \frac{y_2 - y_3}{y_2 - y_1} = c.$$

This is, then, the general solution of (17), and its form at once establishes

PROPERTY 3. *The cross ratio* of any four solutions of (17) is independent of* x.

PROPERTY 4. *If* P *is identically zero, equation* (17) *is linear and of first order. If* P *is not identically zero,* (17) *may be reduced to an equation of the form*

$$v'' + x_1 v' + x_2 v = 0.†$$

The first statement of the property is obvious. If $P \not\equiv 0$, let us substitute $y = \dfrac{z}{P}$ and multiply by P to obtain

$$z' + z^2 + \left(Q - \frac{P'}{P} \right) z + PR = 0.$$

If, now, we put $z = \dfrac{v'}{v}$ and multiply by v, we have

$$v'' + \left(Q - \frac{P'}{P} \right) v' + PRv = 0.$$

Note: The general solution of this equation involves two arbitrary constants. However, they enter into the corresponding solution

---

* By the cross ratio of four numbers a, b, c and d is meant the fraction $\dfrac{\dfrac{a - b}{a - d}}{\dfrac{c - b}{c - d}}$. If a, b, c, and d are metric or projective coördinates of four points A, B, C, and D on a line, this same fraction is said to be the cross ratio of the four points. Its value is invariant under projective transformations, a fact which renders it of fundamental importance in projective geometry.

† Later we shall know this as a linear equation of the second order.

of the original Riccati equation in such a manner that their ratio only is significant and furnishes the one constant essential for a first order equation.

Exercises

1. Form the differential equation whose solution expresses the length of arc s on the hyperbola $x = a \sec \theta$, $y = b \tan \theta$. Do not try to solve the equation obtained.

2. Using $y = \tan x$, an obvious solution, find the complete solution of $y' - y^2 - y \sin 2x + 2 \sin^2 x - 1 = 0$.

3. Show that if two different particular solutions of (17), $y = y_1(x)$ and $y = y_2(x)$, are known, the complete solution can be obtained with only one quadrature. *Hint:* Put $y = \dfrac{y_1 - uy_2}{1 - u}$.

4. Show that $y = 0$, $y = x$, and $y = x^2$ are all solutions of the Riccati equation $y' + \dfrac{y^2}{x^2 - x^3} + y\,\dfrac{x - 2}{x - x^2} = 0$, and write the general solution.

5. Find the Riccati equation which has as particular solutions $y = \dfrac{1}{x}$, $y = \log x$, $y = 2x$.

6. Show that $y = 1$, $y = 2x$, and $y = 2x + 1$ are all solutions of the Riccati equation $y' + \dfrac{y^2}{2x^2 - x} - \dfrac{y(1 + 4x)}{2x^2 - x} + \dfrac{4x}{2x^2 - x} = 0$, and write the general solution. Find the cross ratio of the original three solutions and the solution obtained by putting the arbitrary constant equal to one in the general solution $\dfrac{y - 1}{2x(y - 2x)} = c$; when $x = 1$, when $x = 5$, when $x = a$.

7. Take the three given solutions of the equation of Exercise 6 and the solution corresponding to $c = 3$, and find their cross ratio. Do the same when $c = b$.

8. Show that $y = \tan x$ is a particular solution of the Riccati equation $y' + \dfrac{y^2}{\cos x - 1} + \dfrac{y}{\sin x} = 0$, and thus reduce the equation to a linear equation of the first order, and solve.

16. Applications of differential equations. A class of problems to which differential equations lend themselves effectively may be found in geometry. If one desires to determine the equation of a curve whose slope at each of its points (x, y) is equal to some pre-determined function $f(x, y)$ of the coördinates of the point, he has merely to set

$$y' = f(x, y).$$

Solutions of this equation will represent curves having the desired property. Instead of the slope, one may be interested in some other quantity connected with a curve, whose value, at any point, is expressible in terms of the slope at that point, such as the sub-tangent, $y \dfrac{dx}{dy}$, and the subnormal, yy'. Many other quantities whose measures, at any point, depend only upon the position of the point and the direction of the curve through the point, may be readily expressed in terms of x, y, and y'.

If two one-parameter families of curves occupy the same plane in such a way that each curve of either family crosses, at right angles, every curve of the other family, each of the two families is said to be the system of *orthogonal trajectories* with reference to the other. Systems of curves related in this way have numerous uses in applied science, particularly in connection with fluid flow and potential theory.

If the position of a particle moving in a straight line is given by a coördinate x, and the time after some fixed instant is denoted by t, then the instantaneous velocity v of the particle at the position x and time t is defined by $\dfrac{dx}{dt}$. The condition that the velocity v shall be given by some function f of x and t produces the differential equation

$$\frac{dx}{dt} = f(x, t).$$

In the same manner,

$$\frac{dv}{dt} = g(v, t)$$

expresses the acceleration in terms of the velocity v and the time t.

Forces, acting upon a mass, produce motions of such a nature that (mass)(acceleration) equals the resultant force. Thus, if two forces, F_1 and F_2, both act in the same straight line, we have

$$m \frac{d^2x}{dt^2} = F_1 + F_2,$$

or

$$m \frac{dv}{dt} = F_1 + F_2.$$

A body of weight w pounds has mass w/g.

In electrical work, a condenser is a device capable of holding a quantity q of electricity, spoken of as a *charge*. The presence of such a charge on a condenser is accompanied by a difference in potential e across the terminals, which is proportional to the amount of electricity stored. This fact can be expressed by the equation

$$e = \frac{q}{C}.$$

If q is measured in coulombs and e in volts, then C is said to be the *capacity* of the condenser, in farads.

If a condenser is charged or discharged through a conductor, the instantaneous rate of change of the charge is given by $\frac{dq}{dt}$. This quantity is a measure of the current flowing in the conductor, and we may express the fact by the equation

$$i = \frac{dq}{dt},$$

where i will be the current flowing into the condenser, in amperes, if q is in coulombs and t in seconds. The amount of current which a conductor carries when subject to a constant e.m.f. is proportional to that e.m.f., and is given by the relation

$$e = Ri,$$

where R is called the *resistance* of the conductor. If i is in amperes and e in volts, then R is in ohms.

A (pure) *inductor* is a device which, when placed in an electrical circuit, opposes any change in the current by a difference in potential proportional to the rate of the change. In a circuit containing only a driving e.m.f. of e volts and an inductor, we have the relation

$$e = L \frac{di}{dt},$$

where L is said to be the *inductance* of the inductor and is measured in henries if i is in amperes and t in seconds. If a current i is driven through a resistance R and an inductance L, we have the relation

$$e = Ri + L \frac{di}{dt}.$$

Whether the driving electromotive force, e, is a constant or a function of t, it is seen that the above equation is linear and of the first order.

Exercises

1. Find the system of curves having the property that the tangent at any point passes through $(2, -4)$.

2. Find the system of curves having the property that the subtangent at any point exceeds twice the abscissa of the point by 1.

3. Find the polar equation of the curve passing through $(1, \pi/3)$ and such that the polar subtangent, $\rho^2 \dfrac{d\theta}{d\rho}$, at any point is equal to 2 divided by the radius vector, ρ, of the point.

4. The perpendicular from the origin to the tangent line of a curve is equal to the abscissa of the point of contact. Find the equation of the curve if it passes through $(1, -3)$.

5. Find the equation of the system of curves having the subnormal at every point equal to twice the ordinate of the point of contact, diminished by its abscissa.

6. The normal at any point of a curve and the line joining that point to the origin form an isosceles triangle, with the x-axis as base. Find the equation of the curve.

7. Find the differential equation of the family of orthogonal trajectories of the integral curves of $M\,dx + N\,dy = 0$.

8. Find the orthogonal trajectories of the integral curves of $y(1 - x)\,dx + x^2(1 - y)\,dy = 0$.

9. Find the orthogonal trajectories of the integral curves of the differential equation $(21x + 8y + 1)\,dx + (48x + y + 29)\,dy = 0$.

10. Find the orthogonal trajectories:

    (a) of the system of parabolas $x^2 = ky$.
    (b) of the system of parabolas $y^2 = kx + k$.

11. The area bounded by an arc of a curve, the x-axis, the ordinate $x = a$ and a variable ordinate is twice the length of that arc. Find the equation of the curve.

12. Find the orthogonal trajectories of the system of equilateral hyperbolas $xy = c$, and show that they too are equilateral hyperbolas.

13. Find the orthogonal trajectories of the system of conics $x^2 + \dfrac{y^2}{1 - e^2} = a^2$, in which e is fixed and a is the parameter of the family.

14. Work Exercise 13, modified to have a fixed and e variable.

15. Find the orthogonal trajectories of the system of parabolas whose foci are at $(0, 0)$ and directrices $y = c$, where c is taken as the parameter of the system.

16. A body moves in a straight line with its velocity exceeding by 1 its distance from a fixed point on the line. Find the equation of the motion, if the velocity is 2 when the time is zero.

17. A body moving in a straight line has its acceleration equal to 10 divided by 1 more than the time which has elapsed after a given instant. Find the equation of the motion, if at the given instant the body is 3 units from the origin and has a velocity equal to 2.

18. A body moves in a straight line in such a way that $v = \dfrac{k}{t^{1/2}} + \sin t$. Express the distance in terms of t.

19. A body falling in a liquid is subject to a steady pull of gravity and to a resistance which is proportional to the cube of the velocity. Find the equation of the motion. (*Hint:* Take the mass as unity, and write $v' = g - kv^3$. Rationalize the factors of $g - kv^3$ by the substitution $g = kb^{-3}$.) Show that the velocity approaches a constant.

20. A body of mass m pounds is projected upward at an initial velocity of v_0 feet per second. It encounters resistance equal to kv, and is affected by the steady pull of gravity. Find the equation, expressing v in terms of t. *Hint:* Take v as positive downward, and write $mv' = mg - kv$.

21. An electrical circuit contains a condenser of capacity C farads, and a resistance of R ohms connected in series. The condenser has a charge of q_0 coulombs at the time t_0. Express q in terms of t. *Hint:* $R \dfrac{dq}{dt} + \dfrac{q}{C} = 0$.

22. An electrical circuit contains an inductance of L henries and a resistance of R ohms connected in series. A current i_0 is flowing at the time t_0. Express i in terms of t. (Consider all e.m.f. removed.)

23. A series circuit, with no resistance, contains an inductance L measured in henries, and a constant electromotive force of e volts. Show that the current increases linearly with the time.

24. An electrical circuit contains an inductance of L henries and a resistance of R ohms in series with an electromotive force of the form $E \sin \omega t$ volts, where E and ω are constants. If $i = 0$ when $t = 0$, show that

$$i = \frac{E}{R^2 + L^2\omega^2} (R \sin \omega t - L\omega \cos \omega t) + \frac{EL}{R^2 + L^2\omega^2} \cdot e^{-Rt/L}.$$

As time goes on, note that the last term on the right-hand side approaches zero. On this account it is called the *transient* term. The first term on the right is called the *steady-state* term.

25. Solve Exercise 24 if $R = 12$, $L = 5$, $E = 120$, $\omega = 200$.

26. Put $\tan \alpha = L\omega/R$ in the answer to Exercise 24 and obtain the steady-state term as $E \sin (\omega t - \alpha)/(\sqrt{R^2 + L^2\omega^2})$. The e.m.f. of Exercise 24 is sinusoidal with a coefficient and, therefore, with maximum value equal to E. The steady-state term of the expression for the current is likewise sinusoidal with the maximum value $I = E/\sqrt{R^2 + L^2\omega^2}$. This is analogous to the equation $I = E/R$, which holds when a current driven by a constant e.m.f., E, is retarded by a constant resistance R. In the case at hand the quantity $\sqrt{R^2 + L^2\omega^2}$ is called the *impedance* of the circuit. Note that as $\omega \to 0$, the impedance $\to R$.

27. Solve Exercise 24 with $R = 8$, $L = 6$, $E = 80$, $\omega = 100$. Find the steady-state current when $t = 5$.

28. An electrical circuit contains a resistance of R ohms, a condenser whose capacity is C farads, and a constant electromotive force of E volts. If the charge on the condenser is q_0 when $t = t_0$, find the relation between q and t. Show that q approaches a constant which is independent of R.

29. Under the conditions of Exercise 28, express i in terms of t.

30. An electrical circuit contains a resistance of R ohms, a condenser of capacity C farads, and an e.m.f. which equals $E \sin \omega t$ expressed in volts where E and ω are constants. If the charge on the condensor is zero when $t = 0$, find i in terms of t.

31. By writing $\cot \alpha = -RC\omega$, show that the answer to Exercise 30 may be written as $i = \dfrac{CE\omega}{\sqrt{1 + R^2C^2\omega^2}} \sin (\omega t - \alpha)$.

What would you take to be the impedance of the circuit in this case? (See Exercise 26.)

32. Solve Exercise 30 for the steady-state current when $t = 2$ seconds if $C = \frac{1}{6}$, $R = 8$, $\omega = 120\pi$, $E = 10$.

33. A resistance of R ohms is connected in series with an inductance of L henries and a constant voltage v. At the time t_0, a current i_0 is flowing. Express i in terms of t, and show that i approaches a constant as t increases.

34. Assume that the air pressure p at a point of altitude h above sea level is proportional to the mass of air above the point, and that a portion of air Δm will occupy a volume Δv such that $pk \cdot \Delta v = \Delta m$. Show that $p = c \cdot e^{-kh}$, where c and k are constants.

35. The rate at which a body cools is proportional to the difference in temperature between the body and the surrounding atmosphere. If a body in air at $10°$ will cool from $200°$ to $100°$ in 40 minutes, how long will it take the body to cool from $100°$ to $10°$ in air at $5°$?

36. The rate at which a substance decomposes is assumed to be proportional to the amount of the substance remaining. Write the differential equation expressing this fact, and find its solution. If the amount of the substance not decomposed changes from 6 pounds to 1 pound in 2 hours, find the constant of proportionality and the constant of integration.

37. Find the equation of the Catenary, or curve of equilibrium of a hanging chain. *Hint:* Take the y-axis as the axis of symmetry, and the origin at the minimum point. Let the tension at the point (x, y) be $T(x, y)$, the length of the curve from $(0, 0)$ to (x, y) be (x, y), the weight of the chain from $(0, 0)$ to (x, y) be ks, and recognize that the y component of the tension T is equal to ks, while the x component of T is constant, say ka. This gives the two equations

$$T \frac{dx}{ds} = ka,$$

$$T \frac{dy}{ds} = ks.$$

If we square and add, we obtain $T^2 = k^2(a^2 + s^2)$. The value of T, thus defined, may be placed in the two differential equations, one of which will be in x and s, and the other of which will be in y and s.

Elimination of s between the solutions should give the desired equation.

38. Liquid is discharged from a vessel through an orifice at the rate given by $ca(2gh)^{\frac{1}{2}}$, where h is the head, or height of the surface of the water above the center of the orifice, g is the acceleration of gravity (about 32 feet per second^2), a is the area of the cross section of the orifice, and c is a constant, $\leqq 1$, called the coefficient of discharge, which is dependent upon the physical characteristics of the liquid and the vessel and upon the shape and size of the orifice, but which is ordinarily about 0.6. If the head changes from 10 feet to 9 feet in the first 15 minutes, in what time will the head be 1 foot, assuming that the vessel is cylindrical?

39. A cylindrical tank with vertical axis has a base 12 sq. ft. in area. Near the bottom is an orifice whose area is 2 sq. in., and whose coefficient of discharge is 0.6. It was observed that the discharge through the orifice lowered the head 1 inch in 20 seconds. What was the head to start with? What will the head be after 10 more seconds?

40. A vertical cylindrical tank 4 feet in diameter contains a first liquid with a head of 9 feet above a circular orifice 1 inch in diameter whose coefficient of discharge is $\frac{3}{5}$. A second liquid is flowing into the tank through a pipe $\frac{4}{5}$ inch in inside diameter at a constant linear velocity of 15 feet per second. Assuming g to be 32, express the time t in terms of h. Find the value of h at which it would remain constant.

41. In Exercise 40, find the value of t at which the contents of the tank will be half of each kind of liquid, if the head was 4 feet when the process began: (a) liquids mixed; (b) second liquid floating.

42. If the number of bacteria in a quart of milk doubles in 4 hours, in how much time will the number be multiplied by 25? Assume the rate of growth to be proportional to the number of bacteria present.

43. The rate at which one substance combines with another is supposed to be proportional to the amount of the first substance remaining. If there are 15 pounds of the first substance when $t = 0$ and 5 pounds when $t = 8$, find how much will be left when $t = 5$. Also find the value of t when there is 1 pound left.

44. Two substances are combining in such a way as to produce a third substance. If in x pounds of the product there are αx pounds of the first substance and βx pounds of the second, and if at the beginning of the process there are αa pounds of the first and βb pounds of the second, then the amounts of the two substances remaining after x pounds of the product have been produced are $\alpha(a - x)$ and $\beta(b - x)$, respectively. If the rate of combination is proportional to the product of the remaining amounts, we have $\dfrac{dx}{dt} = k\alpha\beta(a - x)(b - x)$. If $\alpha = \frac{3}{5}$ and there are 300 pounds of the first substance and 200 pounds of the second substance when $t = 0$, and 100 pounds of the product when $t = 1$ hour, find the value of t when there are 400 pounds of the product. Note that $\alpha + \beta = 1$.

45. With the conditions similar to those of Exercise 44, except that $\alpha = \frac{3}{4}$, let the amounts of the first and second substances present when $t = 0$ be 20 and 25 pounds, respectively. If, when $t = 30$ minutes, 20 pounds of the second substance remain, how much of the first substance will remain? How much of each parent substance will there be when $t = 60$ minutes?

46. If a quantity $a - x$ of a substance A is present and changes into a substance B at a rate $k_1(a - x)$, while the substance B is changing into the substance A at a rate $k_2 x$, express x in terms of t.

47. The compound amount A, in dollars, realized if a principal of P dollars is invested at the nominal rate of r per year compounded n times per year for t years is

$$A = P\left(1 + \frac{r}{n}\right)^{nt} \equiv P\left[\left(1 + \frac{r}{n}\right)^{\frac{n}{r}}\right]^{rt}.$$

As the number of times per year for compounding interest increases indefinitely, the amount A approaches the value

$$A = Pe^{rt},$$

which is the formula for the amount after t years if interest is compounded continuously on a principal of P dollars at the nominal rate r. The effective rate, or corresponding rate, for yearly conversion is $(e^r - 1)$, and r is called the *force of interest* corresponding to the effective rate $(e^r - 1)$. Show that the effective rate of 5 per cent is very nearly equivalent to the force 4.9 per cent.

48. A man works for a banking institution which pays him, in addition to his weekly salary, the equivalent of a dollar a day continuously deposited, and continuously converted at the force of

4 per cent. Find the amount in the account at the end of the first 10 years.

49. By natural increase the population of a city doubles every 50 years. Find the expression giving the number of people at a time t years after the period when the population was equal to n_0.

50. The normal growth of the population of a city is the same as in Exercise 49, and each year 1000 people move in from other cities. If the city had 10,000 inhabitants in 1940, what will be its population 50 years later?

51. A circular plate loaded symmetrically with respect to the center is freely supported around its edge. If the angle between the vertical and the normal at a point r units from the center is θ, the plate bends in such a way that the equation $r^2 \dfrac{d^2\theta}{dr^2} + r \dfrac{d\theta}{dr} - \theta = kr^3$ holds, with k a constant. To solve this equation, divide through by r^2, and note that in this form, $\theta'' + \dfrac{\theta'}{r} - \dfrac{\theta}{r^2} = kr$, the equation may be written $\theta'' + \left(\dfrac{\theta}{r}\right)' = kr$. One quadrature produces one arbitrary constant and a linear equation of the first order, $\theta' + \dfrac{\theta}{r} = \dfrac{kr^2}{2} + c$. Find the complete solution.

52. Water is running at the rate of 2 gallons per minute into a tank containing brine. The mixture is running out at the same rate, the concentration being kept uniform by stirring. Find the amount of salt in the tank at the end of one-half hour, if there are always 150 gallons of liquid in the tank and at the beginning the brine contained 60 pounds of salt.

53. Under the same conditions as in Exercise 52, except that the tank contains 150 gallons only at the beginning and the mixture runs out at the rate of 3 gallons per minute, find the amount of salt in the tank at the end of one-half hour.

54. The air in a room 20 feet by 30 feet by 12 feet tested .09 per cent carbon dioxide. Find the percentage of carbon dioxide in the room at the end of 18 minutes if 1000 cubic feet of air containing .04 per cent carbon dioxide is admitted into the room per minute.

17. Miscellaneous exercises on Chapter II. Solve the following:

1. $\left(\dfrac{y-x}{xy}\right) dx + \left(\dfrac{2y^3 + x + y}{y^2}\right) dy = 0.$

2. $\sin\theta\, dr + r\cos\theta\, d\theta = 0.$

3. $(x^2 + y^2)\, dx = x(x\, dy - y\, dx).$

4. $x(5y\, dx + 3x\, dy) - y^2(2y\, dx + x\, dy) = 0.$

5. $(x^2 + y^2)\, dx - 4xy\, dy = 0.$

6. $y\, dx - [x + (x^2 + y^2)^{1/2}]\, dy = 0.$

7. $xy' - 6y = 2x + 1.$

8. $u\dfrac{du}{dv} + vu^2 = v.$

9. $x\, dz + (z - 2z^2 \log x)\, dx = 0.$

10. $(v^3 - 3u)\, dv + (u^2 - 3v)\, du = 0.$

11. $(x + y^2)\, dx - 2xy\, dy = 0.$

12. $\tan x \cot y\, dx + dy = 0.$

13. $y'' = (x - y')\cot x + 1.$ *Hint:* Let $y' = p.$

14. $3y^3(x - 1)\, dx + xy^2(x - 7)\, dy = 0.$

15. $y'' - y' = 1.$

16. $\cos y\, dx + (x \sin y - 1)\, dy = 0.$

17. $\dfrac{dr}{d\theta} - r \tan\theta = r^4 \sec\theta.$

18. $xy'' - y' = 0.$

19. $(1 + e^{u/v})\, du + e^{u/v}\left(1 - \dfrac{u}{v}\right) dv = 0.$

20. $(2x - y + 4)\, dx + (2y + x + 7)\, dy = 0.$

21. $(6y + 3x - 5)\, dx + (2y + x + 2)\, dy = 0.$

22. $y(1 + 2xy)\, dx + x(1 - 2xy)\, dy = 0.$

23. $(\sqrt{st} - 1)s\, dt - (\sqrt{st} + 1)t\, ds = 0.$

24. $y(1 + 3xye^{xy} + 2xye^{-xy})\, dx + x^2y(3e^{xy} + 2e^{-xy})\, dy = 0.$

25. $(12x^2y^2 + y^3)\, dx + (4x^3y + 2xy^2)\, dy = 0.$

26. $(\pi + 2xy - 6y^2)\, dx + (x - 6y)^2\, dy = 0.$

27. $(4x^2 + y^2 + 4x)\, dx + y\, dy = 0.$

28. $3 \sin^2 \theta \sin \varphi \cos \varphi \, d\varphi + 5 \sin \theta \cos \theta \cos^4 \varphi \, d\theta = 0.$

29. $y^2(y \, dx + 2x \, dy) - x^2(y \, dx - 10x \, dy) = 0.$

30. $dr + (r \sec \theta + 1 + \sin \theta) \, d\theta = 0.$

31. $(2u + 1) \, dv + (2 - 4e^{-v}) \, du = 0.$

32. $(2y^2 - 4) \, dx + y(1 + 2xy^2) \, dy = 0.$

33. $(x^2 + 4y^2) \, dy = xy \, dx.$

34. $xy' + (x \tan y/x - y) = 0.$

35. $y' = \left(\dfrac{2x - 3y + 4}{3x - 2y - 1}\right)^2$

36. $(3y - xy^2 - 5x^2y^3) \, dx - x(2 + xy + 10x^2y^2) \, dy = 0.$

37. $(6xy + 6x^2y - 2y^3 + 3e^x) \, dx + (3x^2 - 3y^2) \, dy = 0.$

38. $(1 + x^2) \, y' + xy = \dfrac{2}{x}.$

39. $y \, dy + (xy^2 - 4x) \, dx = 0.$

40. $(ax^2 + 2bxy + cy^2) \, dx + (bx^2 + 2cxy + gy^2) \, dy = 0.$

41. In the differential equation $M \, dx + N \, dy = 0$, M and N are homogeneous polynomials in x and y, of degree 3. If the equation is exact, what are the most general forms for the quantities M and N? Solve the equation formed.

42. Solve the equation $(4x^3 + 9x^2y + 6xy^2 - y^3) \, dx + (3x^3 + 6x^2y - 3xy^2 + 20y^3) \, dy = 0.$

43. The triangle formed by the line tangent to a curve at any point, (x, y), the radius vector to the point, (x, y), and the y-axis, is isosceles, and has the y-axis as base. Find the equation of the curve

44. A water tank has vertical sides, and by means of an orifice at the bottom its level is lowered from 10 feet to 9 feet in 10 minutes Find the time required for the level to fall from 7 feet to 1 foot.

45. The x-intercept of a line tangent to a curve at the point (x, y) is proportional to $x^m y^n$. Find the equation of the curve.

46. An electrical current i is driven by a voltage $v = V \sin \omega$ through an inductance L. (V and ω are constant.) Express i in terms of t.

47. An electrical current i is driven through a resistance R and a condenser of capacity C, by a variable electromotive force $v = V \sin \omega t$. (V and ω are constant.) The initial charge on the condenser is q_0, the initial time t_0, and the initial current i_0.   Express q as a function of t.   *Hint:* The equation is $R \dfrac{dq}{dt} + \dfrac{q}{C} = V \sin \omega t$.

48. Under the conditions of Exercise 47, express i in terms of t.

49. A constant e.m.f. of V volts is applied to a resistance of R ohms and an inductance of L henries, connected in series.   At the time t_0 a current i_0 is flowing.   Express i in terms of t, and show that it approaches a constant as t increases.

50. Replace V in Exercise 49 by $V \sin \omega t$, and solve the problem.

51. A vessel containing liquid is rotated about a vertical axis at a uniform angular velocity ω.   Find the shape assumed by the surface of the liquid.

52. Prove that the differential equation of the orthogonal trajectories of the integral curves of a homogeneous equation is also homogeneous.

53. Find the equation of the family of curves which make the angle $\tan^{-1} \frac{3}{4}$ with each of the integral curves of the differential equation $(7x - 3y + 2)\, dx + (4y - 3x - 5)\, dy = 0$.

54. In books on Calculus* it is shown that if two functions $F(x, y)$ and $G(x, y)$ are so related that $F \equiv \Phi(G)$, then, and only then,

$$\begin{vmatrix} F_x & F_y \\ G_x & G_y \end{vmatrix} \equiv 0.$$

This determinant is known as the *functional determinant*, or *Jacobian*, of the two functions F and G.   Thus, if $G \equiv 1/x^2 y$ and $F \equiv 2 \log x + \log y$, the relation is obviously $F \equiv -\log G$.   Let the student show that the *Jacobian* of F and G vanishes identically for this case.

55. Find the Jacobian of the following pairs of functions; if it vanishes identically, find the functional relationship:

(a) $F \equiv x^2 + y^2$, $G \equiv 2xy$.

(b) $F \equiv \dfrac{(x + y)^2}{x^2 - y^2}$, $G \equiv \dfrac{3x - y}{x - y}$.

56. Show that if $F(x, y) = c$ and $G(x, y) = c$ are two general solutions of the differential equation $M\, dx + N\, dy = 0$, then F is a function of G.   *Hint:* Evidently

$$M \equiv \mu(x, y) F_x \equiv \nu(x, y) G_x$$

---

* Wilson's *Advanced Calculus*, page 62.

and

$$N \equiv \mu(x, y)F_y \equiv \nu(x, y)G_y,$$

where μ and ν are reciprocals of appropriate integrating factors of $M\,dx + N\,dy = 0$.

57. *Prove:* If $F(x, y) = c$ is the general solution of the equation $M\,dx + N\,dy = 0$, and if $G(x, y)$ is a function of $F(x, y)$, then $G(x, y) = c$ also represents the general solution.

58. On page 27 are listed five general solutions of the equation $x\,dy - y\,dx = 0$. Verify that Exercise 56 holds for the first and last by finding the Jacobian of $\dfrac{y}{x}$ and $\dfrac{1}{2}\log\dfrac{y+x}{y-x}$. Find the relation between these functions.

59. Verify by substitution that, since $\dfrac{y}{x} = c$ is the solution of $x\,dy - y\,dx = 0$, the following are also solutions:

(a) $e^{x/y} = c.$ (c) $\tan^{-1}\dfrac{y}{x} = c.$

(b) $\sin\dfrac{x}{y} = c.$ (d) $x^2 - 3xy - y^2 = cy^2.$

60. If $\mu(x, y)$ and $\nu(x, y)$ are two integrating factors of $M\,dx + N\,dy = 0$, show that either $\dfrac{\mu}{\nu}$ is identically equal to some constant, or that $\mu/\nu = c$ is a solution of the equation.

61. Find several solutions of the equation $x\,dy - y\,dx = 0$ from quotients of the integrating factors given on page 27.

62. Show that a differential equation $M\,dx + N\,dy = 0$, which has a solution, has an infinite number of integrating factors. *Hint:* If $f(x, y) = c$ is a solution, then $\varphi(f) = c$ is a solution.

63. Using $y = \sin x$, an obvious solution, find the complete solution of the Riccati equation $y' = y^2 \cdot \csc^2 x + y \cot x - 1$.

64. The air in a room 25 feet by 30 feet by 10 feet tests .1 per cent carbon dioxide. How much air containing .04 per cent of carbon dioxide must be admitted into the room per minute in order that 15 minutes later the air in the room test .08 per cent carbon dioxide?

CHAPTER III

Equations of the First Order, But Not of the First Degree

18. Introduction. We have seen in Chapter I how the differential equation

$$\frac{dy}{dx} = F(x, y) \tag{1}$$

defines a direction at each point (x, y) of the plane or, at least, at each point for which the function $F(x, y)$ has a value. With this picture in mind we have visualized an integral curve of (1) as a curve which has, at each one of its points, the direction called for by (1).

Let us consider, in this light, the equation

$$f(x, y, p) = 0, \tag{2}$$

where $p = dy/dx$ and $f(x, y, p)$ is a function into which p enters to a degree higher than the first. If x and y are assigned fixed values, this equation may be satisfied by more than one value of p. In other words, at a given point more than one direction may be acceptable to the differential equation. Just as the two roots of a quadratic equation may become equal or imaginary, so it may happen that for certain points, (x, y) in the plane, Equation (2), considered as an equation in p, may have some coincident or imaginary roots. If this condition should prevail, it would mean that in the plane there are certain points (x, y) where the differential equation defines fewer directions than the usual number.

19. Singular solutions. Let us consider the family of circles which is represented by the equation

$$(x - c)^2 + y^2 = 25 \tag{3}$$

as shown in Figure 2. The centers of these circles lie on the line $y = 0$. The circles are all tangent to each of the lines $y = 5$ and $y = -5$. If we concern ourselves with the number of these circles

57

which will pass through a given point (x, y), we may draw the following conclusions: (a) if $y^2 > 25$, the number is zero; (b) if $y = \pm 5$, the number is one; (c) if $-5 < y < 5$, the number is two. We may, furthermore, note that when $y = 0$, the two circles have a common vertical tangent line.

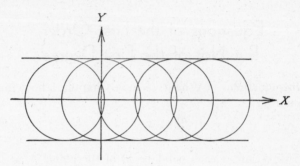

Fig. 2.

Equation (3) may be written as

$$x - c = \pm \sqrt{25 - y^2}$$

and differentiated to obtain the differential equation

$$1 = \mp \frac{yp}{\sqrt{25 - y^2}}, \qquad p = \frac{dy}{dx},$$

or

$$p^2 = \frac{25 - y^2}{y^2}. \tag{4}$$

Equation (4) evidently defines no real values of p if $y^2 > 25$, just one if $y = \pm 5$, and two if $0 < y^2 < 25$. Because he is a student of differential equations, the reader should take the point of view that (4) rather than (3) or Figure 2 is known. Since p is imaginary when $y^2 > 25$, no integral curve can enter such a region. The locus of points, for which (4) defines but one value of p, is made up of the three lines $y = 5$, $y = 0$, $y = -5$. We inquire into the possibility that these lines themselves be solutions of the differential equation. Since their equations are all of the form $y = $ constant, differentiation gives $dy/dx = p = 0$. By referring to (4), we see that $y = \pm 5$ and $p = 0$ satisfy it, but that $y = 0$ and $p = 0$ do not. Thus, the lines, $y = \pm 5$, are solutions of the differential equation.

It is clear from the derivation of (4) from (3) that the latter is the general solution.   If in (3) we assign a particular value to c, we obtain a particular solution.   Since the particular solutions are all circles, the straight line solutions, $y = \pm 5$, are not recoverable from the general solution.   They are, therefore, *singular solutions* in accordance with the following

DEFINITION.   *Any solution of a differential equation not included in the general solution is called a singular solution.*

Now it is shown in algebra that a polynomial equation $F(p) = 0$ of degree n will have n roots.   Any multiple root will also satisfy the derived equation $F'(p) = 0$.   Conversely, any common root of the two equations, $F(p) = 0$ and $F'(p) = 0$, is a multiple root of $F(p) = 0$.   In this case the derived equation is obtained by differentiating both sides with respect to p, other variables being held constant.   We may, therefore, find the locus of points at which (2) determines fewer than the usual number of values of p by finding points (x, y) such that

$$f(x, y, p) = 0 \qquad (2)$$

and

$$\frac{\partial f}{\partial p} (x, y, p) = 0 \qquad (5)$$

are satisfied by the same value of p.

If we consider the example just employed in this way, we seek the locus of points (x, y) for which the two equations,

$$\begin{cases} p^2 y^2 = 25 - y^2 \\ 2py^2 = 0 \end{cases}$$

are satisfied by the same values of P.   Now the second equation is satisfied whenever $y = 0$, but the first is not.   The second equation is also satisfied whenever $p = 0$.   If $p = 0$ is substituted in the first equation, we obtain the consistent equation $y^2 = 25$.   The conclusion, $y = \pm 5$, furnishes the solution sought, but until it can be checked against the general solution, we cannot say that it is *singular*.

Exercises

By the method of the text just displayed find, in each of the problems following, the locus of points at which the differential equation is satisfied by less than the maximum number of values of p. Verify that each such locus represents a singular solution.

1. $y = px + 2p^2 - p$.

General solution is $y = cx + 2c^2 - c$.

2. $p^2 - 3px + 3y = 0$.

General solution is $y = 3cx - 3c^2$.

3. $3p^2 + 2px^3 - 4x^2y = 0$.

General solution is $4y = 2cx^2 + 3c^2$.

4. $2yp^2 - (4x - 5)p + 2y = 0$.

General solution is $4y^2 = c(4x - 5) - c^2$.

5. $xp^2 - 2py + 3x = 0$.

General solution is $y = cx^2 + \dfrac{3}{4c}$.

6. $xp^3 - yp^2 + 1 = 0$.

General solution is $x + cy = c^3$.

7. $27p^3x^2y^6 - 18p^2xy^4(y^3 + 1) - 8x^3 = 0$.

General solution is $x^2 - cy^3 = c^3 + c$.

20. Equations solvable for p or y.   The equation

$$f(x, y, p) = 0 \tag{2}$$

is always theoretically solvable for p if x and y have such values that

$$\frac{\partial f(x, y, p)}{\partial p} \neq 0.$$

If the solution can be effected in terms of elementary functions, then by this method Equation (2), supposedly of higher degree in p, may be replaced by a number of first degree equations.   These may be solved by the methods of the preceding chapter.

If Equation (2) is readily solved for y in terms of x and p, we may write it in the form

$$y = G(x, p). \tag{6}$$

If this is differentiated with respect to x, it gives

$$p = \frac{\partial G(x, p)}{\partial x} + \frac{\partial G(x, p)}{\partial p} \frac{dp}{dx}. \tag{7}$$

Now, (7) is a first order and first degree differential equation in x

and p. It can be solved by the methods of Chapter II. The solution, suitably combined with (6), yields the solution of (2).

Illustration

Find the general solution of the equation

$$xp^2 - 2yp + 9x = 0 \tag{8}$$

and also the singular solution if there is one.

Solution: As the equation cannot be solved for p except by the use of radicals, we shall prefer to solve it for y. So solved, it appears as

$$y = \frac{9x}{2p} + \frac{xp}{2}.$$

If we differentiate this with respect to x, we obtain

$$(p^2 - 9)(p'x - p) = 0. \tag{9}$$

Evidently (9) can be satisfied only if

$$p^2 = 9, \tag{10}$$

or

$$p'x = p. \tag{11}$$

Equation (11) is a differential equation in x and p and may be written as

$$\frac{dp}{p} - \frac{dx}{x} = 0.$$

The solution is $\log (p/x) =$ a constant, or

$$p = 2c_1x. \tag{12}$$

We may now follow either of three courses:

(a) In (12) replace p by dy/dx to solve, obtaining

$$y = c_1x^2 + c_2, \tag{13}$$

and substitute (13) into (8) to find c_2 in terms of c_1.

(b) Eliminate the variable p from (12) and (8).

(c) Regard (8) and (12) as parametric equations of the solution.

Following the alternative (b), we obtain

$$4c_1x^3 - 4c_1xy + 9x = 0,$$

or

$$y = c_1x^2 + \frac{9}{4c_1}. \tag{14}$$

The student should satisfy himself that the alternatives (a) and (c) yield essentially the same result as the above. Because (14) satisfies (8) and contains one arbitrary constant, it is the general solution.

The Equation (10) remains to be considered. If we combine it with (8) by alternative (a), we have

$$p = \frac{dy}{dx} = \pm 3$$

and

$$y = \pm 3x + c_3.$$

Substituting this into (8) gives us

$$9x - 18x \pm 6c_3 + 9x = 0,$$
$$c_3 = 0,$$

and we are left with the equation

$$y = \pm 3x.$$

These equations both satisfy (8), and neither is included in the general solution (14). They are, therefore, singular solutions.

Exercises

Solve the following equations:

1. $p^2 - (2x + 3y)p + 6xy = 0$.

2. $y = 2p + 3p^2$.

3. $x^2p^2 - 3x^2y^3p + 2p - 6y^3 = 0$.

4. $p^2x^2(x^2 - 4) = 1$.

5. $(1 - x^2)p + xy - 5 = 0$.

6. $y - px = x\sqrt{n^2 + p^2}$.

7. $\left(\dfrac{dr}{d\theta}\right)^2 + 2r\left(\dfrac{dr}{d\theta}\right)\tan\theta - r^2\sin^2\theta = r^2(\cos^2\theta - \sec^2\theta)$.

8. $p^3 - (x^2 + xy^2 + y^4)p^2 + (x^3y^2 + x^2y^4 + xy^6)p - x^3y^6 = 0$.

9. $pxy^2(p^2 + 2) = 2p^2y^3 + px^3$.

10. $p^2 - px - 2py + 2xy = 0$.

11. $p^2\cos 2y + p(\sin 2y - \sin 2x \cos 2y) = \sin 2x \sin 2y$.

12. $4x^2(y - px) = 9yp^2$.

13. $(2x + py)^2 = p^2(y^2 + 2x)$.

14. $y - 5x = 3 \cos^{-1} p$.

15. $2px - y + 2 \log p - \log 4 = 0$.

16. $y = 2px + p$.

17. $xy = p^2$.

21. Clairaut's equation. Among the differential equations which can be solved by differentiation are those reducible to the especially interesting type,

$$y = px + \phi(p), \tag{15}$$

called *Clairaut's equation* in honor of the French astronomer and mathematician, Alexis Claude Clairaut (1713–1765). By differentiating with respect to x, we reduce this equation to

$$p = p + [x + \phi'(p)]\frac{dp}{dx}.$$

This evidently will be satisfied only if

$$x = -\phi'(p), \tag{16}$$

or

$$\frac{dp}{dx} = 0.$$

The latter equation leads to the expression

$$p = c,$$

and by combining this with (15) we obtain the general solution

$$y = cx + \phi(c). \tag{17}$$

If we associate (16) with (15), we obtain the simultaneous pair of equations

$$y = -p\phi'(p) + \phi(p), \tag{18}$$
$$x = -\phi'(p)$$

which represent the singular solution of (15).

22. Equations solvable for x. If the Equation (2) can be readily reduced to the form

$$x = \psi(y, p), \tag{19}$$

we may differentiate it with respect to y and obtain

$$\frac{1}{p} = \frac{\partial \psi(y, p)}{\partial y} + \frac{dp}{dy} \frac{\partial \psi(y, p)}{\partial p}, \tag{20}$$

an equation in y and p of the first order and first degree. The solution of (20) may be combined with (19) as (12) was combined with (8) to obtain the solution of (19).

As an illustration of this type of equation let us take

$$16y^2p^3 + 2px - y = 0. \tag{21}$$

Solving for x gives

$$x = \frac{y - 16y^2p^3}{2p},$$

and differentiation of this with respect to y gives

$$\frac{1}{p} = \frac{p\left(1 - 32yp^3 - 48y^2p^2 \dfrac{dp}{dy}\right) - (y - 16y^2p^3) \dfrac{dp}{dy}}{2p^2}.$$

This equation is equivalent to

$$(1 + 32yp^3)(p \, dy + y \, dp) = 0,$$

which can be satisfied only if

$$1 + 32yp^3 = 0, \tag{22}$$

or

$$p \, dy + y \, dp = 0.$$

The second equation yields

$$py = c,$$

and elimination of p between this and (21) gives

$$y^2 = 2cx + 16c^3,$$

or

$$y = \pm \sqrt{2cx + 16c^3}$$

evidently the general solution.

If we return now to (22) and eliminate p between it and (21), we obtain

$$27y^4 + 2x^3 = 0.$$

This equation is not recoverable from the general solution but does satisfy (21). It therefore is a singular solution.

Exercises

Solve the following:

1. $4p^2 + \dfrac{2x}{y} p - 1 = 0.$ **4.** $y^{-\frac{2}{3}}p^2 - 3xp + 9y = 0.$

2. $x = 2p - p^2.$ **5.** $p = \arccos (x - p).$

3. $p^3 - 8xyp + 16y^2 = 0.$ **6.** $x = \dfrac{p}{y} + \log p - \log y.$

7. $\tan y \sec^4 y \, p^2 + 2xp \sec^2 y - \tan y = 0.$

8. $x = p^2 + y.$ **9.** $x = py + p^2.$

10. Solve the following Clairaut equations:

(a) $y = px + \dfrac{a^2}{p}.$

(b) $y = px + 2p^2 - p.$

(c) $y = px + \sqrt{p^3 - p^2 + p - 1}.$

(d) $y = (x - 5)p + p^2.$

(e) $y = px + \log p.$

(f) $(y - px)(3p - 1) = 5p^2.$

(g) $e^{y-px} = p^2.$

(h) $y^2 \log y = pxy + p^2.$ *Hint:* Set $u = \log y.$

11. A differential equation has, as general solution, the relation $y^2 - 2xyc + (1 + x^2)c^2 - 4 = 0.$ Find the singular solution.

12. Find the singular solution of $y = px + \dfrac{1}{p^2}.$

13. The equation $y = \dfrac{c}{2} (x - c)^2,$ where c is any constant, satisfies the differential equation $p^3 - 2xyp + 4y^2 = 0.$ Find the singular solution.

14. Find the singular solution of the equation $p^2 - xp + y = 0.$

15. The general solution of a differential equation is

$$x \cos c + y \sin c = 5.$$

Find the singular solution.

16. Corresponding to each real value of the constant c is a circle whose center has the coördinates $(5 \cos c, 5 \sin c)$, and whose radius equals unity.   Find the equation of the system of circles, its differential equation, and the singular solution of the differential equation.

17. Find the singular solution of the differential equation

$$p^2 - 3xp + y^2 = 0.$$

18. Find the singular solution of $p^2 - pxy + y^2 \log 3y = 0$.

19. Find the singular solution of $xp = y \log y$.

20. Find the singular solution of $p^3 - 2xyp + 4y^2 = 0$.

21. The equation $(1 - x^2)p + xy - 10 = 0$ is satisfied by $y = 10x$.   Is the latter a particular solution or a singular solution?

22. Is $y = 0$ a singular solution or a particular solution of

$$12xp^2 - 12yp + 4y = 0?$$

23. Find the singular solution of $3p^2y^2 - 2pxy + 4y^2 - x^2 = 0$.

24. Solve $yp + 2x = \pm \sqrt{(y^2 + 4x^2)(1 + p^2)}$.

25. Solve $y - px = ax \sqrt{1 + p^2}$.

26. Solve $x^3p^2 + 4x^2py - 5xy^2 = 0$.

27. Solve $(px - y)(px + y) = y(x - y)$.

28. Solve $x^np^t - y^n = 0$.

29. The equation $p^2(3x + 1) - 3p(y + 2) + 9 = 0$ has the general solution $2cy + c^2(y - 3x) - 4 = 0$, and the singular solution $y^2 + 4y - 12x = 0$.   Show that the relation $y - 3x = 0$ is also a solution, and that it is not given by the general solution.   It is the limiting relation approached as the constant c increases beyond all bound.   Such a solution is sometimes called an *infinite* solution.

30. If we set $px - y$ equal to a new variable Y, and differentiate, we obtain

$$dY = p\,dx + x\,dp - dy = (p - y')\,dx + x\,dp = x\,dp.$$

If, now, X is so chosen that $dX = dp$, say $X = p$, then we have

$$P \equiv \frac{dY}{dX} = x.$$

Hence, show that any differential equation of the first order

$$f(x, y, p) = 0$$

becomes
$$f(P, PX - Y, X) = 0,$$
which is likewise of the first order.

31. Show that if the change of variable described in Exercise 30, known as a *transformation of Legendre*, be applied twice, then the result is the original equation.

32. Solve the following equations by applying the transformation of Legendre and solving the resulting differential equation. This gives a relation of the form $F(X, Y, c) = 0$. To return to the original variables, put $X = p$, $Y = px - y$, and obtain $F(p, px - y, c) = 0$. Eliminate p between this and the original equation.

(a) $4p^2x = 3$.

(b) $y = \sqrt{p^2 + (px - y)^2}$.

(c) $xp^2 + 4p - 2y = 0$.

(d) $x = 5p + \sqrt{1 + 4p^2}$.

(e) $p^2x = 1 - x$.

(f) $(y - px)x = y$.

33. Examine the solutions of Exercise 10, above, for infinite solutions.

34. Solve the following by any method, showing all solutions:

(a) $y^2 + 2xyp - (1 - x^2)p^2 = 0$.

(b) $(x^2 - 9)p^2 - 2xyp + y^2 - 9 = 0$.

(c) $px \pm \sqrt{1 + p^2} = 0$.

(d) $x^2(1 + p^3)^2 - a^2 = 0$.

(e) $y = -2p + \sqrt{9 + p^2}$.

(f) $3p^2 + 2px^3 - 4x^2y = 0$.

(g) $y = px + (p - r)(p - s)$, where r and s are constants.

(h) $y = px + \sqrt{a^2 + p^2}$.

(i) $x^2p^2 - (2xy - 1)p + y^2 = 0$.

(j) $(y - px)(3p - 5) = 15p$.

(k) $2x - \log (yp^2) = 0$.

(l) $2y = p^2 + p^3$.

(m) $y = px + x \sqrt{a^2 + p^2}$.

(n) $y^2 \log^2 y + p^2 = y^2$. *Hint:* Let $y = e^z$.

(o) $\dfrac{(ax - 1)^2}{-a^2x^2 + 2ax} = -1 - p^2$.

(p) $p^2 - xp + y = 0$.

(q) $xp^2 - 2yp + 9x = 0$.

(r) $5\left(\dfrac{ds}{dt}\right)^5 + \left(\dfrac{ds}{dt}\right)^2 - s = 0$.

(s) $\sin (y - px) = \dfrac{1}{\pm \sqrt{1 + p^2}}$.

(t) $\left(\dfrac{dr}{d\theta}\right)^3 - (\sin \theta - \csc \theta + r) \left(\dfrac{dr}{d\theta}\right)^2 +$

$(r \sin \theta - r \csc \theta - 1) \dfrac{dr}{d\theta} + r = 0.$

(u) $e^{2x}(y^2 \log y - py) = p^2.$ *Hint:* Set $v = \log y,\ u = e^x.$

35. Is $y = 0$ a singular solution or a particular solution of $y = px$?

36. Show that a family of confocal and coaxial parabolas is self orthogonal.

37. Show that a system of confocal central conics, $\dfrac{x^2}{c^2} + \dfrac{y^2}{c^2 - 1} = 1;\ c^2 \neq 1$, is self orthogonal.

38. Find the system of curves such that the subnormal of any curve at any point equals its subtangent at the same point, multiplied by x^2.

39. The product of the intercepts of a line tangent to a curve is a constant k. Find the curve.

40. Find the curves whose tangents are a constant distance from the point (a, b).

41. The portion of the tangent to a curve cut off by the axes is equal to k. Find the equation of the curve.

42. A circle of radius a rolls on the inside of a circle of radius $4a$ whose center is at the origin. A fixed diameter of the moving circle generates a system of straight lines. Find the singular solution of the differential equation of the system of lines.

43. Express in the form of a Clairaut equation the differential equation whose solutions represent the lines tangent to the curve $x^2 = y^3$.

44. Find the equation of the curve for which $OP = 2 \tan \alpha$, where O is the origin, P is the point where an arbitrary tangent meets OX, and α is the inclination of the tangent.

45. The sum of the x- and y-intercepts of an arbitrary tangent to a curve is 3. Find the equation of the curve.

CHAPTER IV

Linear Differential Equations

23. Introduction. We treat in this chapter the *linear* equation, a most important class of differential equation. The student has already met with linear equations of the first order in Chapter II, Section 13. We now define a linear equation of order n as an equation of the form

$$P_0 \frac{d^n y}{dx^n} + P_1 \frac{d^{n-1}y}{dx^{n-1}} + P_2 \frac{d^{n-2}y}{dx^{n-2}} + \cdots + P_{n-1}\frac{dy}{dx} + P_n y = Q, \quad (1)$$

where $P_0, P_1, \cdots, P_n$ and Q are functions of x alone or constants, with P_0 not identically zero and n a positive integer.

As we shall soon see, this equation has somewhat simpler properties if the function $Q(x)$ in the right-hand side of it is identically zero. If $Q(x) \not\equiv 0$, it is a material help in discussing Equation (1) and seeking its solutions to refer to the equation

$$P_0 \frac{d^n y}{dx^n} + P_1 \frac{d^{n-1}y}{dx^{n-1}} + P_2 \frac{d^{n-2}y}{dx^{n-2}} + \cdots + P_{n-1}\frac{dy}{dx} + P_n y = 0 \quad (2)$$

which is formed from (1) by replacing the right-hand member with zero. This equation is spoken of as the *reduced* or *homogeneous* equation corresponding to (1).

24. Homogeneous, with constant coefficients. Important applications of linear equations occur in which the functions $P_0, P_1, \cdots, P_n$ are constants. If at the same time the right-hand member is zero, the equation has the form

$$a_0 y^{(n)} + a_1 y^{(n-1)} + \cdots + a_{n-1}y' + a_n y = 0, \quad (3)$$

where the $a_0, a_1, \cdots, a_n$ are real constants with $a_0 \neq 0$ and the superscripts (n), $(n-1)$, $\cdots$ mean derivatives with respect to x (or whatever is the independent variable) of the order indicated. It will occur to the thoughtful student that, if a linear combination like (3) of a function and its derivatives cancels to zero, the derivatives must be more or less repetitious in form. If we try, as a possible solution of (3), the equation

$$y = e^{mx}, \tag{4}$$

we have

$$y' = me^{mx}, \quad y'' = m^2 e^{mx}, \quad \cdots, \quad y^{(n)} = m^n e^{mx},$$

and substitution of these into (3) gives the equation

$$a_0 m^n + a_1 m^{n-1} + \cdots + a_{n-1} m + a_n = 0 \tag{5}$$

since $e^{mx} \neq 0$. This is an algebraic equation of degree n. We speak of it as the *characteristic* equation of (3). In general it has n roots or solutions. Sets of two or more of these roots may be equal and pairs of roots may be complex.

The task of solving the characteristic equation is one whose discussion does not properly belong in this book. For such discussions the student may refer to books in college algebra or theory of equations. For the most part the exercises in this book are so selected that the characteristic equations are easy to solve. This is less likely to be true of linear differential equations encountered in practice.

25. Real and distinct roots. From Equations (4) and (5) of Article 24, we infer that if the characteristic equation has n solutions, $m = r_1, m = r_2 \cdots, m = r_n$, then the differential Equation (3) has solutions

$$y = e^{r_1 x}, \quad y = e^{r_2 x}, \quad \cdots, \quad y = e^{r_n x}.$$

We now show that if the numbers $r_1, r_2, \cdots, r_n$ are real and distinct, the general solution is

$$y = c_1 e^{r_1 x} + c_2 e^{r_2 x} + \cdots + c_n e^{r_n x} \tag{6}$$

where $c_1, c_2, \cdots, c_n$ are arbitrary constants.

Two important properties of a linear homogeneous equation may be introduced by the following example. The equation

$$x^2 y'' - 2xy' + 2y = 0$$

has $y = x^2$ as a solution since

$$x^2 (x^2)'' - 2x(x^2)' + 2x^2 \equiv 2x^2 - 4x^2 + 2x^2 \equiv 0.$$

If we put $y = cx^2$, where c is a constant, then we have

$$x^2 (cx^2)'' - 2x(cx^2)' + 2(cx^2) \equiv c[x^2(x^2)'' - 2x(x^2)' + 2x^2]$$

$$\equiv c \cdot 0 = 0,$$

and thus $y = cx^2$ is also a solution.

Again, $y = x$ is a solution, as well as $y = kx$, where k is a constant. *Verify:* If we now set $y = cx^2 + kx$, this too will be a solution since

$$x^2(cx^2 + kx)'' - 2x(cx^2 + kx)' + 2(cx^2 + kx)$$
$$\equiv x^2[c(x^2)'' + k(x)''] - 2x[c(x^2)' + k(x)'] + 2(cx^2 + kx)$$
$$\equiv c[x^2(x^2)'' - 2x(x^2)' + 2x^2] + k[x^2(x)'' - 2x(x)' + 2x]$$
$$\equiv c \cdot 0 + k \cdot 0 = 0.$$

The reader will now appreciate the force of the following two theorems.

THEOREM 1. *If* $y = f(x)$ *satisfies a linear homogeneous differential equation, then* $y = cf(x)$, *where c is an arbitrary constant, also satisfies it.*

THEOREM 2. *If* $y = f(x)$ *and* $y = g(x)$ *both satisfy a linear homogeneous differential equation, then* $y = cf(x) + kg(x)$, *where c and k are arbitrary constants, also satisfies it.*

The extension of Theorem 2 to cases of more than two given solutions is obvious. These theorems follow at once from the properties of linearity of derivatives, which assert that the derivative of a constant times a function is the constant times the derivative of the function, and the derivative of a sum of functions is the sum of their derivatives. A more formal proof may be written out by the student.

Let us return now to a consideration of a homogeneous differential equation with constant coefficients. The most general such equation is displayed in Article 24 as Equation (3). In that article the substitution $y = e^{mx}$ was made which resulted in the characteristic Equation (5). This equation, being of degree n, has n roots, and application of the above theorems indicates that the differential Equation (3) has the solution (6). A proper question for the next consideration is, "Does (6) represent the general solution of (3)?"

The situation may be approached again by an example. As the student should show, the differential equation

$$x^2(1 - \log x)y'' + xy' - y = 0$$

is satisfied by $y = \log x$ and $y = \log x^2$. By the above theorems it follows that

$$y = c_1(\log x) + c_2(\log x^2)$$

also satisfies where c_1 and c_2 are arbitrary constants. But $\log x^2$ is the same as $2 \log x$, and the solution just above may be written as

$$y = c_1 \log x + 2c_2 \log x = (c_1 + 2c_2) \log x$$

or

$$y = c \log x,$$

where we have put c in place of $c_1 + 2c_2$. This solution, containing as it does but one arbitrary constant, cannot be the general solution of any second order differential equation.

The difficulty with the functions $\log x^2$ and $\log x$ (where $y = c_1 \log x + c_2 \log x^2$ fails to be the general solution) is that they satisfy the identity

$$(\log x^2) - 2(\log x) \equiv 0.$$

This is a special case of two functions which are *linearly dependent*. The meaning of linearly *independent* or *dependent* functions is stated in the following definition.

DEFINITION.   *The functions* $f_1(x)$, $f_2(x)$, $\cdots$, $f_n(x)$ *are linearly independent only if the identity,*

$$c_1 f_1(x) + c_2 f_2(x) + \cdots + c_n f_n(x) \equiv 0, \tag{7}$$

has all c's constant and equal to zero.

If the identity (7) is possible with all c's constant and one or more c's not zero, the functions are said to be linearly dependent.

If the functions $e^{r_1 x}$, $e^{r_2 x}$, $\cdots$, $e^{r_n x}$ were linearly dependent, then a set of constants K_1, K_2, $\cdots$, K_n, not all zero, should exist such that

$$K_1 e^{r_1 x} + K_2 e^{r_2 x} + \cdots + K_n e^{r_n x} \equiv 0,$$

and if the notation were so chosen that $K_1 \neq 0$, then we could write

$$e^{r_1 x} = \frac{K_2}{K_1} e^{r_2 x} + \frac{K_3}{K_1} e^{r_3} + \cdots + \frac{K_n}{K_1} e^{r_n x}.$$

In such a case the solution (6) would appear as

$$y = c_1 \left[\frac{K_2}{K_1} e^{r_2 x} + \frac{K_3}{K_1} e^{r_3 x} + \cdots + \frac{K_n}{K_1} e^{r_n x} \right]$$
$$+ c_2 e^{r_2 x} + c_3 e^{r_3 x} + \cdots + c_n e^{r_n x},$$

or

$$y = c_2' e^{r_2 x} + c_3' e^{r_3 x} + \cdots + c_n' e^{r_n x}, \tag{8}$$

where

$$c_i' = c_i + \frac{c_1 K_i}{K_1}, \qquad (i = 2, 3, \cdots, n).$$

Evidently (8) would involve only $n - 1$ arbitrary constants, and could not be the general solution of an nth order differential equation.

A test for the linear dependence of the functions

$$f_1(x), f_2(x), \cdots, f_n(x) \tag{9}$$

is afforded by evaluation of the so-called *Wronskian* (determinant).

$$\begin{vmatrix} f_1(x) & f_2(x) & \cdots & f_n(x) \\ f_1'(x) & f_2'(x) & \cdots & f_n'(x) \\ \cdot & \cdot & \cdots & \cdot \\ \cdot & \cdot & \cdots & \cdot \\ \cdot & \cdot & \cdots & \cdot \\ f_1^{(n-1)}(x) & f_2^{(n-1)}(x) & \cdots & f_n^{(n-1)}(x) \end{vmatrix}. \tag{10}$$

If the functions (9) are linearly dependent, (10) vanishes identically and conversely.*

In the case of constant coefficients, if the n roots $r_1, r_2, \cdots, r_n$ of the characteristic equation are all distinct, the Wronskian of the functions $e^{r_1 x}, e^{r_2 x}, \cdots, e^{r_n x}$ becomes

$$\begin{vmatrix} e^{r_1 x} & e^{r_2 x} & \cdots & e^{r_n x} \\ r_1 e^{r_1 x} & r_2 e^{r_2 x} & \cdots & r_n e^{r_n x} \\ r_1^2 e^{r_1 x} & r_2^2 e^{r_2 x} & \cdots & r_n^2 e^{r_n x} \\ \cdot & \cdot & \cdots & \cdot \\ \cdot & \cdot & \cdots & \cdot \\ \cdot & \cdot & \cdots & \cdot \\ r_1^{n-1} e^{r_1 x} & r_2^{n-1} e^{r_2 x} & \cdots & r_n^{n-1} e^{r_n x} \end{vmatrix}$$

or

$$\begin{vmatrix} 1 & 1 & \cdots & 1 \\ r_1 & r_2 & \cdots & r_n \\ r_1^2 & r_2^2 & \cdots & r_n^2 \\ \cdot & \cdot & \cdots & \cdot \\ \cdot & \cdot & \cdots & \cdot \\ \cdot & \cdot & \cdots & \cdot \\ r_1^{n-1} & r_2^{n-1} & \cdots & r_n^{n-1} \end{vmatrix} e^{(r_1 + r_2 + \cdots + r_n)x}$$

The exponential function $e^{(r_1 + r_2 + \cdots + r_n)x}$ cannot vanish. Therefore, the Wronskian vanishes only if the last determinant vanishes, and this plainly would vanish if two of the roots were equal. This last

---

* See E. B. Wilson, *Advanced Calculus*, page 241.

determinant may be expanded and factored* when it appears as

$$(r_1 - r_2)(r_1 - r_3) \cdots (r_1 - r_n)(r_2 - r_3) \cdots (r_2 - r_n) \cdots (r_{n-1} - r_n).$$

Since no two r's are equal, no factor vanishes, and the functions $e^{r_i x}$ are linearly independent so that (6) is the general solution of (3).

Exercises

1. Find the general solution of each of the following equations:

    (a) $y'' - 2y' - 3y = 0.$

    (b) $3y''' - y'' - 2y' = 0.$

    (c) $2y''' - 5y'' + 2y' = 0.$

    (d) $y'' + 2y' - 8y = 0.$

    (e) $y^{iv} - 4y'' + 3y = 0.$

    (f) $y''' - by'' = a^2 y' - a^2 by.$ (a, b real constants)

    (g) $y^{iv} - 2y''' - y'' + 2y' = 0.$

2. Show that $y_1 \equiv x - \sin 2x$ and $y_2 \equiv 3x - 3 \sin 2x$ are linearly dependent. Show that any two functions that differ by a constant factor are linearly dependent.

3. (a) Show that $y_1 \equiv x + e^x$, $y_2 \equiv 1 + \cos x$, $y_3 \equiv 0$ are linearly dependent.

(b) Show that any set of functions is linearly dependent if $y \equiv 0$ is one of the set.

4. (a) Show that a set of functions is linearly dependent if two of the functions are identical.

(b) Show that a set of functions is linearly dependent if one of the functions is a constant multiple of another.

(c) Show that a set of functions is linearly dependent if a sub-set of those functions is linearly dependent.

5. Verify that $y = 0$ is a solution of (3). If $n - 1$ other solutions are found, are we in a position to write down the general solution?

6. If $y = f(x)$ satisfies Equation (2), show that the substitution $y = \mu f(x)$ and the subsequent substitution $d\mu/dx = v$, made in Equation (1), will lower its order.

7. Solve the equation $y''' + y'' - 2y' = 0$, and find the particular solution for which $y = -1$, $y' = 4$, and $y'' = -8$ when $x = 0$.

---

* See L. E. Dickson, *First Course in Theory of Equations*, Exercise 4, page 108.

8. A particle moves on a straight line in such a way that its acceleration is equal to four times its velocity. At the time $t = 0$ its displacement from the origin is 1 foot and its velocity is 8 feet per second. Find its position and velocity when $t = 2$ seconds.

9. A particle moves in a straight line in such a manner that its acceleration is $\frac{1}{9}$ of its distance from the origin and of the same sign. It starts from the origin with a velocity of 3 units per second. Find its position and velocity at the end of 6 seconds.

10. Verify that $y = e^{2x}$ and $y = xe^{2x}$ are linearly independent solutions of $y'' - 4y' + 4y = 0$ and write the general solution.

26. Complex roots. If we substitute $y = e^{mx}$ into the differential equation

$$y'' - 6y' + 13y = 0, \tag{11}$$

we obtain the characteristic equation

$$m^2 - 6m + 13 = 0.$$

This equation has as roots

$$m = 3 + 2i, \qquad m = 3 - 2i,$$

where $i = \sqrt{-1}$. The method of Section 25 would give as the solution

$$y = c_1 e^{(3+2i)x} + c_2 e^{(3-2i)x} \tag{12}$$

which will, as a matter of fact, satisfy (11) formally. However, it is complex in form and does not always yield real values of y for real values x, c_1, and c_2. Equation (12) can be written as

$$y = e^{3x}[c_1 e^{2ix} + c_2 e^{-2ix}], \tag{13}$$

and the student who is familiar with the identities

$$\left. \begin{array}{l} e^{i\alpha} \equiv \cos \alpha + i \sin \alpha, \\ e^{-i\alpha} \equiv \cos \alpha - i \sin \alpha, \end{array} \right\} \tag{14}$$

will have no trouble to pass from (13) to

$$y = e^{3x}[c_3 \cos (2x) + c_4 \sin (2x)], \tag{15}$$

where $c_3 = c_1 + c_2$ and $c_4 = i(c_1 - c_2)$. Those students who are not familiar with (14) may look up those identities in a book on advanced calculus or, perhaps better, derive the general solution (15) by the method of Exercise 1 below.

Exercises

1. (a) Verify directly that $y = e^{3x} \cos (2x)$ and $y = e^{3x} \sin (2x)$ are solutions of (11), that they are linearly independent, and, hence, that the general solution of (11) is (15).

(b) Verify that if the characteristic equation has as its solution $m = a \pm bi$ (in which case the characteristic equation is $m^2 - 2am + a^2 + b^2 = 0$ and the homogeneous differential equation is $y'' - 2ay' + (a^2 + b^2)y = 0$), then $y = e^{ax} \cos bx$ and $y = e^{ax} \sin bx$ are linearly independent solutions of the differential equation whose general solution is, therefore, $y = e^{ax}[c_1 \cos bx + c_2 \sin bx]$.

2. Solve the following equations:

(a) $y'' - 4y' + 13y = 0$.
(b) $y''' + 6y'' + 10y' = 0$.
(c) $y'' + 6y' + 25y = 0$.

3. Show that if the roots of the characteristic equation of a differential equation include the values $a \pm bi$, the solution

$$y = e^{ax}(c_1 \cos bx + c_2 \sin bx),$$

where c_1 and c_2 are arbitrary real constants, can be written in the equivalent form

$$y = k_1 e^{ax}[\sin (bx + k_2)],$$

where k_1 and k_2 are arbitrary real constants. *Hint:*

$$e^{ax}(c_1 \cos bx + c_2 \sin bx)$$
$$= e^{ax} \cdot \sqrt{c_1^2 + c_2^2} \cdot \left[\frac{c_1}{\sqrt{c_1^2 + c_2^2}} \cos bx + \frac{c_2}{\sqrt{c_1^2 + c_2^2}} \sin bx \right].$$

4. Put the solutions of Exercises 2(a), 2(b), and 2(c) in the form discussed in Exercise 3.

5. Show that a result alternative to the one in Exercise 3 is

$$y = k_1 e^{ax}[\cos (bx + k_2)].$$

6. A particle is in simple harmonic motion on a straight line with its acceleration (-4) times its displacement from the origin. At the end of $\pi/2$ seconds, its velocity is 4 feet per second and its acceleration is 16 feet per second. Find its position and velocity at the end of π seconds.

7. The motion on a straight line, defined by

$$s = e^{-at}(c_1 \cos bt + c_2 \sin bt) \qquad (a > 0),$$

where s is displacement from the origin at the time t, is called *damped harmonic* motion. The quantity e^{-at} is called the *damping factor*, a the *damping constant*, and $2\pi/b$ the period. Show that the equation $\dfrac{d^2s}{at^2} + 2\dfrac{ds}{dt} + 50s = 0$ represents such a motion and find the period.

8. If the equation $\dfrac{d^2s}{dt^2} + 2a\dfrac{ds}{dt} + bs = 0$, $(a > 0)$ is to represent damped harmonic motion, what condition is thus imposed on the coefficients a and b? State in that case the value of the damping factor and the period.

9. For the damped harmonic motion defined by $\dfrac{d^2s}{dt^2} + 6\dfrac{ds}{dt} + 49s = 0$, find the time during which the damping factor decreases by 40%.

10. If the period of a damped harmonic motion is 10π seconds and the damping factor decreases by 37.5% in 4.7 seconds, set up the differential equation which defines the motion.

27. Repeated roots. In applying the method of Section 25 to the equation

$$y'' - 6y' + 9y = 0, \qquad (16)$$

we obtain the characteristic equation

$$m^2 - 6m + 9 = 0$$

which has both roots equal to 3. Evidently $e^{r_1 x}$ and $e^{r_2 x}$ are linearly dependent when $r_1 = r_2$. The solution

$$y = c_1 e^{3x} + c_2 e^{3x}$$

is no more inclusive than the solution

$$y = c_1 e^{3x} \qquad (17)$$

which, having only one arbitrary constant, cannot be the general solution of a differential equation of order 2. To obtain the general solution of (16), we may find a suggestion in the form of the solution (17). By this we see that

$$y = u e^{3x} \qquad (18)$$

is a solution of (16) if u is a constant. We may ask for the most general function u of x such that (18) will satisfy (16). By differentiation

$$y' = u'e^{3x} + 3ue^{3x},$$
$$y'' = u''e^{3x} + 16u'e^{3x} + 9ue^{3x},$$

and by these (16) reduces to

$$u''e^{3x} + u'(6 - 6)e^{3x} + u(9 - 18 + 9)e^{3x} = 0,$$

or

$$u'' = 0.$$

This equation is solved by two integrations which yield

$$u = (c_1 + c_2x)$$

so that the general solution of (16) becomes

$$y = (c_1 + c_2x)e^{3x}.$$

Let us employ the method again, this time with the equation

$$y''' - 6y'' + 12y' - 8y = 0. \tag{19}$$

The characteristic equation

$$m^3 - 6m^2 + 12m - 8 = 0$$

has the triple root $m = 2$. This one root yields the solution

$$y = c_1e^{2x}$$

of (19) which suggests the form

$$y = ue^{2x}. \tag{20}$$

The substitution of (20) into (19) gives the equation

$$u''' = 0$$

which has the solution

$$u = c_1 + c_2x + c_3x^2.$$

The general solution of (19) is, therefore,

$$y = (c_1 + c_2x + c_3x^2)e^{2x}$$

The proof, that if a is a root of the characteristic equation of multiplicity ν, then $y = e^{ax}, y = xe^{ax}, \cdots, y = x^{\nu-1}e^{ax}$ are all solutions of the corresponding homogeneous equation, is easy to make by the use of some symbols, called operators, which will be introduced later in this chapter. In the meantime working a number of the following exercises will prove profitable to the student.

Exercises

1. Show that the differential equation

$$y''' - 8y'' + 20y' - 16y = 0 \tag{21}$$

has the characteristic roots 2, 2, and 4. Then

$$y = ue^{2x} \tag{22}$$

must satisfy (21) with $u =$ a constant. In order that (22) satisfy (21), show that u must satisfy

$$u''' - 2u'' = 0.$$

If we let $u'' = v$, $u''' = v'$, this equation becomes

$$v' - 2v = 0.$$

Solve this equation obtaining

$$v = u'' = c_1 e^{2x}$$

and find u by two integrations. Write, finally, the general solution of (21).

2. Solve the following equations:

(a) $\dfrac{d^3y}{dx^3} + 2\dfrac{d^2y}{dx^2} = 0.$

(b) $y^{iv} - 2y''' + y'' = 0.$

(c) $y^v - 3y^{iv} + 2y''' = 0.$

(d) $\dfrac{d^4y}{dx^4} + 2\dfrac{d^3y}{dx^3} - 3\dfrac{d^2y}{dx^2} - 4\dfrac{dy}{dx} + 4y = 0.$

(e) $\dfrac{d^4y}{dx^4} + \dfrac{d^3y}{dx^3} - 3\dfrac{d^2y}{dx^2} - 5\dfrac{dy}{dx} - 2y = 0.$

(f) $\dfrac{d^4y}{dx^4} - 2\dfrac{d^3y}{dx^3} + 5\dfrac{d^2y}{dx^2} = 0.$

(g) $y''' - 2y'' + y' = 0.$

(h) $y^{vi} + 8y^{iv} + 16y'' = 0.$

3. Show that the characteristic equation of the differential equation

$$y^{iv} - 4y''' + 8y'' - 8y' + 4y = 0$$

has the complex double roots

$$m = 1 \pm i.$$

Verify that $y = xe^x \cos x$ and $y = xe^x \sin x$ are solutions and write the general solution.

4. Write the general solution of

$$y^v + 8y''' + 16y' = 0.$$

28. Right-hand side not zero. Suppose that the general linear equation

$$P_0 \frac{d^n y}{dx^n} + P_1 \frac{d^{n-1} y}{dx^{n-1}} + \cdots + P_{n-1} \frac{dy}{dx} + P_n y = Q(x) \qquad (23)$$

is satisfied by the equation

$$y = F(x) \qquad (24)$$

which is entirely lacking in arbitrary constants. Suppose, moreover, that the homogeneous equation

$$P_0 \frac{d^n y}{dx^n} + P_1 \frac{d^{n-1} y}{dx^{n-1}} + \cdots + P_{n-1} \frac{dy}{dx} + P_n y = 0 \qquad (25)$$

has the general solution

$$y = c_1 f_1(x) + c_2 f_2(x) + \cdots + c_n f_n(x). \qquad (26)$$

By the type of argument used in Section 25 in order to establish Theorems 1 and 2 appearing there, it is easy to see that the equation

$$y = c_1 f_1(x) + c_2 f_2(x) + \cdots + c_n f_n(x) + F(x)$$

satisfies (23). Since this equation contains n essential constants, it must be the general solution. We speak of the right-hand side of Equation (26) as the *complementary function* for the corresponding equation. Naturally the function $F(x)$ is called a *particular integral*. Since the complementary function comes out of the general solution of the homogeneous differential equation, the student already knows how to form it for the case in which the equation has constant coefficients.

The particular integral (24) can often be found by a process known as the method of undetermined coefficients which we will now illustrate. We take the equation

$$y''' - 7y'' + 16y' - 12y = 24x^2 e^x \qquad (27)$$

and soon find its complementary function to be

$$c_1 e^{2x} + c_2 x e^{2x} + c_3 e^{3x}.$$

For a particular integral we try

$$y = Ax^2 e^x + Bxe^x + Ce^x \tag{28}$$

since all derivatives of this reduce to that same form with different coefficients. Thus:

$$y' = Ax^2 e^x + (2A + B)xe^x + (B + C)e^x,$$
$$y'' = Ax^2 e^x + (4A + B)xe^x + (2A + 2B + C)e^x,$$
$$y''' = Ax^2 e^x + (6A + B)xe^x + (6A + 3B + C)e^x.$$

When we multiply y''', y'', y', and y by 1, -7, 16 and -12 as required by (27) and equate the sum to $24x^2 e^x$ identically, we obtain

$$-2Ax^2 e^x + (10A - 2B)xe^x + (-8A + 5B - 2C)e^x \equiv 24x^2 e^x.$$

This identity holds if

$$-2A = 24, \qquad 10A - 2B = 0, \qquad -8A + 5B - 2C = 0,$$

or if

$$A = -12, \qquad B = -60, \qquad C = -102.$$

The particular integral of (27) is, therefore,

$$y = (-12x^2 - 60x - 102)e^x,$$

and its general solution is

$$y = c_1 e^{2x} + c_2 x e^{2x} + c_3 e^{3x} - (12x^2 + 60x + 102)e^x.$$

As is clear from this example, the method of undetermined coefficients consists in assuming a suitable linear combination of functions with unknowns as coefficients. The coefficients are then determined by requiring that the expression satisfy the differential equation. The method may be used only when the right-hand side of the equation is a finite linear combination of functions of the forms x^α, $e^{\beta x}$, $\sin \gamma x$ and $\cos \delta x$, α, β, γ, δ real, with α equal to zero or a positive integer, and of other functions which are products of a finite number of those four forms. In the first column of Table 2 are listed some of the possible terms of $Q(x)$ if the method of undetermined coefficients is to work. In it α, β are supposed real and n is any positive integer. The functions listed in the first column may appear as terms of $Q(x)$ with any numerical coefficients.

The last column gives the form of the particular integral, provided the number listed in the middle column is not one of the charac-

Table 2. Undetermined Coefficients

1	0	A
x^n	0	$A_0 x^n + A_1 x^{n-1} + \cdots + A_n$
$e^{\alpha x}$	α	$A e^{\alpha x}$
$x^n e^{\alpha x}$	α	$e^{\alpha x}[A_0 x^n + A_1 x^{n-1} + \cdots + A_n]$
$e^{\alpha x} \sin (\beta x)$	$\alpha + \beta i$	$e^{\alpha x}[A \cos (\beta x) + B \sin (\beta x)]$
$e^{\alpha x} \cos (\beta x)$	$\alpha + \beta i$	$e^{\alpha x}[A \cos (\beta x) + B \sin (\beta x)]$
$x^n e^{\alpha x} \sin (\beta x)$	$\alpha + \beta i$	$e^{\alpha x} \cos (\beta x)[A_0 x^n + A_1 x^{n-1} + \cdots + A_n]$ $\quad + e^{\alpha x} \sin \beta x [B_0 x^n + B_1 x^{n-1} + \cdots + B_n]$
$x^n e^{\alpha x} \cos (\beta x)$	$\alpha + \beta i$	$e^{\alpha x} \cos (\beta x)[A_0 x^n + A_1 x^{n-1} + \cdots + A_n]$ $\quad + e^{\alpha x} \sin \beta x [B_0 x^n + B_1 x^{n-1} + \cdots + B_n]$

teristic roots of the given equation. If the number listed in the second column is a characteristic root of the given equation with the multiplicity k, the function in the third column should be multiplied by x^k.

Illustration

To solve the equation

$$y'' - 7y' + 10y = 6x + 8e^{2x},$$

note that its characteristic roots are 2 and 5 and its complementary function is $c_1 e^{2x} + c_2 e^{5x}$. Since 0 is not a characteristic root, the function x in the right-hand side indicates the particular integral choice

$$A_0 x + A_1.$$

Since 2 is a characteristic root of multiplicity 1, the function e^{2x} calls for the particular integral

$$A x e^{2x}.$$

Combining these, we write

$$y = A + Bx + Cxe^{2x}.$$

By differentiation we obtain

$$y' = A + 2Cxe^{2x} + Ce^{2x},$$
$$y'' = 4Cxe^{2x} + 4Ce^{2x}.$$

Multiplying y'' by 1, y' by -7, y by 10 and equating the sum of these products to the right-hand member of the given equation, we have

$$(10A - 7B) + 10Bx - 3Ce^{2x} \equiv 6x + 8e^{2x}.$$

From this we draw the equations

$$10A - B = 0, \qquad 10B = 6, \qquad -3C = 8,$$

or

$$A = \tfrac{21}{50}, \qquad B = \tfrac{2}{5}, \qquad C = -\tfrac{8}{3}.$$

The resulting general solution is

$$y = c_1 e^{2x} + c_2 e^{5x} + \tfrac{21}{50} + \tfrac{2}{5}x - \tfrac{8}{3}xe^{2x}.$$

Exercises

1. Solve $\dfrac{d^2y}{dx^2} + 2\dfrac{dy}{dx} = 36 \cos x.$

2. Solve $\dfrac{d^2y}{dx^2} + \dfrac{dy}{dx} - 2y = 2x^2 - 3x.$

3. Solve $\dfrac{d^3y}{dx^3} - \dfrac{d^2y}{dx^2} - 4\dfrac{dy}{dx} + 4y = x^4 - 3x + 5.$

4. Solve $\dfrac{d^3y}{dx^3} - \dfrac{d^2y}{dx^2} - 9\dfrac{dy}{dx} + 9y = 2x + 3.$

5. Solve $\dfrac{d^3y}{dx^3} + \dfrac{d^2y}{dx^2} - 5\dfrac{dy}{dx} + 3y = x^3 - x + 1.$

6. Solve $\dfrac{d^3y}{dx^3} - 3\dfrac{d^2y}{dx^2} + 2\dfrac{dy}{dx} = 2x^2 - 3x + 1.$

7. Solve $\dfrac{d^3y}{dx^3} - \dfrac{d^2y}{dx^2} = 2x + 3.$

8. Solve $\dfrac{d^3y}{dx^3} - 2\dfrac{d^2y}{dx^2} - 3\dfrac{dy}{dx} = x^2 - 5.$

9. Solve $\dfrac{d^4y}{dx^4} + 3\dfrac{d^2y}{dx^2} - 4y = \sin 2x + 6e^{3x}$.

10. Solve $\dfrac{d^3y}{dx^3} - 2\dfrac{d^2y}{dx^2} - 3\dfrac{dy}{dx} = 3\sin x$.

11. Solve $\dfrac{d^4y}{dx^4} - y = -2\sin 2x + \cos 2x$.

12. Solve $\dfrac{d^4y}{dx^4} + 4\dfrac{d^2y}{dx^2} = \sin x - 2\cos 3x$.

13. Find a particular integral of $\dfrac{d^3y}{dx^3} + 9\dfrac{dy}{dx} = 2\cos 3x$.

14. Find a particular integral of $\dfrac{d^4y}{dx^4} + 2\dfrac{d^2y}{dx^2} + y = -\sin x$.

15. Find a particular integral of $\dfrac{d^4y}{dx^4} + 4\dfrac{d^2y}{dx^2} = -\cos 2x$.

16. Find a particular integral of $\dfrac{d^4y}{dx^4} + 5\dfrac{d^2y}{dx^2} + 4y = \cos x + \sin 3x$.

17. Find a particular integral of $\dfrac{d^2y}{dx^2} - 3\dfrac{dy}{dx} + 5y = 3e^{2x}$.

18. Find a particular integral of $\dfrac{d^3y}{dx^3} + 2\dfrac{d^2y}{dx^2} - \dfrac{dy}{dx} = 4e^{-x}$.

19. Find a particular integral of $\dfrac{d^3y}{dx^3} - 4\dfrac{d^2y}{dx^2} + 3\dfrac{dy}{dx} = x + 2e^x$.

20. Find a particular integral of $\dfrac{d^3y}{dx^3} - 6\dfrac{d^2y}{dx^2} + 9\dfrac{dy}{dx} = 2e^{3x}$.

21. Find a particular integral of

(a) $\dfrac{d^2y}{dx^2} - 2\dfrac{dy}{dx} + y = -e^x$.

(b) $\dfrac{d^3y}{dx^3} + \dfrac{d^2y}{dx^2} - 6\dfrac{dy}{dx} = e^x + e^{2x} - 2e^{-3x}$.

22. Find a particular integral of $\dfrac{d^3y}{dx^3} + \dfrac{d^2y}{dx^2} - 6\dfrac{dy}{dx} = e^x + e^{2x} - 2e^{-3x}$.

23. Find a particular integral of $\dfrac{d^2y}{dx^2} + 3\dfrac{dy}{dx} = x^2e^{2x}$.

24. Prove that if the right-hand member of the complete differential equation is of the form $Q(x) \equiv e^{mx} \cdot \varphi(x)$, the substitution $y = e^{mx} \cdot z$ will reduce the given equation to one in z, in which the right-hand member is $\varphi(x)$.

25. Find a particular integral of $\dfrac{d^2y}{dx^2} - 2\dfrac{dy}{dx} - y = e^x \cdot \sin x$.

26. Find a particular integral of $\dfrac{d^3y}{dx^3} - 4\dfrac{d^2y}{dx^2} = e^{3x}(x + 2)$.

27. Find a particular integral of $\dfrac{d^2y}{dx^2} - 4y = 2e^{3x} + \sin x$.

28. Find a particular integral of $\dfrac{d^3y}{dx^3} - 2\dfrac{d^2y}{dx^2} = 2x - \cos x$.

29. Find a particular integral of $\dfrac{d^3y}{dx^3} - \dfrac{dy}{dx} = e^x(x^2 - \sin x)$.

30. Find a particular integral of

$$\frac{d^2y}{dx^2} - (a + b)\frac{dy}{dx} + aby = e^{ax} + 2e^{bx} + \cos x.$$

31. A particle of unit mass moves on a straight line under the action of two forces, one equal to $2\cos 3t$, the other numerically equal to the distance of the particle from the origin and directed towards the origin. At the initial instant, the particle is at the origin and moving with a velocity equal to $+1$. Find the acceleration of the particle at the end of $\pi/2$ seconds.[2] (See Section 16, Chapter II.)

32. A mass weighing 8 pounds moves on a straight line segment AB. It is attracted toward A by a force proportional to its distance from A and toward B by a constant force of 16 pounds. Initially, the mass is at rest 20 feet from A and has an acceleration toward A numerically equal to 4 feet per second[2]. Find the position of the mass at the end of $\pi\sqrt{5}/\sqrt{17}$ seconds.

33. The force exerted by a spring is proportional to the amount by which it is stretched beyond its natural length. A twelve-pound weight attached to the spring elongates it by 2 inches. The weight is drawn down another 4 inches and released. Find the first instant when the spring reaches its natural length.

34. A cylindrical spar buoy 2 feet in diameter and weighing 720 pounds stands vertically in water weighing 62.5 pounds per cubic foot. It is slightly depressed and then released. Find the period of the resulting motion.

29. Method of operators. The method we have used in the preceding section for solving the non-homogeneous equation has the merit of suggesting itself in a tolerably natural way and of being effective when applicable. It yields, however, on the score of generality to the method we present in this section.

We begin by defining the symbol D by means of the equalities:

$$D^m u \equiv \frac{d^m u}{dx^m} \qquad (m \text{ a positive integer}). \quad (29)$$

$$(a_0 D^m + a_1 D^{m-1} + \cdots + a_{m-1}D + a_m)u \equiv a_0 D^m u$$
$$+ a_1 D^{m-1}u + \cdots + a_{m-1}Du + a_m u (a_i \text{ constants}). \quad (30)$$

$$[(D + a)f(D)]u \equiv (D + a)[f(D)u], \text{ where } f(D) \text{ is a}$$
$$\text{polynomial in } D. \quad (31)$$

Manifestly, the expressions D^m and $a_0 D^m + a_1 D^{m-1} + \cdots$ are not factors multiplying u but rather operators which, applied to u, produce a certain result. However, these operators obey a number of laws precisely as if they were numerical factors. Thus:

I. $D(u + v) \equiv \dfrac{d}{dx}(u + v) \equiv \dfrac{du}{dx} + \dfrac{dv}{dx} \equiv Du + Dv,$

II. $D(cu) \equiv \dfrac{d}{dx}(cu) \equiv c\,\dfrac{du}{dx} \equiv cDu,$

III. $D^h(D^k u) \equiv \dfrac{d^h}{dx^h}\left(\dfrac{d^k u}{dx^k}\right) \equiv \dfrac{d^{h+k}u}{dx^{h+k}} \equiv D^{h+k}u,$

IV. $(D + a)[(D + b)u] \equiv (D + b)[(D + a)u].$

By the use of these symbols linear differential equations with constant coefficients may be more simply written. For example,

$$\frac{d^3y}{dx^3} - 8\frac{d^2y}{dx^2} - 8\frac{dy}{dx} + 12y = 0$$

appears as

$$(D^3 - 8D^2 - 8D + 12)y = 0,$$

or

$$(D - 2)^2(D + 3)y = 0.$$

By property IV and a logical extension of it, the quantity

$$(D - a)(D - b)(D - c)y$$

is the same as

$$(D - a)[(D - b)\{(D - c)y\}],$$

so it is possible to operate upon y by a factored operator using one factor at a time.   Moreover, since the factors may be permuted, those factors may be employed in any order.   In view of the fact that

$$(D - a)0 \equiv 0,$$

any solution of

$$(D - c)y = 0$$

is also a solution of

$$(D - a)(D - b)(D - c)y = 0.$$

And, if a, b, c are all different, this equation is equivalent to the three first order equations $(D - a)y = 0$, $(D - b)y = 0$, $(D - c)y = 0$. In like manner the equation

$$(D - a)^3(D - b)^2(D - c)y = 0$$

is equivalent to the three equations

$$(D - a)^3y = 0, \ (D - b)^2y = 0, \ (D - c)y = 0.$$

Note now that the equation

$$(a_0D^n + A_1D^{n-1} + \cdots + a_{n-1}D + a_n)y = 0$$

is of the same form in D as is the characteristic equation of the previous article in m.   We promptly conclude that the above equation has the solution

$$y = e^{ax}(c_1 + c_2x + c_3x^2) + e^{bx}(c_4 + c_5x) + c_6e^{cx}.$$

In order to apply the method of operators to the non-homogeneous equation

$$(D - a)(D - b)(D - c)y = Q(x),$$

it is necessary to be able to "divide" by the operators $D - a$, $D - b$, and $D - c$.   That is, if we had an operator $1/D - a$ which would cancel the effect of the operator $D - a$, we could operate with it upon both sides of the above equation and obtain

$$(D - b)(D - c)y = \frac{1}{D - a} Q(x) = P(x).$$

Operation upon both sides of this by $\dfrac{1}{D-b}$ and then by $\dfrac{1}{D-c}$ would produce in turn

$$(D-c)y = \frac{1}{D-b}P(x) = R(x)$$

and

$$y = \frac{1}{D-c}R(x) = S(x).$$

Now if

$$(D-a)u = v, \tag{32}$$

operation upon both sides by $\dfrac{1}{D-a}$ will produce

$$u = \frac{1}{D-a}v.$$

But we may solve (32) by writing it in the form

$$\frac{du}{dx} - au = v$$

and by employing the integrating factor e^{-ax} as shown in Section 13, Chapter II. We thus obtain the equivalent exact equation

$$e^{-ax}\frac{du}{dx} - aue^{-ax} = ve^{-ax},$$

whose solution is

$$ue^{-ax} = \int ve^{-ax}\,dx + C,$$

or

$$u = e^{ax}\int ve^{-ax}\,dx + Ce^{ax}.$$

We conclude, finally, that it is reasonable to define the operator $\dfrac{1}{D-a}$ by the equation

$$\frac{1}{D-a}v = e^{ax}\int ve^{-ax}\,dx + Ce^{ax},$$

where C is an arbitrary constant.

Ordinarily the inverse operator is employed only for finding particular integrals so that the arbitrary constants may be dropped.

Illustration

In order to solve the equation

$$(D - 2)^2(D - 1)y = 36e^{3x} + 12,$$

we apply in succession the operators $\dfrac{1}{D - 2}$, $\dfrac{1}{D - 2}$, and $\dfrac{1}{D - 1}$, dropping all constants of integration, and obtain

$$
\begin{aligned}
(D - 2)(D - 1)y &= e^{2x} \int (36e^x + 12e^{-2x})\, dx \\
&= e^{2x}(36e^x - 6e^{-2x}) \\
&= 36e^{3x} - 6, \\
(D - 1)y &= e^{2x} \int (36e^x - 6e^{-2x})\, dx \\
&= e^{2x}(36e^x + 3e^{-2x}) \\
&= 36e^{3x} + 3, \\
y &= e^x \int (36e^{2x} + 3e^{-x})\, dx \\
&= e^x(18e^{2x} - 3e^{-x}) \\
&= 18e^{3x} - 3.
\end{aligned}
$$

This is, of course, a particular integral. Annexing the complementary function, we have the general solution

$$y = c_1 e^x + c_2 e^{2x} + c_3 x e^{2x} + 18e^{3x} - 3.$$

Exercises

1. By the method of this section, find the complete solution of:

(a) $\dfrac{d^2 y}{dx^2} - 2\dfrac{dy}{dx} = \cos x.$

(b) $\dfrac{d^3 y}{dx^3} + 2\dfrac{d^2 y}{dx^2} - 3\dfrac{dy}{dx} = x + 2.$

(c) $\dfrac{d^2 y}{dx^2} - a\dfrac{dy}{dx} + b\dfrac{dy}{dx} - aby = 2e^{3x}.$

(d) $\dfrac{d^3 y}{dx^3} - 2\dfrac{d^2 y}{dx^2} - \dfrac{dy}{dx} + 2y = -xe^x.$

(e) $\dfrac{d^3 y}{dx^3} - 4\dfrac{d^2 y}{dx^2} + 4\dfrac{dy}{dx} = e^x - \sin 2x.$

2. By the method of this section, show that the complete solution of $(D - a)^k y = 0$ is $y = e^{ax}(c_1 + c_2 x + c_3 x^2 + \cdots + c_k x^{k-1}).$

3. Verify that

$$[f(D)]e^{rx} \equiv (D^n + a_1 D^{n-1} + a_2 D^{n-2} + \cdots + a_{n-1}D + a_n)e^{rx}$$
$$\equiv e^{rx}(r^n + a_1 r^{n-1} + \cdots + a_{n-1}r + a_n)$$
$$\equiv e^{rx} \cdot f(r).$$

30. Method of variation of parameters. In this section we take up a method of finding a particular integral of a linear differential equation applicable not only to the equation with constant coefficients but also to any linear differential equation for which the complementary function has been found. It is called the method of variation of parameters (sometimes called the method of variation of constants), due to Lagrange.*

Let the equation be

$$\frac{d^n y}{dx^n} + P_1 \frac{d^{n-1}y}{dx^{n-1}} + P_2 \frac{d^{n-2}y}{dx^{n-2}} + \cdots + P_{n-1}\frac{dy}{dx} + P_n y = Q(x), \quad (33)$$

and let the reduced equation have the complete solution

$$y = c_1 y_1 + c_2 y_2 + \cdots + c_n y_n. \tag{34}$$

The method consists in seeking to modify the c's in such a manner that (34) becomes a solution of (33). For that purpose, let us think of the c's as functions of x, to be determined presently. From (34), by differentiation, we have

$$y' = (c_1 y_1' + c_2 y_2' + \cdots + c_n y_n') + (c_1' y_1 + c_2' y_2 + \cdots + c_n' y_n),$$

and we impose, as one condition on the c's, that

$$c_1' y_1 + c_2' y_2 + \cdots + c_n' y_n \equiv 0,$$

so that

$$y' = c_1 y_1' + c_2 y_2' + \cdots + c_n y_n',$$

and hence,

$$y'' = (c_1 y_1'' + c_2 y_2'' + \cdots + c_n y_n'') + (c_1' y_1' + c_2' y_2' + \cdots + c_n' y_n').$$

We now impose a second condition, that

$$c_1' y_1' + c_2' y_2' + \cdots + c_n' y_n' \equiv 0,$$

which gives

$$y'' = c_1 y_1'' + c_2 y_2'' + \cdots + c_n y_n''.$$

Differentiating again, we obtain

$$y''' = (c_1 y_1''' + c_2 y_2''' + \cdots + c_n y_n''')$$
$$+ (c_1' y_1'' + c_2' y_2'' + \cdots + c_n' y_n''),$$

and again imposing the condition

---

* (1736–1813); one of the greatest mathematicians of all time.

$$c_1'y_1'' + c_2'y_2'' + \cdots + c_n'y_n'' \equiv 0,$$

we have

$$y''' = c_1y_1''' + c_2y_2''' + \cdots + c_ny_n'''.$$

Continuing in this manner, we arrive, finally, at

$$y^{(n)} = (c_1y_1^{(n)} + c_2y_2^{(n)} + \cdots + c_ny_n^{(n)})$$
$$+ (c_1'y_1^{(n-1)} + c_2'y_2^{(n-1)} + \cdots + c_n'y_n^{(n-1)}).$$

We now set the last parenthesis equal to $Q(x)$.

The conditions thus imposed on the c's form a linear system of n equations in the n variables $c_1', c_2', \cdots, c_n'$, displayed as follows:

$$\begin{cases}
c_1'y_1 + c_2'y_2 + \cdots + c_n'y_n \equiv 0 \\
c_1'y_1' + c_2'y_2' + \cdots + c_n'y_n' \equiv 0 \\
c_1'y_1'' + c_2'y_2'' + \cdots + c_n'y_n'' \equiv 0 \\
\quad \cdot \qquad \cdot \qquad \quad \cdot \\
\quad \cdot \qquad \cdot \qquad \quad \cdot \\
c_1'y_1^{(n-2)} + c_2'y_2^{(n-2)} + \cdots + c_n'y_n^{(n-2)} \equiv 0 \\
c_1'y_1^{(n-1)} + c_2'y_2^{(n-1)} + \cdots + c_n'y_n^{(n-1)} \equiv Q(x).
\end{cases} \qquad (35)$$

The determinant of this system is

$$\begin{vmatrix}
y_1 & y_2 & \cdots & y_n \\
y_1' & y_2' & \cdots & y_n' \\
y_1'' & y_2'' & \cdots & y_n'' \\
\cdot & \cdot & & \cdot \\
\cdot & \cdot & & \cdot \\
y_1^{(n-2)} & y_2^{(n-2)} & \cdots & y_n^{(n-2)} \\
y_1^{(n-1)} & y_2^{(n-1)} & \cdots & y_n^{(n-1)}
\end{vmatrix},$$

the Wronskian of $y_1, y_2, \cdots, y_n$, and is not identically zero, by virtue of the hypothesis that these y's are linearly independent (Section 25, page 73). Hence, the system of equations (35) can be solved for c_i', and the expressions for the c's may be found by quadratures.

We still have to show that (34) is a solution of (33), if the c's satisfy (35). Now if we substitute

$$\begin{cases}
y = c_1y_1 + c_2y_2 + \cdots + c_ny_n \\
y' = c_1y_1' + c_2y_2' + \cdots + c_ny_n' \\
y'' = c_1y_1'' + c_2y_2'' + \cdots + c_ny_n'' \\
\quad \cdot \qquad \cdot \qquad \quad \cdot \\
\quad \cdot \qquad \cdot \qquad \quad \cdot \\
y^{(n-1)} = c_1y_1^{(n-1)} + c_2y_2^{(n-1)} + \cdots + c_ny_n^{(n-1)} \\
y^{(n)} = c_1y_1^{(n)} + c_2y_2^{(n)} + \cdots + c_ny_n^{(n)} + Q(x)
\end{cases}$$

in (33), the left-hand side becomes

$$c_1[y_1^{(n)} + P_1 y_1^{(n-1)} + \cdots + P_{n-1} y_1' + P_n y_1]$$
$$+ c_2[y_2^{(n)} + P_1 y_2^{(n-1)} + \cdots + P_{n-1} y_2' + P_n y_2] + \cdots$$
$$+ c_n[y_n^{(n)} + P_1 y_n^{(n-1)} + \cdots + P_{n-1} y_n' + P_n y_n] + Q(x),$$

and hence, it is identically equal to $Q(x)$, since each y_i is, by hypothesis, a solution of the reduced equation, and therefore each bracket equals zero identically. Thus (34), with the c's in the form determined, is indeed a solution of (33).

The actual task of solving (35) for c_i', and then performing the quadratures for finding the c's, may, of course, become too laborious to be effectively used in solving (33). The application of the method, nevertheless, is wide.

Consider as an illustration:

$$\frac{d^3 y}{dx^3} - \frac{1}{2} \frac{d^2 y}{dx^2} = e^{-x/2}.$$

The complete solution of the reduced equation is, obviously, $y = c_1 + c_2 x + c_3 e^{x/2}$. Differentiate, and obtain

$$y' = c_2 + \frac{c_3}{2} e^{x/2} + (c_1' + c_2' x + c_3' e^{x/2}),$$

and set $c_1' + c_2' x + c_3' e^{x/2} \equiv 0,$ (a)

$$y'' = \frac{c_3}{4} e^{x/2} + \left(c_2' + \frac{c_3'}{2} e^{x/2} \right),$$

and set $c_2' + \frac{c_3'}{2} e^{x/2} \equiv 0,$ (b)

$$y''' = \frac{c_3}{8} e^{x/2} + \left(\frac{c_3'}{4} e^{x/2} \right),$$

and set $\frac{c_3'}{4} e^{x/2} \equiv e^{-x/2}.$ (c)

From (a), (b), and (c) we obtain:

$$c_3' \equiv 4e^{-x}, \qquad \text{hence } c_3 \equiv -4e^{-x},$$
$$c_2' \equiv -2e^{-x/2}, \qquad \text{hence } c_2 \equiv 4e^{-x/2},$$
$$c_1' \equiv 2xe^{-x/2} - 4e^{-x/2}, \text{ hence } c_1 \equiv -4xe^{-x/2},$$

and a solution of the equation (a particular integral) is

$$y = -4xe^{-x/2} + 4e^{-x/2} \cdot x - 4e^{-x} \cdot e^{x/2} \equiv -4e^{-x/2}.$$

The complete solution is, therefore,

$$y = c_1 + c_2 x + c_3 e^{x/2} - 4e^{-x/2}.$$

Exercises

1. Solve by the method of variation of parameters:

(a) $\dfrac{d^2y}{dx^2} + a^2y = \cot ax.$ (c) $\dfrac{d^2y}{dx^2} + \dfrac{dy}{dx} - 12y = x - \sin x.$

(b) $\dfrac{d^3y}{dx^3} - a^2\dfrac{dy}{dx} = e^{2ax} \sin^2 x.$ (d) $\dfrac{d^3y}{dx^3} + \dfrac{dy}{dx} = e^x + 2x - 1.$

2. Verify that $y = x$ and $y = x^2$ are solutions of $\dfrac{d^2y}{dx^2} - \dfrac{2}{x}\dfrac{dy}{dx} + \dfrac{2}{x^2}y = 0$, and, hence, that the complete solution is $y = c_1x + c_2x^2$. Find, by the method of variation of parameters, a particular solution or $\dfrac{d^2y}{dx^2} - \dfrac{2}{x}\dfrac{dy}{dx} + \dfrac{2}{x^2}y = x^3 \log x.$

3. Verify that $y = x$ is a solution of $x^2\dfrac{d^2y}{dx^2} - x\dfrac{dy}{dx} + y = 0.$ Set $y = xu$ in the given equation, and obtain, as a solution of the resulting equation in u, $u = c_1 \log x + c_2$. (Hence, $y = c_1x \log x + c_2x$ is the general solution.) By variation of parameters, find next a particular solution of

$$x^2\frac{d^2y}{dx^2} - x\frac{dy}{dx} + y = \frac{(\log x)^3}{x}.$$

4. Show how the discussion in the preceding text establishes the theorem: "The general solution of the reduced equation being known, the integration of the complete linear differential equation of order n is effected by n quadratures."

31. The linear equation with variable coefficients. When the linear differential equation has constant coefficients, its treatment is complete, inasmuch as its integration reduces to solving a certain algebraic equation, *viz.*, the characteristic equation. The difficulties that may arise in solving that algebraic equation are of no official concern in the subject of differential equations. The case is different when the coefficients in the equation are variable. There is then no general method available for its integration. We do take note, however, of certain highly special types for which methods of integration are at hand, *viz.*, the so-called *Cauchy* linear equation, and the *exact* linear equation.

32. Cauchy's linear equation. The Cauchy equation* is defined as one of the type

$$x^n \frac{d^n y}{dx^n} + a_1 x^{n-1} \frac{d^{n-1} y}{dx^{n-1}} + \cdots + a_{n-1} x \frac{dy}{dx} + a_n y = Q(x), \quad (36)$$

where the a's are constants.

The substitution $x = e^t$ will transform any Cauchy linear differential equation of order n into a linear differential equation of order n in which the coefficients are constants. To see that this is so, note that

$$x \frac{dy}{dx} = \frac{dy}{dt} = Dy,$$

$$x^2 \frac{d^2 y}{dx^2} = \frac{d^2 y}{dt^2} - \frac{dy}{dt} = D(D - 1)y,$$

$$x^3 \frac{d^3 y}{dx^3} = \frac{d^3 y}{dt^3} - 3 \frac{d^2 y}{dt^2} + 2 \frac{dy}{dt} = D(D - 1)(D - 2)y,$$

$$\cdots \cdots \cdots \cdots \cdots \cdots \cdots \cdots \cdots$$

$$\cdots \cdots \cdots \cdots \cdots \cdots \cdots \cdots \cdots$$

$$x^n \frac{d^n y}{dx^n} = D(D - 1)(D - 2) \cdots (D - n + 1)y,$$

where D is now understood to represent differentiation with respect to t. When these expressions are placed in (36), the latter becomes

$$[D(D - 1)(D - 2) \cdots (D - n + 1) + a_1 D(D - 1)(D - 2)$$
$$\cdots (D - n + 2) + \cdots + a_{n-1} D + a_n] y = Q(e^t).$$

This equation has constant coefficients and is readily solved by the methods already described for such equations.

Illustration

To solve the differential equation

$$x^2 \frac{d^2 y}{dx^2} - 3x \frac{dy}{dx} - 5y = 0, \quad (37)$$

we make the substitution $x = e^t$ and the consequent substitutions $x^2 \frac{d^2 y}{dx^2} = D(D - 1)y$, $x \frac{dy}{dx} = Dy$, and obtain the new equation

---

* So called after Augustin Louis Cauchy (1789–1857). Also called the Euler equation; also, by others, the homogeneous linear equation. The last term is obviously undesirable, as the term "homogeneous" has already been used in a different sense.

$$[D(D - 1) - 3D - 5]y = 0,$$

or

$$[D^2 - 4D - 5]y = 0.$$

The characteristic equation for this having the roots 5 and −1, the general solution is written down at once as

$$y = c_1 e^{5t} + c_2 e^{-t}.$$

Transformed back in terms of x, this gives,

$$y = c_1 x^5 + c_2 x^{-1}$$

as the general solution of (37).

Exercises

1. Solve by the above method:

(a) $x^2 \dfrac{d^2y}{dx^2} - 4x \dfrac{dy}{dx} + 6y = 0.$

(b) $x^2 \dfrac{d^2y}{dx^2} - 5x \dfrac{dy}{dx} + 8y = x^3 \sinh x.$

(c) $x^3 \dfrac{d^3y}{dx^3} + 2x^2 \dfrac{d^2y}{dx^2} - 6x \dfrac{dy}{dx} = 0.$

(d) $x^3 \dfrac{d^3y}{dx^3} + 3x^2 \dfrac{d^2y}{dx^2} + x \dfrac{dy}{dx} = a^2 x \dfrac{dy}{dx}.$

(e) $x^3 \dfrac{d^3y}{dx^3} - 2x^2 \dfrac{d^2y}{dx^2} = 2x^3 - x.$

2. Show that the equation

$$(a + bx)^n \frac{d^ny}{dx^n} + a_1(a + bx)^{n-1} \frac{d^{n-1}y}{dx^{n-1}} + \cdots + a_{n-1}(a + bx) \frac{dy}{dx}$$
$$+ a_n y = Q(x)$$

can be solved by the substitution $a + bx = e^t$.

3. Solve by the method of Exercise 2.

(a) $(2 - x)^2 \dfrac{d^2y}{dx^2} + (2 - x) \dfrac{dy}{dx} - 15y = 0.$

(b) $(1 + 2x)^2 \dfrac{d^2y}{dx^2} - (2 + 4x) \dfrac{dy}{dx} - 12y = 3x + 1.$

4. Solve the equation $x^2 \dfrac{d^2y}{dx^2} - 3x \dfrac{dy}{dx} + 5y = 0$ by using the substitution $y = x^r$. *Hint:* Note that the equation becomes a quadratic equation in r whose two solutions give two linearly independent solutions of the original differential equation.

5. Solve by the method of Exercise 4:

(a) $x^2 \dfrac{d^2y}{dx^2} + 3x \dfrac{dy}{dx} + y = 0.$

(b) $x^3 \dfrac{d^3y}{dx^3} + 3x^2 \dfrac{d^2y}{dx^2} + x \dfrac{dy}{dx} = 0.$

(c) $x^3 \dfrac{d^3y}{dx^3} - 2x \dfrac{dy}{dx} = 0.$

6. Solve:

(a) $x^2 \dfrac{d^2y}{dx^2} - x \dfrac{dy}{dx} + 10y = 0.$

(b) $x^2 \dfrac{d^2y}{dx^2} + x \dfrac{dy}{dx} + 4y = 0.$

(c) $(1 - 3x)^2 \dfrac{d^2y}{dx^2} - 3(1 - 3x) \dfrac{dy}{dx} - 9y = [\log{(1 - 3x)}]^2.$

(d) $(3 + x)^3 \dfrac{d^3y}{dx^3} + 3(3 + x)^2 \dfrac{d^2y}{dx^2} + (6 + 2x) \dfrac{dy}{dx} = 0.$

33. Exact linear equations. If we differentiate the linear equation

$$R_0 y^{(n-1)} + R_1 y^{(n-2)} + \cdots + R_{n-2} y' + R_{n-1} y = S(x) + c, \quad (38)$$

where the R_i are functions of x, we obtain another linear equation

$$P_0 y^{(n)} + P_1 y^{(n-1)} + \cdots + P_{n-2} y'' + P_{n-1} y' + P_n y = Q(x), \quad (39)$$

where the P_i are functions of x such that

$$\begin{cases} Q(x) \equiv S'(x) \\ P_0 \equiv R_0 \\ P_1 \equiv R_0' + R_1 \\ P_2 \equiv R_1' + R_2 \\ \quad \cdot \qquad \cdot \qquad \cdot \\ \quad \cdot \qquad \cdot \qquad \cdot \\ P_{n-1} \equiv R_{n-2}' + R_{n-1} \\ P_n \equiv R_{n-1}' \end{cases} \quad (40)$$

and hence,

$$
\begin{cases}
S(x) \equiv \displaystyle\int Q(x)dx + c \\
R_0 \equiv P_0 \\
R_1 \equiv P_1 - P_0' \\
R_2 \equiv P_2 - P_1' + P_0'' \\
\quad \cdot \qquad \cdot \qquad \cdot \qquad \cdot \\
\quad \cdot \qquad \cdot \qquad \cdot \qquad \cdot \\
R_{n-2} \equiv P_{n-2} - P_{n-3}' + P_{n-4}'' - \cdots + (-1)^{n-2}P_0^{(n-2)} \\
R_{n-1} \equiv P_{n-1} - P_{n-2}' + P_{n-3}'' - \cdots + (-1)^{n-1}P_0^{(n-1)}.
\end{cases}
\tag{41}
$$

Under these circumstances Equation (39) is said to be *exact* and to have (38) as its *first integral*.*

From the last equation in (40) and the last in (41), it is seen that

$$
P_n - R_{n-1}' \equiv P_n - P_{n-1}' + P_{n-2}'' - P_{n-3}''' + \cdots \\
+ (-1)^n P_0^{(n)} \equiv 0. \tag{42}
$$

Thus, this relation is a necessary condition for the exactness of (39). It is also clearly sufficient, for whenever it is satisfied we can build the functions R_i and $S(x)$ by formulas (41), and (40) will be satisfied.

To illustrate, let us consider the linear equation

$$
(x^2 + 1)y'' + 4xy' + 2y = 2 \cos x - 2x,
$$

of the form (39), with $n = 2$, $P_0 \equiv x^2 + 1$, $P_1 \equiv 4x$, $P_2 \equiv 2$. Setting up (42), we obtain

$$
P_2 - P_1' + P_0'' \equiv 2 - 4 + 2 = 0;
$$

therefore the relation holds, the given equation is exact, and its first integral is

$$
R_0 y' + R_1 y = \int (2 \cos x - 2x)dx + c_1,
$$

where

$$
R_0 \equiv P_0 \equiv x^2 + 1, \\
R_1 \equiv P_1 - P_0' \equiv 4x - 2x \equiv 2x;
$$

---

* The notion of exactness is also applicable to other than linear equations. Thus, any equation $f(x, y, y', y'', \cdots, y^{(n)}) = 0$ is said to be *exact* if a function $\varphi(x, y, y', y'', \cdots, y^{(n-1)})$ exists such that $d\varphi/dx \equiv f$. The differential equation $\varphi(x, y, y', y'', \cdots, y^{(n-1)}) = c$ is then defined as the *first integral* of $f(x, y, y', y'', \cdots, y^{(u)}) = 0$. However, in the general case, no test for exactness is available, and no formula for the first integral exists.

that is,

$$(x^2 + 1)y' + 2xy = 2 \sin x - x^2 + c_1.$$

This first integral happens to be exact also, since, for it, $P_0 \equiv x^2 + 1$, $P_1 \equiv 2x$, and $P_1 - P_0' \equiv 0$, and its first integral is

$$R_0 y = \int (2 \sin x - x^2 + c_1) \, dx + c_2,$$

where $R_0 \equiv P_0 \equiv x^2 + 1$; that is,

$$(x^2 + 1)y = -2 \cos x - \frac{x^3}{3} + c_1 x + c_2.$$

In this example we have arrived at a complete solution of the equation proposed. But such will not always be the case, for the first integral of an exact equation is not always itself exact, and all we may expect of (39), in general, when (42) is satisfied, is that it be replaced by its first integral, *i. e.*, by a linear equation of next lower order.

In the particular case, however, in which the given linear equation is exact and of order two, its first integral is linear and of order one, and, consequently, it can be integrated, whether or not it is exact.

Exercises

1. (a) Show that $(2x - 1)y''' + (4 + x)y'' + 2y' = 0$ is exact, and find its first integral.

(b) Show that the first integral of the equation in (a) is also exact, and derive its first integral as

$$(2x - 1)y' + xy = c_1 x + c_2.$$

(c) Show that the last equation is not exact. Obtain its solution (and hence the solution of the original equation in (a)).

2. Solve:

(a) $(x + \sin x)y''' + 3(1 + \cos x)y'' - 3 \sin x \cdot y' - \cos x \cdot y = - \sin x.$

(b) $(e^x + 2x)y^{iv} + 4(e^x + 2)y''' + 6e^x y'' + 4e^x y' + e^x y = \frac{1}{x^5}.$

(c) $\sin x \cdot y''' + (2 \cos x + 1)y'' - \sin x \cdot y' = \cos x.$

(d) $(x^2 + 1)y''' + 8xy'' + 10y' = 3 - \frac{1}{x^2} + 2 \log x.$

(e) $(x + 2)^2 y''' - y' = \frac{-8}{x^3} - \frac{8}{x^2} - \frac{1}{x} - 1.$

3. (a) Show that the linear equation with constant coefficients,

$$y^{(n)} + a_1 y^{(n-1)} + a_2 y^{(n-2)} + \cdots + a_{n-2} y'' + a_{n-1} y' + a_n y = Q(x),$$

is exact if, and only if, $a_n = 0$. What is its first integral in that case?

(b) State the condition that must be satisfied by the coefficients of the Cauchy linear equation

$$a_0 x^n y^{(n)} + a_1 x^{n-1} y^{(n-1)} + \cdots + a_{n-1} xy' + a_n y = Q(x)$$

if it is to be exact. Show that, in case the condition is satisfied, the first integral is reducible to a Cauchy linear equation.

(c) Show that if a second order linear equation

$$P_0 y'' + P_1 y' + P_2 y = Q(x)$$

is exact and its first integral lacks the term in y, then $P_2 = 0$. State the converse proposition.

4. (a) Show that a necessary and sufficient condition that $\mu(x)$ be an integrating factor of

$$P_0 y^{(n)} + P_1 y^{(n-1)} + \cdots + P_{n-2} y'' + P_{n-1} y' + P_n y = 0, \quad \text{(A)}$$

is that it satisfy the equation,

$$\mu P_n - (\mu P_{n-1})' + (\mu P_{n-2})'' - \cdots + (-1)^n (\mu P_0)^{(n)} = 0, \quad \text{(B)}$$

called the *adjoint equation* of (A). Note that it is a linear differential equation in μ, and of order n.

(b) Find the adjoint equation of

$$x^3 y''' + xy' - y = 0. \tag{C}$$

The result is found to be

$$x^3 \mu''' + 9x^2 \mu'' + 19x\mu' + 8\mu = 0. \tag{D}$$

(c) Obtain $\mu = x^{-2}$ as one solution of (D). Verify that its use will make (C) exact and yield a first integral

$$xy'' - y' + \frac{y}{x} = c_1.$$

(d) Find the adjoint equation of (D), *i. e.*, the equation satisfied by ν, where ν is an integrating factor of (D). The result is

$$x^3 \nu''' + x\nu' - \nu = 0. \tag{E}$$

Note that (E) and (C) are identical equations. This result is general and is embodied in the following .

Theorem. *Every integral of the adjoint equation is an integrating factor of the given equation; likewise, every integral of a given homogeneous linear equation is an integrating factor of its adjoint equation.*

(e) Prove the second statement in the above theorem.

(f) Find the adjoint equation of $xy'' + y' - x^2y = 0$.

34. One variable absent. Before we take up systems of linear equations, we take a brief glance at two special types of equations which are amenable to simple treatment whether they be linear or non-linear.

First consider a second order differential equation in which the dependent variable is absent, *i. e.*, one of the form

$$f\left(\frac{d^2y}{dx^2}, \frac{dy}{dx}, x\right) = 0.$$

If we set $p = dy/dx$, this takes the form

$$f\left(\frac{dp}{dx}, p, x\right) = 0,$$

a first order equation in p and x. If we can solve this and obtain $p = g(x, c_1)$, then y is found as $y = c_2 + \int g(x, c_1)\,dx$. Again, should the independent variable be absent from the second order equation, *i. e.*, if we are confronted with an equation of the form

$$f\left(\frac{d^2y}{dx^2}, \frac{dy}{dx}, y\right) = 0,$$

then $p = \dfrac{dy}{dx}$ leads to $\dfrac{d^2y}{dx^2} = \dfrac{dp}{dx} = \dfrac{dp}{dy}\dfrac{dy}{dx} = p\dfrac{dp}{dy}$, and our equation takes the form

$$f\left(p\frac{dp}{dy}, p, y\right) = 0.$$

If we can solve this first order equation to obtain

$$p = g(y, c_1),$$

then x is derived as

$$x = c_2 + \int \frac{dy}{g(y, c_1)}.$$

Note that the above method will in any event lower the order of the equation by 1 if either the dependent or the independent variable is absent. Thus, $f\left(\dfrac{d^n y}{dx^n}, \dfrac{d^{n-1} y}{dx^{n-1}}, \cdots, \dfrac{dy}{dx}, x\right) = 0$ will be transformed into

$$f\left(\frac{d^{n-1} p}{dx^{n-1}}, \frac{d^{n-2} p}{dx^{n-2}}, \cdots, p, x\right) = 0,$$

while $\dfrac{dy}{dx} = p,\ \dfrac{d^2 y}{dx^2} = p\dfrac{dp}{dy},\ \dfrac{d^3 y}{dx^3} = p^2\dfrac{d^2 p}{dy^2} + p\left(\dfrac{dp}{dy}\right)^2$ etc. will transform

$$f\left(\frac{d^n y}{dx^n}, \frac{d^{n-1} y}{dx^{n-1}}, \cdots, \frac{dy}{dx}, y\right) = 0$$

into an equation in p and y of order $n - 1$.

Exercises

1. Solve:

    (a) $xy'' - 2y' = 0$.   (b) $xy'' - y' = 3x^2$.

    (c) $(1 + x^2)y'' + 1 + y'^2 = 0$, where $y = 2$, $y' = 1$ when
$$x = 0.$$

    (d) $y'' - 2yy' = 0$.   (e) $2yy'' - y'^2 = 1$.

    (f) $yy'' - y'^2 = 4y^2 \cdot \log y$, where $y = e$, $y' = 2e$ when
$$x = 1.$$

    (g) $y'' - y'^2 = 1$. Do it in two ways.

    (h) $x^2 \dfrac{d^3 y}{dx^3} - 2x \dfrac{d^2 y}{dx^2} + 2 \dfrac{dy}{dx} = 0$

35. Simultaneous linear equations. We bring this chapter to a close by considering a system of two equations in two dependent variables, both functions of the same independent variable. Such a system is called *linear* if the dependent variables and their derivatives enter to the first degree in each of the equations. Thus,

$$\begin{cases} P_0 x^{(m)} + P_1 x^{(m-1)} + \cdots + P_m x + Q_0 y^{(n)} + Q_1 y^{(n-1)} \\ \qquad\qquad\qquad\qquad\qquad + \cdots + Q_n y = T_1(t), \quad (43) \\ R_0 x^{(u)} + R_1 x^{(u-1)} + \cdots + R_u x + S_0 y^{(v)} + S_1 y^{(v-1)} \\ \qquad\qquad\qquad\qquad\qquad + \cdots + S_v y = T_2(t), \end{cases}$$

is such a system, if the derivatives are with respect to t and $P_0 \cdots$, P_m; $Q_0, \cdots, Q_n$; $R_0, \cdots, R_u$; $S_0, \cdots, S_v$ are functions of t alone.

A pair of functions, $x = f(t)$, $y = g(t)$, that satisfies each of the two equations identically is said to be a solution of the system.*

We shall restrict ourselves to a system with constant coefficients, *i. e.*, one of the type

$$\begin{cases} [f_1(D)]x + [g_1(D)]y = T_1(t), \\ [f_2(D)]x + [g_2(D)]y = T_2(t), \end{cases} \tag{44}$$

where D is an operator denoting differentiation with respect to t, while $f_i(D)$ and $g_i(D)$ $(i = 1, 2)$ are polynomials in D with constant coefficients. We illustrate the method of treating such a pair of equations by the following example.

Let the given system be

$$\begin{cases} \dfrac{d^2x}{dt^2} - 9x + \dfrac{dy}{dt} + 3y = \sin 2t, \\ \dfrac{dx}{dt} + x - \dfrac{dy}{dt} = 2t, \end{cases}$$

or

$$\begin{cases} (D^2 - 9)x + (D + 3)y = \sin 2t, \\ (D + 1)x - Dy = 2t. \end{cases}$$

To eliminate one of the variables, say y, operate on the first equation by D, and on the second by $(D + 3)$, obtaining

$$\begin{cases} (D^3 - 9D)x + D(D + 3)y = 2 \cos 2t, \\ (D^2 + 4D + 3)x - D(D + 3)y = 6t + 2. \end{cases}$$

Adding the two, we get

$$(D^3 + D^2 - 5D + 3)x = 2 \cos 2t + 6t + 2.$$

a linear equation in x alone.

By the methods of the preceding sections, we obtain as the complementary function, *i. e.*, the solution of the reduced equation,

$$x = c_1 e^t + c_2 t e^t + c_3 e^{-3t}.$$

---

* It is proved in the theory of differential equations that such a system of n linear equations in n dependent variables, functions of the same independent variable, has a unique solution for the range of values of the independent variable t, $a \leqq t \leqq b$, if in that range $P_0(t) \neq 0$; $Q_0(t) \neq 0$; $R_0(t) \neq 0$; $S_0(t) \neq 0$; $\cdots$ and $\dfrac{P_1}{P_0}, \ldots, \dfrac{P_m}{P_0}; \dfrac{Q_1}{Q_0}, \ldots, \dfrac{Q_n}{Q_0}; \dfrac{R_1}{R_0}, \ldots, \dfrac{R_u}{R_0}; \dfrac{S_1}{S_0}, \ldots, \dfrac{S_v}{S_0}$, are continuous functions of t.

For a particular integral, we use the method of Section 28 and assume

$$x = A \sin 2t + B \cos 2t + Et + F,$$

$$\therefore \qquad Dx = 2A \cos 2t - 2B \sin 2t + E,$$

$$D^2x = -4A \sin 2t - 4B \cos 2t,$$

$$D^3x = -8A \cos 2t + 8B \sin 2t,$$

so that

$$(D^3 + D^2 - 5D + 3)x = (18B - A) \sin 2t - (18A + B) \cos 2t$$
$$+ 3Et + (3F - 5E)$$

$$\equiv 2 \cos 2t + 6t + 2,$$

whence,

$$18B - A = 0,$$
$$18A + B = -2,$$
$$3E = 6,$$
$$3F - 5E = 2,$$

so that

$$A = \frac{-36}{325},\ B = \frac{-2}{325},\ E = 2,\ F = 4,$$

and the complete solution is

$$x = c_1 e^t + c_2 t e^t + c_3 e^{-3t} - \frac{36}{325} \sin 2t - \frac{2}{325} \cos 2t + 2t + 4.$$

We now have the choice of either substituting this value of x into one of the given equations and solving for y, or repeating the above process in order to eliminate x from the given pair of equations. By the first plan, we get from the second of the given equations

$$Dy = (D + 1)x - 2t$$

$$= (D + 1)\left(c_1 e^t + c_2 t e^t + c_3 e^{-3t} - \frac{36}{325} \sin 2t - \frac{2}{325} \cos 2t + 2t + 4\right)$$
$$- 2t$$

$$= (2c_1 + c_2)e^t + 2c_2 t e^t - 2c_3 e^{-3t} - \frac{32}{325} \sin 2t - \frac{74}{325} \cos 2t + 6,$$

whence,

$$y = (2c_1 + c_2)e^t + 2c_2 e^t(t - 1) + \frac{2}{3} c_3 e^{-3t} + \frac{16}{325} \cos 2t - \frac{37}{325}$$
$$\sin 2t + 6t + c_4.$$

These expressions for x and y are solutions of the system of equations only if they satisfy both equations. If we substitute them into the first of the two given equations, we have

$$(D^2 - 9)\left(c_1 e^t + c_2 t e^t + c_3 e^{-3t} - \frac{36}{325}\sin 2t - \frac{2}{325}\cos 2t + 2t + 4\right)$$

$$+ (D + 3)\left[(2c_1 - c_2)e^t + 2c_2 t e^t + \frac{2}{3}c_3 e^{-3t} + \frac{16}{325}\cos 2t\right.$$

$$\left. - \frac{37}{325}\sin 2t + 6t + c_4\right] \equiv \sin 2t,$$

which reduces to

$$\sin 2t - 30 + 3c_4 \equiv \sin 2t,$$

whence, $c_4 = 10$. The complete solution of the system is thus

$$x = c_1 e^t + c_2 t e^t + c_3 e^{-3t} - \frac{36}{325}\sin 2t - \frac{2}{325}\cos 2t + 2t + 4,$$

$$y = (2c_1 - c_2)e^t + 2c_2 t e^t + \frac{2}{3}c_3 e^{-3t} + \frac{16}{325}\cos 2t - \frac{37}{325}\sin 2t$$

$$+ 6t + 10.$$

To proceed by the second method, we operate on the two given equations by $(D + 1)$ and $(D^2 - 9)$, respectively, obtaining

$$\begin{cases} (D + 1)(D^2 - 9)x + (D^2 + 4D + 3)y = \sin 2t + 2\cos 2t, \\ (D + 1)(D^2 - 9)x - (D^3 - 9D)y = -18t, \end{cases}$$

and, by subtracting

$$(D^3 + D^2 - 5D + 3)y^* = \sin 2t + 2\cos 2t + 18t,$$

so that the complementary function is $y = k_1 e^t + k_2 t e^t + k_3 e^{-3t}$, and a particular integral turns up (using again the method of Section 28 if we choose), as

$$y = -\frac{37}{325}\sin 2t + \frac{16}{325}\cos 2t + 6t + 10.$$

We obtain as the complete solution

$$y = k_1 e^t + k_2 t e^t + k_3 e^{-3t} - \frac{37}{325}\sin 2t + \frac{16}{325}\cos 2t + 6t + 10.$$

Obviously, we have no reason to assume k_1, k_2, k_3 identical with c_1, c_2, c_3; hence, it remains to find how these constants are related.

---

* The operator in the left-hand member of this equation is the same as in the equation for x. Let the student operate on (44) and convince himself that this is generally true.

To that end, substitute the values of x and y already found into either of the given equations. We choose the second, as the simpler one, and obtain

$$\left[(2c_1 + c_2)e^t + 2c_2te^t - 2c_3e^{-3t} - \frac{32}{325} \sin 2t - \frac{74}{325} \cos 2t + 6 + 2t \right]$$
$$- \left[k_1e^t + k_2te^t + k_2e^t - 3k_3e^{-3t} - \frac{74}{325} \cos 2t - \frac{32}{325} \sin 2t + 6 \right]$$
$$\equiv 2t,$$

or

$$(2c_1 + c_2 - k_1 - k_2)e^t + (2c_2 - k_2)te^t - (2c_3 - 3k_3)e^{-3t} + 2t \equiv 2t.$$

For this to be an identity, we must have

$$\begin{cases} k_1 + k_2 = 2c_1 + c_2, \\ k_2 = 2c_2, \\ 3k_3 = 2c_3, \end{cases} \quad \text{whence,} \quad \begin{cases} k_1 = 2c_1 - c_2, \\ k_2 = 2c_2, \\ k_3 = \frac{2}{3} c_3. \end{cases}$$

With these values of k_1, k_2, and k_3, we obtain

$$y = (2c_1 - c_2)e^t + 2c_2te^t + \frac{2}{3} c_3e^{-3t} + \frac{16}{325} \cos 2t - \frac{37}{325} \sin 2t$$
$$+ 6t + 10,$$

as above.*

Exercises

1. Solve the following systems of equations:

(a) $\begin{cases} \dfrac{dx}{dt} + \dfrac{dy}{dt} - y = e^t, \\ 2\dfrac{dx}{dt} + \dfrac{dy}{dt} + 2y = \cos t. \end{cases}$

(b) $\dfrac{dx}{dt} + 2x - y = \dfrac{dy}{dt} - x + 3y = 0.$

---

* In the system of equations solved here, one was of order two, and the other of order one, while the number of arbitrary constants in the solution turned out to be three. This is in consonance with the so-called Existence Theorem, which asserts the existence and uniqueness of the solution of a system of linear differential equations, under the conditions stated in the preceding footnote. The theorem also asserts that the number of arbitrary constants in the general solution equals (at most) the sum of the orders of the several equations of the system.

(c) $\dfrac{dx}{3t - 2y} = \dfrac{dy}{4 + 2x} = dt.$

(d) $\dfrac{dx}{dt} + \dfrac{dy}{dt} - 3y = \dfrac{d^2x}{dt^2} + \dfrac{dy}{dt} = 0.$

(e) $\begin{cases} \dfrac{d^2x}{dt^2} + \dfrac{d^2y}{dt^2} + \dfrac{dy}{dt} = \sinh 2t, \\[2mm] 2\dfrac{d^2x}{dt^2} + \dfrac{d^2y}{dt^2} = 2t. \end{cases}$

(f) $\begin{cases} \dfrac{d^2x}{dt^2} - \dfrac{x}{4} - \dfrac{dy}{dt} = e^{2t} + 1, \\[2mm] \dfrac{dy}{dt} - y = t - 2. \end{cases}$

(g) $\begin{cases} \dfrac{d^2x}{dt^2} - \dfrac{dx}{dt} + \dfrac{dy}{dt} = 0, \\[2mm] \dfrac{d^2x}{dt^2} - x + \dfrac{d^2y}{dt^2} = 0. \end{cases}$

(h) $\begin{cases} \dfrac{d^2x}{dt^2} - \dfrac{dy}{dt} = -2e^{2t}, \\[2mm] \dfrac{d^3x}{dt^3} + 2\dfrac{dx}{dt} = 12e^{2t} - \sin t. \end{cases}$

2. Prove that if $\begin{cases} x = f_1(t) \\ y = g_1(t) \end{cases}$ and $\begin{cases} x = f_2(t) \\ y = g_2(t) \end{cases}$ are two solutions of the homogeneous system

$$\begin{cases} [F_1(D)]x + [G_1(D)]y = 0 \\ [F_2(D)]x + [G_2(D)]y = 0 \end{cases},$$

then

$$\begin{cases} x = c_1 f_1(t) + c_2 f_2(t) \\ y = c_1 g_1(t) + c_2 g_2(t) \end{cases},$$

where c_1 and c_2 are arbitrary constants, is also a solution.

3. Solve the system

$$\begin{cases} \dfrac{dx}{dt} = x + 2y \\[2mm] \dfrac{dy}{dt} = 3x + 2y \end{cases}$$

by assuming as a solution

$$\begin{cases} x = Ae^{mt}, \\ y = Be^{mt}. \end{cases}$$

Hint: The substitution will yield

$$\begin{cases} A(1 - m) + 2B = 0, \\ 3A + (2 - m)B = 0, \end{cases}$$

and this pair of equations will be satisfied by values of A and B other than $A = B = 0$ if and only if

$$\begin{vmatrix} 1 - m & 2 \\ 3 & 2 - m \end{vmatrix} = 0.$$

This is called the characteristic equation of the given system. It is satisfied by $m = -1$ and $m = 4$. The equations in A and B yield $B = -A$ when $m = -1$, and $B = \dfrac{3A}{2}$ when $m = 4$, with A arbitrary. Hence, the solutions of the system are

$$\begin{cases} x = A_1 e^{-t} \\ y = -A_1 e^{-t} \end{cases}$$

and

$$\begin{cases} x = A_2 e^{4t} \\ y = \dfrac{3A_2}{2} e^{4t} \end{cases}.$$

By Exercise 2,

$$\begin{cases} x = A_1 e^{-t} + A_2 e^{4t} \\ y = -A_1 e^{-t} + \dfrac{3A_2}{2} e^{4t} \end{cases}$$

is also a solution. It is the general solution, since it has two arbitrary constants.

4. Solve by the method of Exercise 3:

(a) $\begin{cases} \dfrac{dx}{dt} = 4x + 2y, \\ \dfrac{dy}{dt} = -x + y. \end{cases}$
(b) $\begin{cases} \dfrac{dx}{dt} = -3y, \\ \dfrac{dy}{dt} = -x + 2y. \end{cases}$

5. Verify that if the characteristic equation of

$$\begin{cases} \dfrac{dx}{dt} = ax + by, \\ \dfrac{dy}{dt} = cx + dy, \end{cases} \tag{I}$$

viz., $\begin{vmatrix} a - m & b \\ c & d - m \end{vmatrix} = 0$, has a double root m, then

$$\begin{cases} x = A_1 e^{mt} + A_2 t e^{mt}, \\ y = B_1 e^{mt} + B_2 t e^{mt}, \end{cases}$$

is the complete solution of (I), where A_1 and A_2 are arbitrary constants and B_1 and B_2 are determined by A_1 and A_2.

6. Solve by using Exercise 5:

(a) $\begin{cases} \dfrac{dx}{dt} = 4x - y, \\ \dfrac{dy}{dt} = x + 2y. \end{cases}$ (b) $\begin{cases} \dfrac{dx}{dt} = x + y, \\ \dfrac{dy}{dt} = -x + 3y. \end{cases}$

7. Verify that if the characteristic equation of the system (I) of Exercise 5 has the complex roots $p \pm qi$ (p, q, real), then the complete solution is

$$\begin{cases} x = e^{pt}(A_1 \sin qt + A_2 \cos qt), \\ y = e^{pt}(B_1 \sin qt + B_2 \cos qt), \end{cases}$$

where A_1 and A_2 are arbitrary, while B_1 and B_2 are determined by A_1 and A_2.

8. Solve, using Exercise 7:

(a) $\begin{cases} \dfrac{dx}{dt} = 2x - y, \\ \dfrac{dy}{dt} = x + 2y. \end{cases}$ (b) $\begin{cases} \dfrac{dx}{dt} = 4x - 5y, \\ \dfrac{dy}{dt} = x + 2y. \end{cases}$

9. Extend the method of Exercise 3 to the system:

$$\begin{cases} \dfrac{dx}{dt} = 2x, \\ \dfrac{dy}{dt} = 3x - 2y, \\ \dfrac{dz}{dt} = 2y + 3z. \end{cases}$$

Solution: Assume $x = A e^{mt}$, $y = B e^{mt}$, $z = C e^{mt}$.   Substitution yields

$$\begin{aligned} (2 - m)A & & = 0, \\ 3A - (2 + m)B & & = 0, \\ 2B + (3 - m)C & = 0. \end{aligned}$$

Hence, the characteristic equation of the system is

$$\begin{vmatrix} 2-m & 0 & 0 \\ 3 & -2-m & 0 \\ 0 & 2 & 3-m \end{vmatrix} = 0,$$

satisfied by $m = 2$, $m = -2$, and $m = 3$. For $m = 2$, we have

$$B = \frac{3A}{4}, \ C = -\frac{3A}{2}, \ A \text{ undetermined;}$$

for $m = -2$, we have

$$A = 0, \ C = -\frac{2B}{5}, \ B \text{ undetermined;}$$

while for $m = 3$, we have

$$A = 0, \ B = 0, \ C \text{ undetermined.}$$

Hence, three distinct solutions are

$$\begin{cases} x = Ae^{2t}, \\ y = \frac{3A}{4} e^{2t}, \\ z = -\frac{3A}{2} e^{2t}, \end{cases} \qquad \begin{cases} x = 0, \\ y = Be^{-2t}, \\ z = -\frac{2B}{5} e^{-2t}, \end{cases} \qquad \begin{cases} x = 0, \\ y = 0, \\ z = Ce^{3t}. \end{cases}$$

The theorem of Exercise 2 is also applicable to a homogeneous system of more than two equations, and thus

$$\begin{cases} x = Ae^{2t}, \\ y = \frac{3A}{4} e^{2t} + Be^{-2t}, \\ z = -\frac{3A}{2} e^{2t} - \frac{2B}{5} e^{-2t} + Ce^{3t}, \end{cases}$$

is a solution. This is, in fact, the complete solution, since it has three arbitrary constants.

10. Solve, as in Exercise 9:

(a) $\begin{cases} \dfrac{dx}{dt} = -3x + 48y - 28z, \\[2mm] \dfrac{dy}{dt} = -4x + 40y - 22z, \\[2mm] \dfrac{dz}{dt} = -6x + 57y - 31z. \end{cases}$ (b) $\begin{cases} \dfrac{dx}{dt} = 6x - 72y + 44z, \\[2mm] \dfrac{dy}{dt} = 4x - 43y + 26z, \\[2mm] \dfrac{dz}{dt} = 6x - 63y + 38z. \end{cases}$

11. The x-component of the velocity of a moving particle equals the sum of its coördinates, the y-component of its velocity is twice its abscissa.   Find its path, if at the start of its motion it is at $(1, 0)$.

36. Miscellaneous exercises on Chapter IV.

1. Solve the following:

(a) $y''' - y' = 0$.

(b) $y''' + 3y' - 4y = 0$.

(c) $y^{iv} - 2ay''' + a^2 y'' = x^2 - 1$.

(d) $y''' + 2y'' - 4y' - 8y = e^{3x} + 2$.

(e) $y^{iv} - 3y''' + \dfrac{11}{4} y'' - \dfrac{3}{4} y' = \cos x$.

(f) $y''' - 2y'' - 3y' + 10y = 0$.

(g) $y^{iv} - 8y''' + 20y'' = x^2 + e^{3x}$.

(h) $y^{iv} + 2y''' - 3y'' - 4y' + 4y = 32 \sin 2x - 24 \cos 2x$.

(i) $y''' - 2y'' - a^2 y' + 2a^2 y = \sinh x$.

(j) $4y''' - 8y'' - 11y' - 3y + 18e^x = 0$.

(k) $y''' - 3ay'' + 3a^2 y' - a^3 y = e^{ax}$.

(l) $y^{iv} + 2a^2 y'' + a^4 y = \cosh ax$.

(m) $x^2 y'' - 4xy' + 6y = x^4 - x^2$.

(n) $y''' + \dfrac{3}{x} y'' - \dfrac{2}{x^2} y' + \dfrac{2}{x^3} y = 6x \log x - 6 \log x$
$$- x - 8.$$

(o) $(2 - x)^2 y'' + (2 - x)y' - 3y = 0$.

(p) $\dfrac{y''}{x} - \dfrac{3y'}{x^2} + \dfrac{4y}{x^3} = \dfrac{5}{x^2}$.

(q) $(3 + 2x)^3 y''' + 2(3 + 2x)^2 y'' + 4(3 + 2x)y' = 0$

(r) $y''' - y'' - 2y' = x^3 \cdot e^{2x}$.

(s) $y'' - 2y' + y = \dfrac{2e^x}{(x - 1)^2}$.

(t) $y'' = 4e^{2y}$; $y = 0$, $y' = -\sqrt{3}$ when $x = 0$.

(u) $yy'' - (y')^2 = 2y'$.

(v) $(1 - x^2)y'' + xy' = 1$.

2. In each of the following, find the particular solution satisfying the conditions stated:

(a) $y'' - 6y' + 13y = 0$; $y = 0$, $y' = 4e^{3\pi}$, when $x = \pi$.

(b) $y''' + y'' - 10y' + 8y = 16x - 20$; $y = 0$, $y' = 7$,
$$y'' = -15, \text{ when } x = 0.$$

(c) $x^2 y'' - 5xy' + 13y = 0$; $y = 2$, $y' = 4$, when $x = 1$.

3. Show the following equations to be exact; integrate them as far as possible:

(a) $(x^2 + 3x)y'' + (3x - 1)y' + y = (20x + 30)(x^2 + 3x)^{\frac{1}{3}}$.

(b) $y''' - \sin x \cdot y'' - 2 \cos x \cdot y' + y \sin x = \log x$.

(c) $xy''' + \log x \cdot y'' + \dfrac{2}{x} y' - \dfrac{1}{x^2} y = 2x$.

(d) $xy^{iv} + 5y''' = 24$.

(e) $y^{iv} \sin x + 4y''' \cos x - 6y'' \sin x - 4y' \cos x + y \sin x$
$$= 6 \csc^4 x \cdot \cot x.$$

4. (a) Find the adjoint equation of $xy'' + 2y' - xy = e^x$. Show that e^x and e^{-x} are solutions of the adjoint equation, and, employing them as integrating factors of the given equation, find its general solution.

(b) Find integrating factors of $x^2y'' + 6xy' + 6y = 0$, by solving its adjoint equation.

(c) Show that the equation $(x^2 + x)y'' + (2x + 1)y' + 2y = 0$ is self-adjoint, i. e., is identical with the adjoint equation.

5. In the exercises below, known solutions of the reduced equation are enclosed in parentheses; solve or reduce to an equation of lower order by substituting for y a new dependent variable, u times the given function:

(a) $y'' \sin 2x - y' \cos 2x + 2y \sin 2x = \cos 2x \sqrt{\sin 2x}$;
$$(y = \cos 2x).$$

(b) $y'' \cdot x^2 \cos x + y'(x^2 \sin x - 2x \cos x)$
$$+ y(2 \cos x - x \sin x) = \dfrac{x^3}{\sec x}; \ (y = x \sin x).$$

(c) $(1 - \log x)y'' + \dfrac{y'}{x} - \dfrac{y}{x^2} = \dfrac{1 - \log x}{\log x}; \ (y = \log x)$.

(d) $xy'' - y' + \dfrac{y}{x} = 3x^2; \ (y = x; y = x \log x)$.

(e) $(x^2 - 2x)y''' + y''(2x - x^2) - 2y' + 2y = 0$;
$$(y = e^x; y = x^2).$$

6. (a) Show that the homogeneous linear equation whose solutions are $y = y_1(x)$, $y = y_2(x)$, $y = y_3(x)$, is

$$\begin{vmatrix} y & y' & y'' & y''' \\ y_1 & y_1' & y_1'' & y_1''' \\ y_2 & y_2' & y_2'' & y_2''' \\ y_3 & y_3' & y_3'' & y_3''' \end{vmatrix} = 0.$$

(b) Write down the homogeneous linear equation whose solutions are $y = y_1(x)$, $y = y_2(x)$, $y = y_3(x)$, and $y = y_4(x)$.

(c) Write down the homogeneous linear equation whose solutions are $y = x^2$, and $y = 2x$.

(d) Write down the homogeneous linear equation whose solutions are $y = e^x$, $y = x$, $y = x^2$.

7. Show that the second order linear equation

$$y'' + Py' + Qy = R$$

may be changed to one of the form

$$u'' + Su = T,$$

and find S and T in terms of P, Q, and R.   *Hint:* Set $y = u \cdot v$, and reduce the equation to

$$u'' \cdot v + u'(2v' + vP) + u(v'' + v'P + vQ) = R.$$

Now define v by

$$2v' + vP = 0 \ (\therefore \ v = e^{-\frac{1}{2}\int P \, dx}),$$

and obtain the desired result.

8. Solve the following by applying the method of Exercise 7:

(a) $y'' + y' \cot x - \dfrac{17 + \csc^2 x}{4} y = 0.$

(b) $y'' + \dfrac{y'}{x} - \dfrac{4x^2 + 1}{4x^2} y = \dfrac{e^x}{\sqrt{x}}.$

(c) $x^2 y'' + 4x^3 y' + (4x^4 + 2x^2 + 1)y = 0.$

(d) $y'' + y' \log x + \left(\dfrac{x - 4}{2x^2} + \dfrac{\log^2 x}{4} \right) y = \sqrt{\dfrac{e^x}{x^x}}.$

9. Show that the second order linear equation

$$y'' + Py' + Qy = R$$

may, by a change of independent variable from x to z

$\left(i. \ e., \text{ by } y' = \dfrac{dy}{dz} \cdot z', \ y'' = \dfrac{dy}{dz} \cdot z'' + \dfrac{d^2y}{dz^2} \cdot z'^2 \right)$ be transformed into

$$\frac{d^2y}{dz^2} + \frac{Pz' + z''}{z'^2} \cdot \frac{dy}{dz} + \frac{Q}{z'^2} y = \frac{R}{z'^2}.$$

Note: We may make the coefficient of y constant by defining z by $z'^2 = \pm Q$ (choosing the sign which will make z' real).   If it happens that this choice of z renders the coefficient of $\dfrac{dy}{dz}$ also constant, the new equation will have all its coefficients constant and will be readily integrable. Thus, in the case of the equation $y'' + \dfrac{4x^2 - 1}{x} y'$ $- 4x^2 y = 4x^4$, we try $z'^2 = 4x'$ $(\therefore z' = 2x, \; z'' = 2, \; z = x^2)$; then $\dfrac{Pz' + z''}{z'^2} = 2$, and the transformed equation is $\dfrac{d^2y}{dz^2} + 2\dfrac{dy}{dz}$ $- y = z$, with the solution

$$y = c_1 e^{(-1+\sqrt{2})z} + c_2 e^{(-1-\sqrt{2})z} - z - 2.$$

The solution of the original equation is, therefore,

$$y = c_1 e^{(-1+\sqrt{2})x^2} + c_2 e^{(-1-\sqrt{2})x^2} - x^2 - 2.$$

10. Solve the following by applying the method of Exercise 9:

(a) $y'' - (2e^x + 1)y' + e^{2x} \cdot y = e^{3x}$.

(b) $y'' + (\sin x - \cot x)y' + y \sin^2 x = 0$.

(c) $y'' - \left(3 \tan x + \dfrac{1}{\sin x \cos x}\right) y' - y \cdot \tan^2 x = 0$.

11. Test the following for the applicability of either the method of Exercise 7 or that of Exercise 9, and solve:

(a) $y'' - 4xy' - (1 - 4x^2)y = e^{x^2}$.

(b) $y'' + \dfrac{5}{4x} y' - \dfrac{1}{4x^2} y = \dfrac{\log x}{4x^2}$.

(c) $y'' - \dfrac{y'}{x \log x} - y \log^2 x = 0$.

(d) $y'' + y' \tan x + \left(\dfrac{1}{2} + \dfrac{3 \tan^2 x}{4} - \dfrac{6}{x^2}\right) y = \sqrt{\cos x}$.

(e) $y'' + y' \sqrt{x} + y\left(\dfrac{x}{4} + \dfrac{1}{4\sqrt{x}} - 9\right) = xe^{-\frac{1}{3}x^{3/2}}$.

12. (a) Prove that the Riccati equation $y' = P + Qy + Ry^2$, where P, Q, and R are functions of x alone, is transformed by the substitution $y = -\dfrac{1}{R} \cdot \dfrac{du/dx}{u}$ into the linear equation

$$u'' - u'\left(Q + \dfrac{dR/dx}{R}\right) + u \cdot PR = 0,$$

if R is not identically zero.

(b) Apply the above substitution to

$$y' = -\frac{3}{x^3} + \left(2 - \frac{3}{x}\right)y + x^3 y^2,$$

and obtain

$$u'' - 2u' - 3u = 0.$$

Solve this for u, and from the solution derive

$$y = -\frac{1}{x^3} \cdot \frac{3c_1 e^{3x} - c_2 e^{-x}}{c_1 e^{3x} + c_2 e^{-x}} = -\frac{1}{x^3} \cdot \frac{3e^{3x} - ce^{-x}}{e^{3x} + ce^{-x}}.$$

where $c = \dfrac{c_2}{c_1}$.

(c) Solve $y' = -\dfrac{20}{x^3} - \dfrac{y}{x} + xy^2.$

(d) Solve $y' = \dfrac{\log^2 x}{x} + \dfrac{2 \log^2 x + 1}{x \log x} y + \dfrac{y^2}{x}.$

(e) Solve $y' = -4 \csc x + (3 - \cot x)y + y^2 \sin x.$

(f) Prove that if three solutions, $y = y_1,\, y = y_2,\, y = y_3$, of a Riccati equation are known, the equation is given by

$$\begin{vmatrix} y' & 1 & y & y^2 \\ y_1' & 1 & y_1 & y_1^2 \\ y_2' & 1 & y_2 & y_2^2 \\ y_3' & 1 & y_2 & y_3^2 \end{vmatrix} = 0.$$

(g) Write down the Riccati equation whose three solutions are $y = \log x,\, y = x,\, y = 1$.

13. Solve the following systems of equations:

(a) $\begin{cases} \dfrac{dx}{dt} = 4x + 3y, \\[2mm] \dfrac{dy}{dt} = 8x + 2y. \end{cases}$
   (b) $\begin{cases} \dfrac{du}{dx} + 13v = 3u, \\[2mm] \dfrac{dv}{dx} + 9v = 4u. \end{cases}$

(c) $\dfrac{dx}{dt} - 6x + 2y = \dfrac{dy}{dt} - 2x - 2y = 0.$

(d) $\begin{cases} \dfrac{du}{dx} = u - 4y + z, \\[2mm] \dfrac{dy}{dx} = -2y + z, \\[2mm] \dfrac{dz}{dx} = 4z. \end{cases}$
   (e) $\begin{cases} \dfrac{dx}{dt} + y = t^2 + 6t + 1, \\[2mm] x - \dfrac{dy}{dt} = 3t^2 - 3t - 1. \end{cases}$

(f) $\begin{cases} \dfrac{dx}{dt} + \dfrac{dy}{dt} + 2x + y = e^{2t} + t, \\[3mm] \dfrac{dx}{dt} + \dfrac{dy}{dt} - x + 3y = e^{-t} - 1. \end{cases}$

(g) $x - \dfrac{dx}{dt} - 2y = \dfrac{d^2x}{dt^2} - 2\dfrac{dy}{dt} - 2t + \cos 2t = 0.$

(h) $\dfrac{d^2x}{dt^2} - \dfrac{dx}{dt} + \dfrac{dy}{dt} = \dfrac{dx}{dt} + \dfrac{d^2y}{dt^2} + \dfrac{dy}{dt} = 0.$

(i) $\dfrac{d^2x}{dt^2} + 6x + 7y = 0 = \dfrac{d^2y}{dt^2} + 3x + 2y - 2t.$

14. A particle moving on a straight line is said to be in simple harmonic motion if its acceleration is proportional to its distance from a fixed point on the line and is directed toward that point. Denoting the distance of the particle from that point at the time t by s, show that the differential equation of its motion is $\dfrac{d^2s}{dt^2} = -k^2s$. Solve this equation on the basis that at $t = 0$, $s = h$, and $v = 0$. Show that the motion is periodic, and of period $\dfrac{2\pi}{k}$; also that the amplitude is h.

Note: The differential equation of this Exercise is of the form $\dfrac{d^2s}{dt^2} = f(s)$. A possible method of integrating such an equation is to multiply it by $2\dfrac{ds}{dt}$, obtaining $2\dfrac{ds}{dt} \cdot \dfrac{d^2s}{dt^2} = 2f(s)\dfrac{ds}{dt}$, or $\left(\dfrac{ds}{dt}\right)^2 = \displaystyle\int 2f(s) \cdot ds \equiv \varphi(s) + c_1$; whence, $\dfrac{ds}{\sqrt{\varphi(s) + c_1}} = \pm dt$, and the variables are separated.

Let the student work out the given equation by this method.

15. If the acceleration of a particle under the force of gravity is inversely proportional to the square of its distance from the center of the earth, and is directed toward the center, find the velocity at the surface of the earth of a particle falling from an infinite distance.

Hint: Show that the equation of its motion is $\dfrac{d^2s}{dt^2} = -\dfrac{k^2}{s^2}$. Use the method of the above note. (This equation is non-linear.) Also use the initial conditions: $(s = \infty,\ v = 0)$ and $\left(s = R,\ \dfrac{d^2s}{dt^2} = -g\right)$, where R is the radius of the earth.

16. A particle moves on a straight line in a resisting medium, and the resistance is proportional to the velocity. Assuming that the particle starts with a velocity v_0 from a position $s = s_0$, show that as time goes on the particle approaches the position $s = s_0 + \dfrac{v_0}{k^2}$, where $(-k^2)$ is the constant of proportionality.

17. A particle moves on a straight line in a resisting medium, under an attraction proportional to its distance from a fixed center on the line; the attraction is directed toward the center, and the resistance is proportional to the speed. Assuming the constants of proportionality to be 25 and 6, respectively, also that the particle starts from the center with a velocity of 8 ft. per sec., show that the particle will have an infinite number of oscillations and will approach a state of rest at the center. Find the period of the vibrations. This is a case of *damped vibrations* in mechanics.

18. (a) A pendulum of length l is suspended from a fixed point and is constrained to move in a vertical plane through the point of suspension. Assume that the weight is concentrated at a point in the bob (hence the string weightless), and that there is no resistance; show that the motion is represented by the equation

$$l \frac{d^2\theta}{dt^2} = -g \sin \theta,$$

where θ is the angle that the string makes with the vertical at the time t. Use the method of the note to Exercise 14, and obtain

$$\frac{d\theta}{\sqrt{c_1 l + 2g \cos \theta}} = \pm \frac{dt}{\sqrt{l}}.$$

This integral cannot be expressed in terms of elementary functions.

(b) Solve the equation in (a), modified to the case in which θ remains tolerably small throughout the motion, so that $\sin \theta$ is approximately equal to θ. Find the period. Note that the equation is now of the same form as that in Exercise 14, and the motion represented by it is simple harmonic motion.

19. A particle moves in a plane in such a manner that its velocity component in the direction of each coördinate axis is equal to the other coördinate. Find its possible paths.

20. A beam of length l feet is supported at both ends, and is loaded at the center by a weight of w tons. Find the deflection of the beam at any point, and the maximum deflection. *Hint:* It is proved in mechanics that the bending moment at any cross-section (defined as the algebraic sum of the moments, about the center of the section, of all forces acting on one side of the section) is equal to $\dfrac{EI}{R}$, where E is the modulus of the elasticity for the material of the beam, I is the moment of inertia of the cross-section about a horizontal axis through its center, and R is the radius of curvature, at the cross-section, of the curve into which the beam is bent.

Now, $R = \dfrac{(1 + y'^2)^{3/2}}{y''}$, as the student will recall from his elementary calculus, and hence the bending moment is

$$\frac{EI}{R} = EIy''(1 + y'^2)^{-3/2} = EIy'' \left[1 - \frac{3}{2} y'^2 + \frac{15}{8} y'^4 - \cdots \right].$$

If the bending is slight, the slope y' is very small, and we may neglect y'^2 and higher powers and obtain EIy'' for the right-hand member.

The differential equation of the curve assumed by the beam is thus obtained by equating the bending moment at a distance x from a suitably assumed origin, to EIy''.

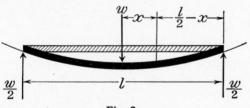

Fig. 3.

For the problem stated, take the origin at the lowest point of the (deflected) beam, which, by symmetry, is its mid-point, and the y-axis at right angles to the beam. The bending moment at any section for which x is positive is $\dfrac{w}{2}\left(\dfrac{l}{2} - x\right)$; hence, the differential equation of the curve is

$$EIy'' = \frac{w}{2}\left(\frac{l}{2} - x\right),$$

whence, by direct integration,

$$EIy' = \frac{w}{2}\left(\frac{lx}{2} - \frac{x^2}{2}\right) + c_1,$$

where $c_1 = 0$, since $y' = 0$ at $x = 0$, and from this

$$EIy = \frac{w}{2}\left(\frac{lx^2}{4} - \frac{x^3}{6}\right) + c_2,$$

where $c_2 = 0$, since $y = 0$ at $x = 0$, and we have

$$y = \frac{w}{24EI}\,(3lx^2 - 2x^3).$$

Since we have imposed the restriction, above, that x be positive, we must repeat the process with the contrary assumption, *i. e.*, the assumption that x is negative. The result thus obtained will be

$$y = \frac{w}{24EI}\,(3lx^2 + 2x^3),$$

and therefore we see that the two results may be combined into the one equation

$$y = \frac{w}{24EI}\,(3lx^2 - 2|x|^3).$$

The maximum value of y obviously corresponds to $x = \pm\dfrac{l}{2}$, at which it has the value $Y = \dfrac{w}{48EI}\,l^3$, and the deflection at any cross-section is

$$Y - y = \frac{w}{48EI}\,l^3 - \frac{w}{24EI}\,(3lx^2 - 2|x|^3) = \frac{w}{48EI}\,(l^3 - 6lx^2 + 4|x|^3).$$

21. A beam l feet in length is supported at the ends and is carrying a uniformly distributed load of w tons per foot run. Find its maximum deflection, and the deflection at any cross-section.

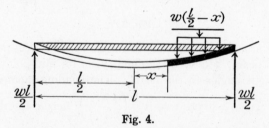

Fig. 4.

Hint: The bending moment at the section indicated is

$$\frac{wl}{2}\left(\frac{l}{2} - x\right) - \frac{w}{2}\left(\frac{l}{2} - x\right)^2 = \frac{w}{2}\left(\frac{l^2}{4} - x^2\right),$$

for the point of application of the force $\dfrac{wl}{2}$ is at a distance $\dfrac{l}{2} - x$ from the section, and for the force $w\left(\dfrac{l}{2} - x\right)$, the distance is $\dfrac{1}{2}\left(\dfrac{l}{2} - x\right)$; also, the second force imparts a moment opposite in sign to that imparted by the first.

22. (a) A beam l feet in length is fixed at one end and is carrying a load of w tons at the other end. Find its maximum deflection, and the deflection at any point.

(b) A beam 30 feet in length is fixed at one end and is carrying a uniformly distributed load of 1 ton per foot run. Find its maximum deflection, and the deflection at any point.

(c) A beam 40 feet in length is fixed at one end. It is loaded at the free end with a weight of 2 tons, and is carrying a total weight of 60 tons evenly distributed over the beam. Find the slope and the amount of deflection at the free end.

23. A particle is projected upward, and moves against gravity and a resistance which is proportional to the velocity. If the constant of proportionality is k^2, and if the initial velocity is v_0, show that the particle will come to rest at the instant defined by

$$t = \frac{1}{k^2} \log \frac{v_0 k^2 + g}{g}.$$

24. (a) An electrical circuit contains an inductor of L henries, a condenser of C farads, and a resistor of R ohms connected in series with a generator. If the generator delivers a voltage difference $E(t)$ between its terminals (when t is time measured in seconds), show that the charge q on the condenser is such that

$$L \frac{d^2 q}{dt^2} + R \frac{dq}{dt} + \frac{1}{C} q = E(t).$$

Hint: (See Section 16, Chapter II.)

(b) Under the above conditions show that

$$L \frac{d^2 i}{dt^2} + R \frac{di}{dt} + \frac{1}{C} i = E'(t),$$

where i is the current measured in amperes flowing at time t and $E'(t)$ is the derivative of $E(t)$ with respect to t.

25. An electrical generator delivers a voltage given by $E = 1700$ sin $20t$. It is connected in series with an inductor of 1 henry, a resistor of 20 ohms, and a condenser of capacity $\frac{1}{500}$ farads. If at time $t = 0$ no current is flowing but the condenser has a charge of -4 coulombs, find i and q in terms of t.

26. If in the circuit of the preceding exercise the generator is replaced by a battery delivering a constant e.m.f. of 5000 volts, find q and i in terms of t if $q = 0$ and $i = 0$ when $t = 0$. Also find the limits of i and q as $t \to \infty$.

27. In the solution of a problem on the order of the last two above, the terms which approach zero as t approaches infinity are called *transient* terms while the other terms are called *steady state* terms. If a circuit contains an inductor of 1 henry, a resistor of 60 ohms, a condenser of capacity $4(10^{-4})$ farads, and a generator delivering $100 \sin 40t$ volts and if q and i are both zero when $t = 0$, find the value of the transient term when $t = 0.01$ second and also find the maximum value of the steady state current.

28. A particle moves under damped harmonic motion defined by the equation $\dfrac{d^2s}{dt^2} + 4\dfrac{ds}{dt} + bs = 0$. Find b and the constants of integration if at the time $t = 0$, $s = 6$, the velocity is (-20) and the acceleration is 32.

29. A cylindrical spar buoy 16 inches in diameter and standing vertically in water weighing 62.5 pounds per cubic foot is slightly depressed and then released. The period of the resulting motion is $6\sqrt{2\pi/g}$ seconds. Find the weight of the spar buoy.

30. A suspension spring with a sixteen-pound weight attached to it is observed to make 30 complete oscillations in 20 seconds. Knowing that this weight will stretch the spring 3 inches and that the air resistance is proportional to the speed, find the constant of proportionality. (Take $g = 32$ ft./sec^2.)

31. The x-component of the acceleration of a moving particle is equal to twice its ordinate, the y-component of its acceleration equals one-half its abscissa. Find the equation of its path, if at the time $t = 0$, the particle is at the origin and the x- and y-components of its velocity are each equal to 1.

32. The force exerted by a spring is proportional to the amount it is stretched beyond its natural length. A nine-pound weight hanging at rest at the end of a spring stretches it 2 inches. The weight is drawn down another 2 inches and released. Find the equation of the ensuing motion, also its period and amplitude.

33. Solve Exercise 32 under the modifying condition that the motion is retarded by a force which, measured in pounds, equals $\frac{1}{75}$ of the absolute value of the velocity of the weight, measured in feet per second.

34. The sole force acting on a particle moving in a plane is the force of attraction to a fixed point, O, in that plane, the force being inversely proportional to the square of the distance of the particle from O. Show that the locus of the particle is a conic with O as focus. *Hint:* Show that with the particle at $P(r, \theta)$ the components of the force along and at right angles to OP are, respectively,

$$\frac{d^2r}{dt^2} - r\left(\frac{d\theta}{dt}\right)^2 \text{ and } r\frac{d^2r}{dt^2} + 2\frac{dr}{dt}\cdot\frac{d\theta}{dt}.$$

Hence,

$$\frac{d^2r}{dt^2} - r\left(\frac{d\theta}{dt}\right)^2 = \frac{-k}{r^2}, \qquad\qquad \text{(A)}$$

and

$$r\frac{d^2\theta}{dt^2} + 2\frac{dr}{dt}\cdot\frac{d\theta}{dt} = 0. \qquad\qquad \text{(B)}$$

Equation (B) gives at once

$$r^2\frac{d\theta}{dt} = h \qquad\qquad (h \text{ a constant}). \quad \text{(C)}$$

Set $r = \dfrac{1}{u}$ and write Equation A in terms of derivatives with respect to θ, making use of (C). The final result is

$$r = \frac{\dfrac{h^2}{k}}{1 + \dfrac{ch^2}{k}\cos(\theta - d)}.$$

35. In the electrical network of Figure 5 the current through the elements L_1, R_1, and C_1 has been designated by i_1 and that through L_2, R_2, and C_2 by i_2. By Kirchoff's law the current through the elements L_{12}, R_{12}, C_{12} is $i_1 - i_2$. The charges on the three condensers C_1, C_2, and C_{12} are integrals of the currents i_1, i_2, and $i_1 - i_2$. Hence q_{12}, the charge on C_{12}, equals

$$\int^t (i_1 - i_2)\, dt = \int^t i_1\, dt - \int^t i_2\, dt = q_1 - q_2 + K,$$

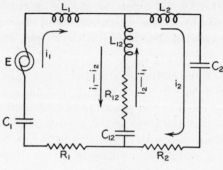

Fig. 5.

where K is a constant. By the addition of voltages around the two parts of the circuit, show that the following equations are obtained:

$$\left[(L_1 + L_{12})D^2 + (R_1 + R_{12})D + \left(\frac{1}{C_1} + \frac{1}{C_{12}}\right)\right] q_1$$
$$- \left(L_{12}D^2 + R_{12}D + \frac{1}{C_{12}}\right) q_2 = E - \frac{K}{C_{12}},$$

$$- \left(L_{12}D^2 + R_{12}D + \frac{1}{C_{12}}\right) q_1$$
$$+ \left[(L_2 + L_{12})D^2 + (R_2 + R_{12})D + \left(\frac{1}{C_2} + \frac{1}{C_{12}}\right)\right] q_2 = \frac{K}{C_{12}},$$

$$\left[(L_1 + L_{12})D^2 + (R_1 + R_{12})D + \left(\frac{1}{C_1} + \frac{1}{C_{12}}\right)\right] i_1$$
$$- \left(L_{12}D^2 + R_{12}D + \frac{1}{C_{12}}\right) i_2 = \frac{dE}{dt},$$

$$- \left(L_{12}D^2 + R_{12}D + \frac{1}{C_{12}}\right) i_1$$
$$+ \left[(L_2 + L_{12})D^2 + (R_2 + R_{12})D + \left(\frac{1}{C_2} + \frac{1}{C_{12}}\right)\right] i_2 = 0.$$

36. In the electrical circuit of Figure 6 all currents are zero when $t = 0$ and $E = 100 \sin 300t$. Express the currents in terms of time.

37. Prove that the two circuits as shown in Figure 7 are equivalent if $\frac{1}{L} = \frac{1}{L_1} + \frac{1}{L_2}$, i.e., the sum of the reciprocals of the inductances of two inductors is the reciprocal of the inductance of the pair when connected in parallel. *Hint:* In each case set up the differential equation for the current through the resistor.

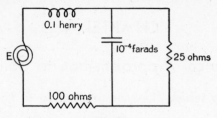

0.1 henry

10^{-4} farads

25 ohms

E

100 ohms

Fig. 6.

38. Prove that the sum of the reciprocals of the resistances of two resistors is the reciprocal of their resistance when connected in parallel.

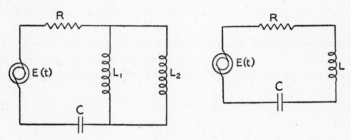

R

E(t)

L_1

L_2

C

R

E(t)

L

C

Fig. 7.

39. Prove that the sum of the capacities of two condensers is the capacity of the pair connected in parallel.

40. Prove that the sum of the reciprocals of the capacities of two condensers is the reciprocal of the capacity of the pair when connected in series.

41. Find the inductance of two inductors of inductances L_1 and L_2 if the two are connected in series.

42. Find the resistance of two resistors of resistance R_1 and R_2 if the two are connected in parallel.

CHAPTER V

Numerical Approximation to Solutions

37. Taylor's series. Let our problem be to find a particular solution of

$$y' = f(x, y), \tag{1}$$

say, the solution passing through (x_0, y_0). It may well happen that no method is available for integrating (1) formally, in which case resort may be had to some means of finding an approximation to the solution desired.

One such method has been indicated in Exercise 6, page 16, and the student will do well to re-read the discussion of that exercise. To illustrate the method again, let the particular solution of

$$y' = x - y^2 \tag{2}$$

passing through $\left(0, \dfrac{1}{2}\right)$ be desired. We compute, for $\left(0, \dfrac{1}{2}\right)$,

$$y' = x - y^2 = -\frac{1}{4},$$

$$y'' = 1 - 2yy' = \frac{5}{4},$$

$$y''' = -2yy'' - 2y'^2 = -\frac{11}{8},$$

$$y^{iv} = -2yy''' - 6y'y'' = \frac{13}{4},$$

$$y^{v} = -2yy^{iv} - 8y'y''' - 6y''^2 = -\frac{123}{8}, \text{ etc.}$$

The series

$$y = \frac{1}{2} + x\left(-\frac{1}{4}\right) + \frac{x^2}{2!} \cdot \frac{5}{4} + \frac{x^3}{3!}\left(-\frac{11}{8}\right) + \frac{x^4}{4!} \cdot \frac{13}{4}$$
$$+ \frac{x^5}{5!}\left(-\frac{123}{8}\right) + \cdots \tag{3}$$

is, indeed, the Taylor expansion, about $\left(0, \frac{1}{2}\right)$, of that function

$$y = f(x) \tag{4}$$

which satisfies (2) and for which $y = \frac{1}{2}$ when $x = 0$, *i.e.*, it is the Taylor expansion of the particular solution sought.

In general, it is not possible to obtain (4) explicitly from its Taylor expansion, in fact, if it were possible, (1) probably would be readily integrable in the first place.

A finite number of terms of the series (3) will, then, serve as an approximation to (4), and hence if the value of y in (4) is desired, say for $x = .2$, we compute it as

$$y = \frac{1}{2} + (.2)\left(-\frac{1}{4}\right) + \frac{.04}{2} \cdot \frac{5}{4} + \frac{.008}{6}\left(-\frac{11}{8}\right) + \frac{.0016}{24} \cdot \frac{13}{4}$$

$$+ \frac{.00032}{120}\left(-\frac{123}{8}\right) + \cdots = .47334, \text{ approximately.}$$

38. Picard's method. Let us now turn to another method devised by the eminent French mathematician Émile Picard.

To solve the problem proposed at the beginning of this section, start with

$$y_1 \equiv y_0 + \int_{x_0}^{x} f(x, y_0)\,dx.$$

Form, next,

$$y_2 \equiv y_0 + \int_{x_0}^{x} f(x, y_1)\,dx,$$

then

$$y_3 \equiv y_0 + \int_{x_0}^{x} f(x, y_2)\,dx,$$

and

$$y_4 \equiv y_0 + \int_{x_0}^{x} f(x, y_3)\,dx.$$

By continuing this process, we obtain a sequence of functions of x,

$$y_0, y_1, y_2, y_3, y_4, \cdots,$$

all of which take on the value y_0 at $x = x_0$, and, furthermore, such that

$$\begin{cases} y_1' \equiv f(x, y_0)^* & \therefore \ (y_1')_{x=x_0} = f(x_0, y_0), \\ y_2' \equiv f(x, y_1) & \therefore \ (y_2')_{x=x_0} = f(x_0, y_0), \\ y_3' \equiv f(x, y_2) & \therefore \ (y_3')_{x=x_0} = f(x_0, y_0), \\ y_4' \equiv f(x, y_3) & \therefore \ (y_4')_{x=x_0} = f(x_0, y_0), \text{ etc.} \end{cases} \tag{5}$$

These functions are not themselves solutions of (1), since they do not identically satisfy $y_i' = f(x, y_i)$ $(i = 1, 2, 3, 4, \cdots)$, but it is proved that the successive functions in the sequence form better and better approximations to the solution sought. Indeed, Picard proved that this sequence tends to a limit which is precisely the solution in question.

For the example (2) worked in this section, Picard's method would yield $\left(\text{with } x_0 = 0, \ y_0 = \dfrac{1}{2}, \text{ and } f(x, y) \equiv x - y^2 \right)$

$$y_1 \equiv \frac{1}{2} + \int_0^x \left(x - \frac{1}{4} \right) dx \equiv \frac{1}{2} - \frac{x}{4} + \frac{x^2}{2},$$

$$y_2 \equiv \frac{1}{2} + \int_0^x \left[x - \left(\frac{1}{2} - \frac{x}{4} + \frac{x^2}{2} \right)^2 \right] dx \equiv \frac{1}{2} - \frac{x}{4} + \frac{5x^2}{8} - \frac{3x^3}{16}$$

$$+ \frac{x^4}{16} - \frac{x^5}{20},$$

$$y_3 \equiv \frac{1}{2} + \int_0^x (x - y_2^2) \, dx,$$

etc. The value of y for $x = .2$ would be found as

$$(y_1)_{x=.2} = .47$$
$$(y_2)_{x=.2} = .47358,$$

where the second would be a better approximation to the value sought than the first, while $(y_3)_{x=.2}$ would be a still better approximation.

It is evident that the labor involved in performing the successive integrations weakens the effectiveness of the method as a practical means of approximation. It is however, of great theoretical significance.

Exercises

1. (a) Obtain the approximate solution of $y' = xy$ which passes through $\left(\dfrac{1}{2}, 1 \right)$, in the form of a Taylor series. Using the

---

* Wood's *Advanced Calculus*, page 141, Equation (1).

first 4 terms of the series, compute the value of y in the above solution for $x = .55$.

(b) Obtain the approximate solution in (a) by Picard's method.   Compute y_2 for $x = .55$.

(c) Compare the results in (a) and (b) with the value of y in the exact solution, for $x = .55$.

2. Obtain the approximate solution of $y' = \log xy$ which passes through $(1, 1)$, in the form of a Taylor series.   Use the first three terms of the series to compute the value of y in the above solution, for $x = 1.1$.

3. By Picard's method, obtain the approximation to the solution of $y' = x - y$ which passes through $(0, 2)$, down to y_4.   Compare each of y_1, y_2, y_3, y_4 with the values given by the exact solution.

4. Show that the successive approximations, by Picard's method, to the solution of $y' = -y$ through (x_0, y_0), tend to the limit $y = y_0 e^{x_0 - x}$, i.e., to the exact solution.

5. Show that all the approximations, by Picard's method, to the solution of $y' = x$ through (x_0, y_0) are identical with the exact solution.

6. (a) Obtain the approximate solutions to $y' = x + y^2$ through $(0, 0)$:

   i. By Picard's method.
   ii. As a Taylor series.

(b) Compute the values of y in the two parts of Exercise 6(a) for $x = -.1$.

7. Extend formulas (5) of the text to show that y_i, in the Picard sequence of approximations, has all its x-derivatives up to and including the ith, but not, in general, the $(i + 1)^{\text{st}}$, equal at (x_0, y_0) to its value as determined by $f(x, y)$, where i equals 1, 2, 3, $\cdots$.

8. Obtain, by Picard's method, an approximation to that solution of the system

$$\begin{cases} \dfrac{dy}{dx} = z, \\[2mm] \dfrac{dz}{dx} = x - y^2, \end{cases}$$

which is satisfied by $y = 1$ and $z = 2$, when $x = 0$.   *Hint:* Picard's sequence of approximations to a particular solution of

$$\begin{cases} \dfrac{dy}{dx} = f(x, y, z), \\[2mm] \dfrac{dz}{dx} = g(x, y, z), \end{cases}$$

satisfied by (x_0, y_0, z_0), is

$$\begin{cases} y_1 \equiv y_0 + \displaystyle\int_{x_0}^{x} f(x, y_0, z_0) \, dx, \\[2mm] z_1 \equiv z_0 + \displaystyle\int_{x_0}^{x} g(x, y_0, z_0) \, dx, \end{cases}$$

$$\begin{cases} y_2 \equiv y_0 + \displaystyle\int_{x_0}^{x} f(x, y_1, z_1) \, dx, \\[2mm] z_2 \equiv z_0 + \displaystyle\int_{x_0}^{x} g(x, y_1, z_1) \, dx, \end{cases}$$

etc.

9. Obtain, by Picard's method, a third approximation to that solution of

$$\begin{cases} \dfrac{dy}{dx} = x + z^2, \\[2mm] \dfrac{dz}{dx} = y - x, \end{cases}$$

for which $y = 0$ and $z = 1$, when $x = 0$.

10. Obtain, by Picard's method, a third approximation to that solution of

$$\begin{cases} \dfrac{dy}{dx} = z^2, \\[2mm] \dfrac{dz}{dx} = y + u, \\[2mm] \dfrac{du}{dx} = u - z, \end{cases}$$

for which $y = 1$, $z = 0$, and $u = 1$, when $x = 0$.

11. (a) Obtain an approximation to the solution of Exercise 8 as two simultaneous Taylor series. *Hint:* At $(0, 1, 2)$, we have

$$\begin{cases} y' = z = 2, \\ z' = x - y^2 = -1, \end{cases}$$
$$\begin{cases} y'' = z' = -1, \\ z'' = 1 - 2yy' = 1 - 4 = -3, \end{cases}$$

$$\begin{cases} y''' = z'' = -3, \\ z''' = -2yy'' - 2y'^2 = 2 - 8 = -6, \end{cases}$$

etc.

(b) Obtain an approximate solution for Exercise 9 as two simultaneous Taylor series.

(c) Obtain an approximate solution for Exercise 10 as three simultaneous Taylor series.

12. Derive the formulas analogous to formula (5) of the text for the case of two simultaneous equations, as discussed in Exercise 8.

13. Obtain an approximation to that solution of $y'' = x + y^2 - 2y'$ for which $y = 1$ and $y' = 1$, when $x = 0$:

(a) in the form of a Taylor series;

(b) by Picard's method.

Hint: For (b), replace the given equation by the system

$$\begin{cases} \dfrac{dy}{dx} = z, \\ \dfrac{dz}{dx} = x + y^2 - 2x. \end{cases}$$

14. Obtain an approximation to that solution of $y'' = x + y - y^2$ for which $y = -1$ and $y' = 1$, when $x = 0$:

(a) in the form of a Taylor series;

(b) by Picard's method.

39. Milne's method. The methods of the foregoing sections, while of great theoretical significance, are not ordinarily expedient to use in practice.   Indeed, unless the differential equation is so simple as to be readily solved exactly, the integrations encountered under the method of Picard become hopelessly complicated.   The method of Taylor's series involves successive differentiations which likewise tend to become involved.   However, if x is kept comparatively close to x_0, only a few terms of the series may be needed for approximating y.   The method, therefore, furnishes us with starting values of y, *e.g.*, the value of y corresponding to $x = x_0 + h$, $x_0 + 2h$, $x_0 + 3h$.

In this section we take up a highly efficient method, due to W. E. Milne*, for extending the solution.   It requires just such a start as may be had by the use of a series.

---

* "Numerical Integration of Ordinary Differential Equations," *The American Mathematical Monthly*, Vol. 33 (1926), pp. 455–460.

We turn again to the differential equation

$$y' = f(x, y) \tag{1}$$

with the initial condition $x = x_0$, $y = y_0$. We assume that, by any method whatever, we have found the values of y for $x = x_0 + h$, $x_0 + 2h$, and $x_0 + 3h$. Milne's method consists in finding y for $x = x_0 + 4h$ by the formula

$$y_4 = y_0 + \frac{4h}{3} (2y_1' - y_2' + 2y_3') \tag{6}$$

where $y_4 = y(x_0 + 4h)$, $y_3 = y(x_0 + 3h)$, $y_2 = y(x_0 + 2h)$, and $y_1 = y(x_0 + h)$, while $y_i' = f(x_0 + ih, y_i)$, $i = 1, 2, 3, 4$.

Having the values of y_1, y_2, and y_3, obtained by some other method, as we have previously stated, we compute the values of y_1', y_2', and y_3' by substituting (x_1, y_1), (x_2, y_2), and (x_3, y_3) into (1). Next we find y_4 by (6) and then y_4' by substituting (x_4, y_4) into (1). These values of y_4 and y_4' just found are tentative values of y and y' corresponding to $x = x_4 = x_0 + 4h$. When found, they should be checked by the formula

$$y_4 = y_2 + \frac{h}{3} (y_4' + 4y_3' + y_2'). \tag{7}$$

Formulas (6) and (7) both arise from the obvious relation

$$y_n = y_i + \int_{x_i}^{x_n} y' \, dx$$

by replacing the integral with an approximate integral. Equation (6) employs the formula

$$\int_{x_0}^{x_0+4h} f(x) \, dx = \frac{4h}{3} [2f(x_0 + h) - f(x_0 + 2h) + 2f(x_0 + 3h)], \tag{8}$$

while (7) comes from

$$\int_{x_0}^{x_0+2h} f(x) \, dx = \frac{h}{3} [f(x_0) + 4f(x_0 + h) + f(x_0 + 2h)]. \tag{9}$$

Now (8) and (9) do not hold exactly except under highly special conditions. The error in (9) may be shown to be expressible in the form

$$- \frac{h^5}{90} f^{iv}(\xi), \tag{10}$$

where ξ is some number between x_0 and $x_0 + 2h$. The error in (8) is of the form

$$\frac{28h^5}{90} f^{iv}(\eta), \tag{11}$$

where η lies between x_0 and $x_0 + 4h$.

The values of these error expressions (10) and (11) cannot be computed exactly in the application of Milne's method because, in general, the function of x representing y' is not known. Moreover, the derivations of these error expressions fail to indicate the precise values of ξ and η. If $f(x) = y'$, the error expressions in (10) and (11) reduce to $-\dfrac{h^5}{90} \cdot \dfrac{d^5y}{dx^5}$ and $+\dfrac{28h^5}{90} \cdot \dfrac{d^5y}{dx^5}$. Under ordinary circumstances $\dfrac{d^5y}{dx^5}$ remains essentially constant over the interval from x_0 to $x_0 + 4h$. Under these conditions the difference between the values for y_4, as given by

$$y_4^{(1)} = y_0 + \frac{4h}{3} [2y_1' - y_2' + 2y_3'] \tag{12}$$

and

$$y_4^{(2)} = y_2 + \frac{h}{3} [y_2' + 4y_3' + y_4'], \tag{13}$$

represents $\dfrac{29}{90} h^5 \dfrac{d^5y}{dx^5}$. One-twenty-ninth of this is the error in y_4 as given by (10). Hence the following rule: *If*

$$\left| \frac{y_4^{(1)} - y_4^{(2)}}{29} \right| \tag{14}$$

is insignificant in the number of places tabulated as values of y, *accept the value of* $y_4^{(2)}$ *as correct.** *If (14) is significant, Milne's method can only be used with a smaller value of* h.

Illustration

Given the differential equation

$$y' = 2y - x$$

_____

* This is in accordance with the statement made by Milne in his original exposition of the method. It is the experience of the authors that this is too optimistic and that a more practical rule would substitute the divisor 10 in place of 29 in the expression (14).

and four points, (1, 1), (1.1, 1.1054), (1.2, 1.2229) and (1.3, 1.3554) on the same integral curve of it, let us find, by Milne's method, the values of y corresponding to $x = 1.4, 1.5,$ and 1.6.

The given values, as well as the results obtained, are shown in Table 3. The calculation of $y(1.4)$ is made by Formula (6) as

Table 3.

x	y	y'
1	1	1
1.1	1.1054	1.1108
1.2	1.2229	1.2458
1.3	1.3554	1.4108
1.4	1.5063	1.6126
1.5	1.6794	1.8588
1.6	1.8799	2.1598

$$y(1.4) = 1 + \frac{4(.1)}{3} [2(1.4108) - 1.2458 + 2(1.1108)]$$
$$= 1.5063.$$

By the differential equation we find

$$y'(1.4) = 2(1.5063) - 1.4 = 1.6126.$$

Then, by (7)

$$y(1.4) = 1.2229 + \frac{.1}{3} [1.6126 + 4(1.4108) + 1.2458] = 1.5063,$$

a value which agrees with the value previously obtained. Hence, we assume that it is correct and enter it in Table 3. The method is repeated to add other rows to the table, as follows.

$$y(1.5) = 1.1054 + \frac{.4}{3} [2(1.6126) - 1.4108 + 2(1.2458)] = 1.6795,$$

$$y'(1.5) = 2(1.6795) - 1.5 = 1.8590,$$

$$y(1.5) = 1.3554 + \frac{.1}{3} [1.8590 + 4(1.6126) + 1.4108] = 1.6794,$$

$$y(1.6) = 1.2229 + \frac{.4}{3} [2(1.8588) - 1.6126 + 2(1.4108)] = 1.8798,$$

$$y'(1.6) = 2(1.8798) - 1.6 = 2.1596,$$

$$y(1.6) = 1.5063 + \frac{.1}{4} [2.1596 + 4(1.8588) + 1.6126] = 1.8799.$$

The fact that the check value of y has not differed from the tentative value more than one unit in the fourth decimal place suggests that we might be able to increase the value of h to .2. To this end we draw up Table 4, taking alternate rows from Table 3. From this table, using (6) and (7) we obtain

Table 4.

x	y	y'
1	1	1
1.2	1.2229	1.2458
1.4	1.5063	1.6126
1.6	1.8799	2.1598

$$y(1.8) = 1 + \frac{4(.2)}{3}\,[2(2.1598) - 1.6126 + 2(1.2458)] = 2.3863,$$

$$y'(1.8) = 2(2.3863) - 1.8 = 2.9726,$$

$$y(1.8) = 1.5063 + \frac{.2}{3}\,[2.9726 + 4(2.1598) + 1.6126] = 2.3879.$$

Thus, the check value of $y(1.8)$ differs from the tentative value by 0.0016. One 29th part of this difference is not negligible, since we are keeping four decimal places. We conclude that $h = .2$ is too large and if we want to extend the integral curve further than the points of Table 3 we shall have to go back to $h = .1$.

Exercises

1. In each of the following cases fill in the blanks in the given table which lists sets of points on an integral curve of the corresponding differential equation.

(a) $\dfrac{dy}{dx} = x + y$,

x	0	0.1	0.2	0.3	0.4	0.5
y	1	1.1103	1.2428	1.3997		

(b) $\dfrac{dy}{dx} = \dfrac{y - x}{y + x}$,

x	0	0.1	0.2	0.3	0.4	0.5
y	1	1.091	1.168	1.233		

(c) $\dfrac{dy}{dx} = y - xy$,

x	1	1.2	1.4	1.6	1.8	2.0	2.2
y	1	0.9802	0.9231	0.8353			

2. For the following differential equations, find by any method three more points on the integral curve through the point given and then proceed to the given value of x, by the method of Milne.

(a) Find y at $x = 1.5$ on the integral curve of $xy' = y - 3x$ through $(1, 2.000)$.

(b) Find y at $x = 0.50$ on the integral curve of $y' = \sin x + \cos y$ through $(0.00, 0.00)$.

40. Milne's method extended. The principles employed in the derivation of Milne's method lend themselves to analogous methods requiring more or fewer than four points on the curve. If computation is done by hand, then Formulas (14) and (13) are ideal because the multiplications and divisions required by them are so easily done. If calculating machines are available, it may be worth while to use more involved formulas. One pair of formulas, which can be used, consists of

$$y_6^{(1)} = y_0 + \frac{3h}{10} [11y_1' - 14y_2' + 26y_3' - 14y_4' + 11y_5'] \qquad (15)$$

and

$$y_6^{(2)} = y_2 + \frac{2h}{45} [7y_2' + 32y_3' + 12y_4' + 32y_5' + 7y_6'] . \qquad (16)$$

The error involved in (15), which is used for advancing after six points are known, is expressible in the form $\frac{41}{140} h^7 \frac{d^7y}{dx^7}$, while the error in the check Formula (16) is $-\frac{8}{945} h^7 \frac{d^7y}{dx^7}$. Of course, the derivatives d^7y/dx^7 are evaluated at different places between x_0 and $x_0 + 6h$ in these two expressions. Playing again upon the constancy of this derivative in that interval, we see that the difference between $y_6^{(1)}$ and $y_6^{(2)}$ is about 34.6 times the error in $y_6^{(2)}$. Accordingly, we accept $y_6^{(2)}$ as correct if $\left| \dfrac{y_6^{(1)} - y_6^{(2)}}{34} \right|$ is negligible in the number of places kept. In practice this is found to be too optimistic, and we suggest the change of 34 to 12.

Illustration

The solution of the differential equation

$$y' = 2y - x,$$

which passes through the point $(1, 1)$, also passes through the points of the table shown.

Table 5.

x	y	y'
1	1	1
1.2	1.2230*	1.2460
1.4	1.5064	1.6128
1.6	1.8800	2.1600
1.8	2.3883	2.9766
2.0	3.0973	4.1946

By (15) we obtain
$$y_6^{(1)} = 4.1052,$$
$$y_6' = 6.0104,$$
and by (16)
$$y_6^{(2)} = 4.1058.$$

The difference between $y_6^{(2)}$ and $y_6^{(1)}$ is .0006, and this divided by 12 is barely negligible in four decimals. We conclude that $y_6 = 4.1058$.

41. Starting the solution. The Milne method requires the possession of four "consecutive" points on the curve before it can be started. If the function $f(x, y)$, y being an unknown function of x in the equation
$$y' = f(x, y),$$
can be differentiated several times with respect to x without excessive labor, and if these derivatives are reasonably small at the starting point (x_0, y_0), then the three additional points required may be best obtained by use of a Taylor series as shown in Article 37. In other cases the procedure described below is available.

Just as the Milne method finds a fifth point on the curve, given four points, so similar methods can find a second point, given one, a third point, given two, and a fourth point, given three. We shall first set down all of the formulas which will be required. In these formulas the symbol I_i^j is used with the understanding that

$$I_i^j = \int_{x_i}^{x_j} y' \, dx, \qquad \text{where} \qquad x_j = x_i + (j - i)h.$$

*The values in Table 5 are computed from the exact solution and differ slightly from the corresponding values in Tables 3 and 4. Corresponding to $x = 1.2$ the value of y correct to eight figures is 1.2229562.

One ordinate formula for advancing:

$$I_0^1 = hy_0'.$$ (17)

Two ordinate formula for checking:

$$I_0^1 = \frac{h}{2}(y_0' + y_1').$$ (18)

Two ordinate formula for advancing:

$$I_0^2 = 2hy_1'.$$ (19)

Three ordinate formulas for checking:

$$I_0^1 = \frac{h}{12}(5y_0' + 8y_1' - y_2'),$$ (20)

$$I_0^2 = \frac{h}{3}(y_0' + 4y_1' + y_2').$$ (21)

Three ordinate formula for advancing:

$$I_0^3 = \frac{3h}{4}(y_0' + 3y_2').$$ (22)

Four ordinate formulas for checking:

$$I_0^1 = \frac{h}{24}(9y_0' + 19y_1' - 5y_2' + y_3'),$$ (23)

$$I_0^2 = \frac{h}{3}(y_0' + 4y_1' + y_2'),$$ (24)

$$I_0^3 = \frac{3h}{8}(y_0' + 3y_1' + 3y_2' + y_3').$$ (25)

Four ordinate formula for advancing:

$$I_0^4 = \frac{4h}{3}[2y_1' - y_2' + 2y_3'].$$ (26)

Six ordinate formula for advancing:

$$I_0^6 = \frac{3h}{10}[11y_1' - 14y_2' + 26y_3' - 14y_4' + 11y_5'].$$

Five ordinate formula for checking:

$$I_2^6 = \frac{2h}{45}[7y_2' + 32y_3' + 12y_4' + 32y_5' + 7y_6'].$$

Illustration

Let $y' = 2y - x$ and let $(1, 1)$ be given.   In the notation of the above formulas, we have $x_0 = 1$, $y_0 = 1$, $y_0' = 2(1) - 1 = 1$.   If we take $h = .1$, we have by (17)

$$y_1 = 1 + .1(1) = 1.1,$$
$$y_1' = 2(1.1) - (1.1) = 1.1,$$

and we have the partial table below.

x	y	y'
1	1	1
1.1	1.1	1.1

Checking by (18) we find

$$y_1 = 1 + \frac{.1}{2} (1 + 1.1) = 1.105,$$
$$y_1' = 2(1.105) - 1.1 = 1.110,$$

and the modified table becomes

x	y	y'
1	1	1
1.1	1.105	1.110

Another check by (18) gives

$$y_1 = 1 + \frac{.1}{2} (1 + 1.110) = 1.1053,$$
$$y_1' = 2(1.1053) - 1.1 = 1.1106,$$

and the table becomes

x	y	y'
1	1	1
1.1	1.1053	1.1106

If we recheck by (18), these values are repeated so that no further refinement can be made to four decimal places by use of (18).   We therefore apply Formula (19) to obtain

$$y_2 = 1 + 2(.1)(1.1106) = 1.2212,$$
$$y_2' = 2(1.2212) - 1.2 = 1.2424,$$

and our tentative three point table is

x	y	y'
1	1	1
1.1	1.1053	1.1106
1.2	1.2212	1.2424

We now check not only y_2 but also y_1, using Formulas (20) and (21). We obtain

$$y_1 = 1 + \frac{.1}{12} [5(1) + 8(1.1106) - 1.2424] = 1.1053,$$

$$y_2 = 1 + \frac{.1}{3} [1 + 4(1.1106) + 1.2424] = 1.2228,$$

$$y_2' = 2(1.2228) - 1.2 = 1.2456,$$

and the new table

x	y	y'
1	1	1
1.1	1.1053	1.1106
1.2	1.2228	1.2456

New checks by (20) and (21) yield

$$y_1 = 1 + \frac{.1}{12} [5(1) + 8(1.1106) - 1.2456] = 1.1053,$$

$$y_2 = 1 + \frac{.1}{3} [1 + 4(1.1106) + 1.2456] = 1.2229,$$

$$y_2' = 2(1.2229) - 1.2 = 1.2458.$$

Since the only change on the last check was small, we assume that either these values of y_1 and y_2 are correct or that they will be corrected by later checks.

Proceeding to advance by (22), we have

$$y_3 = 1 + \frac{3(.1)}{4} [1 + 3(1.2458)] = 1.3553,$$

$$y_3' = 2(1.3553) - 1.3 = 1.4106,$$

and the tentative four point table is

x	y	y'
1	1	1
1.1	1.1053	1.1106
1.2	1.2229	1.2458
1.3	1.3553	1.4106

For the last time we check all three new points using (23), (24), and (25) for this purpose.   We find

$$y_1 = 1 + \frac{.1}{24} [9(1) + 19(1.1106) - 5(1.2458) + 1.4106] = 1.1053,$$

$$y_2 = 1 + \frac{.1}{3} [1 + 4(1.1106) + 1.2458] = 1.2229,$$

$$y_3 = 1 + \frac{3(.1)}{8} [1 + 3(1.1106) + 3(1.2458) + 1.4106] = 1.3555,$$

and we have our final four point table

Table 6.

x	y	y'
1	1	1
1.1	1.1053	1.1106
1.2	1.2229	1.2458
1.3	1.3555	1.4110

Proceeding now by the usual Milne method and checking only the last new value at each stage, we may add to this start indefinitely.   We then obtain the column headed y (approximate) in the table below.   The column marked y (correct) is tabulated from the exact solution

$$y = \frac{2x + 1 + e^{2x-2}}{4}.$$

Table 7.

x	y (approximate)	y (correct)	error
1	1	1	0
1.1	1.1053	1.1053	0
1.2	1.2229	1.2229	0
1.3	1.3555	1.3555	0
1.4	1.5064	1.5064	0
1.5	1.6796	1.6796	0
1.6	1.8800	1.8800	0
1.7	2.1138	2.1138	0
1.8	2.3883	2.3883	0
1.9	2.7125	2.7124	.0001
2.0	3.0974	3.0973	.0001

42. Halving the interval. It may happen that after a number of steps have been made by the Milne method, using a particular value for h, a stage may be reached at which the errors become intolerable. The remedy for this is to use a smaller value for h. If, for example, we halve the value of h, calling the last four established y-values y_0, y_1, y_2, y_3, we need the values which we might designate by $y_{3\frac{1}{2}}$ and $y_{5\frac{1}{2}}$, viz., the values corresponding to $x = x_0 + \dfrac{3h}{2}$ and $x = x_0 + \dfrac{5h}{2}$. Evidently

$$y_{5\frac{1}{2}} = y_2 + \int_{x_2}^{x_2 + \frac{1}{2}h} y'\, dy$$

and

$$y_{3\frac{1}{2}} = y_1 + \int_{x_1}^{x_1 + \frac{1}{2}h} y'\, dx.$$

The integral $\displaystyle\int_{x_2}^{x_2 + \frac{1}{2}h} y'\, dx$ may be designated by $I_2^{2.5}$ and approximated by

$$I_2^{2.5} = \frac{h}{384}\, [7y_0' - 37y_1' + 197y_2' + 25y_3'].\tag{27}$$

By use of this approximation we obtain

$$y_{5\frac{1}{2}} = y_2 + \frac{h}{384}\, [7y_{-1}' - 37y_0' + 197y_1' + 25y_2'].$$

Illustration

Let it be required to insert into the table

x	y	y'
1.6	1.8800	2.1600
1.7	2.1138	2.5276
1.8	2.3838	2.9676
1.9	2.7125	3.5250
2.0	3.0974	4.1948

the values of y corresponding to $x = 1.85$ and $x = 1.95$. By the above formulas

$$y(1.95) = 2.7125 + \frac{.1}{384}\, [7(2.5276) - 37(2.9676)$$

$$+\ 197(3.5250) + 25(4.1948)]$$

$$= 2.7125 + .1842 = 2.8967,$$

$$y(1.85) = 2.3838 + \frac{.1}{384} [7(2.1600) - 37(2.5276)$$
$$+ 197(2.9676) + 25(3.5250)]$$
$$= 2.3838 + .1548 = 2.5386,$$

and now we produce the table

Table 8.

x	y	y'
1.85	2.5386	3.2272
1.90	2.7125	3.5250
1.95	2.8967	3.8434
2.00	3.0974	4.1948

from which we could proceed, if desired, by Milne's method with $h = 0.05$.

Exercises

1. Use the foregoing method of starting the solution of the differential equation

$$\frac{dy}{dx} = \frac{1}{2} - xy^2$$

through the point $(0, 0)$. Take $h = 0.2$ and find the y-values corresponding to $x = 0.2, 0.4,$ and 0.6 keeping four decimal places.

2. If $y' = x - y^2$ and $y = .5$ when $x = 0$, find y corresponding to $x = .05, .10, .15, .20,$ and $.25$ correct to four significant figures as nearly as it can be done by the above method.

3. A projectile is fired from a point on level ground with an initial velocity of 1000 feet per second. The angle of elevation of the gun is such that the initial horizontal component of velocity is 800 feet per second. The projectile meets resistance which in pounds is numerically equal to its mass times the cube of its velocity times the constant, 0.00000005. Using numerical methods, trace the flight of the projectile until it returns to the ground and find the time of flight and the range. *Hints:* If m represents the mass and θ the inclination of the path, the force $-0.00000005 \ mv^3$ pounds may be resolved into $-0.00000005 \ mv^3 \cos \theta$ pounds of horizontal force and $-0.00000005 \ mv^3 \sin \theta$ pounds of vertical force.

Moreover, $v \cos \theta = \dfrac{dx}{dt}$ and $v \sin \theta = \dfrac{dy}{dt}$, and the equations governing the motion are

$$\frac{d^2x}{dt^2} = -0.00000005 \left[\left(\frac{dx}{dt}\right)^2 + \left(\frac{dy}{dt}\right)^2 \right] \frac{dx}{dt},$$

$$\frac{d^2y}{dt^2} = -0.00000005 \left[\left(\frac{dx}{dt}\right)^2 + \left(\frac{dy}{dt}\right)^2 \right] \frac{dy}{dt} - 32.16.$$

If we set $\dfrac{dx}{dt} = \alpha$, $\dfrac{dy}{dt} = \beta$, these equations appear as

$$\frac{d\alpha}{dt} = -0.00000005(\alpha^2 + \beta^2)\alpha,$$

$$\frac{d\beta}{di} = -0.00000005(\alpha^2 + \beta^2)\beta - 32.16.$$

Initially, $\alpha = 800$ and $\beta = 600$; if we take $h = 1$ second, we may tabulate α and β. From the table of values of α and β we may tabulate x and y, using numerical integration. When the solution is located between $t = 31$ and $t = 32$, we may employ Formula (27) to shorten the interval first to $h = 0.5$ and then to $h = 0.25$ in order to make interpolation more reliable.

CHAPTER VI

Integration in Series

43. Equations of the first order. We propose, in this chapter, to study the problem of approximating to the general solution of an ordinary differential equation by means of a power series.

We begin with an illustration, given

$$y' = x + \frac{1}{y}, \tag{1}$$

let us assume its solution to be

$$y = A_0 + A_1 x + A_2 x^2 + A_3 x^3 + A_4 x^4 + \cdots, \tag{2}$$

the coefficients in the series to be determined presently, in such a manner that (2) satisfies (1) formally.

Now, since the right-hand side of (1) has the properties of continuity, single-valuedness, etc., demanded in the Existence Theorem, we know that for any point $(0, A_0)$ (with the exception of $(0, 0)$, where the conditions of the Theorem fail to be met), there exists a unique solution

$$y = f(x) \tag{3}$$

which is continuous for some range of values of x in the neighborhood of $x = 0$, and which takes on the value A_0 at $x = 0$. Again, the series in (2) converges for some range of values of x in the neighborhood of $x = 0$,* and hence represents some continuous function which takes on the value A_0 at $x = 0$. After (2) has been made to satisfy (1) formally by the proper choice of coefficients, the function represented by it must be identical with (3), by the uniqueness of the solution. (It is not to be expected, however, that the explicit form of (3) will be in evidence from its expansion (2). In fact, if such is the case the equation is usually integrable directly,

---

* That a power series like (2) converges over some interval about $x = 0$, is proved in the Theory of Functions of a Real Variable. To be sure, the length of the interval may be zero in the case of some series, *i. e.*, $x = 0$ may be the only value of x for which the series converges.

and no recourse to integration in series is necessary.) We now differentiate (2) to obtain

$$y' = A_1 + 2A_2x + 3A_3x^2 + 4A_4x^3 + 5A_5x^4 + \cdots .^* \quad (4)$$

Hence, by (1), or, what is the same, by

$$yy' - xy - 1 = 0, \quad (5)$$

$$(A_0 + A_1x + A_2x^2 + A_3x^3 + \cdots)(A_1 + 2A_2x + 3A_3x^2 + 4A_4x^3 + \cdots) - (A_0x + A_1x^2 + A_2x^3 + A_3x^4 + \cdots) - 1 \equiv 0.$$

Hence,†

$$A_0A_1 + (2A_0A_2 + A_1^2)x + (3A_0A_3 + 3A_1A_2)x^2 + (4A_0A_4 + 4A_1A_3 + 2A_2^2)x^3 + (5A_0A_5 + 5A_1A_4 + 5A_2A_3)x^4 + \cdots - (A_0x + A_1x^2 + A_2x^3 + A_3x^4 + \cdots) - 1 \equiv 0. \quad (6)$$

Since (6) is to be an identity, the coefficients of every power of x on the left-hand side must equal zero. Whence,

$$\begin{cases} A_0A_1 - 1 = 0, \\ 2A_0A_2 + A_1^2 - A_0 = 0, \\ 3A_0A_3 + 3A_1A_2 - A_1 = 0, \\ 4A_0A_4 + 4A_1A_3 + 2A_2^2 - A_2 = 0, \\ 5A_0A_5 + 5A_1A_5 + 5A_2A_3 - A_3 = 0, \text{ etc.}; \end{cases} \quad (7)$$

and

$$\begin{cases} A_1 = \dfrac{1}{A_0}, \\ A_2 = \dfrac{A_0 - A_1^2}{2A_0} = \dfrac{A_0^3 - 1}{2A_0^3}, \\ A_3 = \dfrac{A_1 - 3A_1A_2}{3A_0} = \dfrac{3 - A_0^3}{6A_0^5}, \\ A_4 = \dfrac{A_2 - 2A_2^2 - 4A_1A_3}{4A_0} = \dfrac{7A_0^3 - 15}{24A_0^7}, \text{ etc.} \end{cases} \quad (8)$$

The equalities (7), and hence (8), may be extended as far as desired, and it is thus possible to find as many coefficients of (2) as desired in

---

* A power series may be differentiated term by term within its interval of convergence, and the resulting series will converge to the derivative of the function represented by the original series.

† Two power series $B_0 + B_1x + B_2x^2 + B_3x^3 + \cdots$ and $C_0 + C_1x + C_2x^2 + C_3x^3 + \cdots$ may be multiplied within their common interval of convergence, and the product is the series $B_0C_0 + (B_0C_1 + B_1C_0)x + (B_0C_2 + B_1C_1 + B_2C_0)x^2 + (B_0C_3 + B_1C_2 + B_2C_1 + B_3C_0)x^3 + \cdots$.

terms of A_0, while A_0 itself remains arbitrary.   Substituting from (8) into (2), we obtain as the general solution of (1) the infinite series

$$y = A_0 + \frac{1}{A_0}\, x + \frac{A_0^3 - 1}{2A_0^3}\, x^2 + \frac{3 - A_0^3}{6A_0^5}\, x_3 + \frac{7A_0^3 - 15}{24A_0^7}\, x^4 + \cdots \quad (9)$$

The student may satisfy himself that by extending the set of equalities (7), any coefficient A_m may be found in terms of A_0, $A_1, \cdots, A_{m-1}$, and hence in terms of A_0; therefore, precisely one arbitrary constant will enter in (9), as was, of course, to be expected from the order of (1).

Since every function of x cannot be developed as a power series in $x\left(e.\, g.,\, \log x, \frac{1}{x}\right)$, we need not expect to be able to approximate to the general solution of every equation

$$y' = F(x, y) \quad (10)$$

by means of a series (2).*   The solution may in such a case be obtained as a power series in $x - a(a \neq 0)$.   See Exercise 6 below.

Exercises

1. Integrate in series

$$y' = x^2 + x + \frac{y}{x}.$$

Show that the solution is a finite power series: $y = Ax + x^2 + \dfrac{x^3}{2}$ (A arbitrary).   Integrate the equation directly, and compare results.

2. Integrate in series

$$y' = xe^x + \frac{y}{x}.$$

(*Hint:* Replace e^x by its development as a power series.)   Show that the solution is

$$y = A_1 x + x^2 + \frac{x^3}{2!} + \frac{x^4}{3!} + \frac{x^5}{4!} + \cdots \qquad (A_1\ \text{arbitrary})$$

$$= (A_1 - 1)x + x\left(1 + x + \frac{x^2}{2!} + \frac{x^3}{3!} + \frac{x^4}{4!} + \cdots\right)$$

$$= Ax + xe^x \qquad (A\ \text{arbitrary}).$$

Integrate the equation directly, and compare results.

---

* Such an impossibility will show up in the list of equalities corresponding to (7) of the text, since the coefficients of (2) will fail to be determined by them.

3. Integrate in series:

(a) $y' = \dfrac{x^2 + y}{x}.$ (b) $y' = x + 2xy.$

(c) $(x + 1)(y' - e^x) + y = 0.$

4. Integrate in series:

(a) $y' = \dfrac{y}{1 + xy}.$ (c) $y' = \dfrac{x + y}{1 + y}.$

(b) $y' = x - y^2.$ (d) $y' = \dfrac{x}{x^2 - y}.$

5. Integrate in series: $y' = \dfrac{y}{x - y}.$ In working this problem, the student will note that the first equality in the set analogous to (7) of the text is $A_0(1 + A_1) = 0.$ By assuming A_0 arbitrary and $A_1 = -1,$ we obtain the series representing the general solution. If we assume $A_0 = 0,$ the succeeding equalities in the set will make all the coefficients equal to zero, and will thus lead to the finite series $y = 0.$

6. (a) Show that $y' = \dfrac{x + y}{x}$ cannot be solved for y as a power series in $x.$

(b) Solve $y' = \dfrac{x + y}{x}$ for y as a power series in $x - 1.$ *Hint:* Set

$$x - 1 = z \left(\therefore \frac{dy}{dz} = \frac{dy}{dx} \right).$$

The equation becomes

$$\frac{dy}{dz} = \frac{z + 1 + y}{z + 1}.$$

Assume

$$y = A_0 + A_1 z + A_2 z^2 + A_3 z^3 + \cdots,$$

and obtain

$$y = A_0 + (1 + A_0)z + \frac{1}{2} z^2 - \frac{1}{6} z^3 + \frac{1}{12} z^4 - \frac{1}{20} z^5 + \cdots$$

$$= A_0 x + (x - 1) + \frac{1}{2} (x - 1)^2 - \frac{1}{6} (x - 1)^3 + \frac{1}{12} (x - 1)^4$$

$$- \frac{1}{20} (x - 1)^5 + \cdots.$$

This result may be put in a simpler form by noting that

$$y' = A_0 + 1 + (x - 1) - \frac{(x-1)^2}{2} + \frac{(x-1)^3}{3} - \frac{(x-1)^4}{4} + \cdots$$

$$= A_0 + 1 + \log x$$

$\left(\text{verify that the coefficient of } (x-1)^n \text{ in the last expansion is } \dfrac{(-1)^{n-1}}{n}\right)$,

whence, $y = A_0 x + x \log x$ (the constant of the last integration being zero by $x = 1$, $y = A_0$) is the general solution. Integrate the given equation directly, and compare the results.

7. Integrate in series:

(a) $y' = \dfrac{x^2 + x + y}{x + 1}$.   (b) $y' = \dfrac{x^2 - x + y}{x}$.

44. Linear equations of the second order. Equations of the type

$$Py'' + Qy' + Ry = 0, \tag{11}$$

where P, Q, and R are polynomials in x and P is not identically zero, are encountered a great deal in applied mathematics. Later in this chapter we will study in some detail three particular equations of this type.

To start with now, we take as an illustration the equation

$$x^2 y'' + x^3 y' + (x^2 - 2)y = 0. \tag{12}$$

Let us assume a solution of the form

$$y = a_0 x^m + a_1 x^{m+s} + \cdots + a_k x^{m+ks} + \cdots, \quad a_0 \neq 0, \tag{13}$$

the values of m and s and the a's to be determined presently. Since the right-hand side of (13) is a sum of terms each of the form ax^p, we may reduce the work of substituting (13) into (12) by substituting a typical term and using the result as a pattern. Thus, if

$$y = x^p, \; y' = px^{p-1}, \; y'' = p(p-1)x^{p-2},$$

the left-hand side of (12) becomes

$$p(p-1)x^p + px^{p+2} + x^{p+2} - 2x^p,$$

or

$$(p+1)(p-2)x^p + (p+1)x^{p+2}$$

or

$$f(p)x^p + g(p)x^{p+2},$$

where
$$f(p) \equiv (p + 1)(p - 2)$$
and
$$g(p) \equiv p + 1.$$

The fact that the exponents of x differ by 2 suggests that in (13) we might set $s = 2$ advantageously. Therefore, we now write the proposed solution as

$$y = a_0 x^m + a_1 x^{m+2} + \cdots + a_k x^{m+2k} + \cdots, \quad a_0 \neq 0, \quad (14)$$

with the a's and m still to be determined.

From the above deductions it follows that if
$$y \equiv a x^p,$$
then
$$x^2 y'' + x^3 y' + (x^2 - 2)y \equiv a f(p) x^p + a g(p) x^{p+2}. \quad (15)$$

By the use of (15), while substituting (14) into (12), we obtain

$$\begin{aligned}
0 = \; & a_0 f(m) x^m + [a_0 g(m) + a_1 f(m + 2)] x^{m+2} \\
& + [a_1 g(m + 2) + a_2 f(m + 4)] x^{m+4} \\
& + \cdots \\
& + [a_k g(m + 2k) + a_{k+1} f(m + 2k + 2)] x^{m+2k+2} \\
& + \cdots.
\end{aligned}$$

Since we expect this equation to hold for every value of x or at least every value within the interval of convergence of (14), each coefficient must vanish. We conclude that

$$f(m) = 0, \quad (16)$$
$$a_k g(m + 2k) + a_{k+1} f(m + 2k + 2) = 0, \; k = 0, 1, 2, \cdots. \quad (17)$$

Equation (16) follows since $a_0 \neq 0$. This equation determines the value of m and is called the *indicial equation*. Equation (17) determines relations between consecutive a's and will be spoken of as the *recurrence relation*.

In the illustration at hand the indicial equation is

$$(m + 1)(m - 2) = 0,$$
whence
$$m = 2 \text{ or } m = -1.$$

The recurrence relation is

$$a_k(m + 2k + 1) + a_{k+1}(m + 2k + 3)(m + 2k) = 0,$$

or

$$a_{k+1} = \frac{-(m + 2k + 1)a_k}{(m + 2k + 3)(m + 2k)}, \qquad k = 0, 1, 2, \cdots.$$

For $m = 2$ this becomes

$$a_{k+1} = \frac{-(2k + 3)a_k}{(2k + 5)(2k + 2)}, \qquad k = 0, 1, 2, \cdots,$$

or

$$a_1 = \frac{-3a_0}{(5)(2)}, \qquad a_2 = \frac{-5a_1}{(7)(4)}, \qquad a_3 = \frac{-7a_2}{(9)(6)}, \cdots.$$

From these we find

$$a_2 = \frac{(5 \cdot 3)a_0}{(7 \cdot 5)(4 \cdot 2)}, \qquad a_3 = \frac{-(7 \cdot 5 \cdot 3)a_0}{(9 \cdot 7 \cdot 5)(6 \cdot 4 \cdot 2)}, \cdots,$$

and write, as the corresponding solution of (12),

$$y = a_0 x^2 - \frac{3x^4}{(2)(5)} + \frac{(3 \cdot 5)x^6}{(2 \cdot 4)(5 \cdot 7)} - \frac{(3 \cdot 5 \cdot 7)x^8}{(2 \cdot 4 \cdot 6)(5 \cdot 7 \cdot 9)} + \cdots = a_0 y_1(x),$$

where a_0 is an arbitrary constant.

For $m = -1$ the recurrence relation takes the form

$$a_{k+1} = \frac{-2ka_k}{(2k - 1)(2k + 2)}, \qquad k = 0, 1, 2, \cdots,$$

from which we obtain, by putting $k = 0$,

$$a_1 = 0.$$

The coefficients a_2, a_3, $\cdots$, which are constant times a_1, are also zero, and the corresponding solution is

$$y = a_0 x^{-1},$$

where a_0 is again an arbitrary constant.

The functions $y_1(x)$ and x^{-1} are evidently linearly independent since otherwise one would be a constant times the other. The complete solution of our differential equation is, therefore,

$$y = A y_1(x) + B x^{-1},$$

where A and B are arbitrary constants.

It is easily shown that the series representing $y_1(x)$ converges for every value of x. If the ratio test is applied to the form (14) of the series, the test ratio is seen to be

$$\frac{a_{k+1}x^{m+2k+2}}{a_k x^{m+2k}} = \frac{a_{k+1}}{a_k}x^2 = \frac{-x^2 g(m+2k)}{f(m+2k+2)},$$

the last equality coming from the recurrence relation.   Now from the form of f and g the test ratio may be written as

$$\frac{-x^2(m+2k+1)}{(m+2k+2)^2 - (m+2k+2) - 2}.$$

Upon dividing numerator and denominator by k, we see that the limit of this ratio is zero as $k \to \infty$, regardless of the value of x which establishes convergence.

The situation in other problems might be different.   In the above case the convergence for every value of x actually follows from the fact that $g(p)$ is linear in p while $f(p)$ is quadratic.   If g and f had both been quadratic, $i.e.$,

$$g(p) = \alpha p^2 + \beta p + \gamma, \qquad (\alpha \neq 0)$$
$$f(p) = a p^2 + b p + c, \qquad (a \neq 0)$$

we should have had as test ratio

$$\frac{-x^2[\alpha(m+2k)^2 + \beta(m+2k) + \gamma]}{a(m+2k+2)^2 + b(m+2k+2) + c}.$$

Dividing numerator and denominator by k^2 before allowing k to approach infinity, we would have found as the limit of the test ratio,

$$\frac{-\alpha x^2}{a}.$$

The series would have converged for

$$\left|\frac{\alpha x^2}{a}\right| < 1$$

and diverged for

$$\left|\frac{\alpha x^2}{a}\right| > 1.$$

With a similar argument we may see that if g should have been of degree higher than f, the series would have diverged for every value of x, unless possibly for $x = 0$.

As a second illustration let us consider the equation

$$x^4 y'' + (2 - x^3)y' - 3x^2 y = 0.$$

As before, we make the trial substitution

$$y = x^p.$$

From this we find

$$x^4y'' + (2 - x^3)y' - 3x^2y = 2px^{p-1} + (p - 3)(p + 1)x^{p+2}.$$

The question arises as to which of the two functions, $(p - 3)(p + 1)$ or $2p$, to call $f(p)$. The foregoing discussion of convergence indicates that $f(p)$ must be of at least as high a degree as $g(p)$ if the series representing the solution is to have a non-zero interval of convergence. Therefore, we must select

$$f(p) = (p - 3)(p + 1),$$
$$g(p) = 2p,$$

and have the pattern substitution

$$x^4y'' + (2 - x^3)y' - 3x^2y = f(p)x^{p+2} + g(p)x^{p-1}.$$

This indicates that the exponents of x in the series solution must be descending by three, and we assume the solution

$$y = a_0x^m + a_1x^{m-3} + a_2x^{m-6} + \cdots + a_kx^{m-3k} + \cdots \quad (a_0 \neq 0).$$

After making the substitution, we have

$$
\begin{aligned}
0 = {} & a_0f(m)x^{m+2} + [a_0g(m) + a_1f(m - 3)]x^{m-1} \\
& + [a_1g(m - 3) + a_2f(m - 6)]x^{m-4} \\
& + \cdots \\
& + [a_kg(m - 3k) + a_{k+1}f(m - 3k - 3)]x^{m-3k-1} \\
& + \cdots.
\end{aligned}
$$

The indicial equation

$$f(m) \equiv (m - 3)(m + 1) = 0$$

gives the values

$$m = 3, \qquad m = -1.$$

The recurrence relation gives

$$a_{k+1} = \frac{-a_kg(m - 3k)}{f(m - 3k - 3)} = \frac{-2(m - 3k)a_k}{(m - 3k - 6)(m - 3k - 2)}.$$

For $m = 3$ this appears as

$$a_{k+1} = \frac{2(k - 1)a_k}{(k + 1)(3k - 1)},$$

or

$$a_1 = \frac{-2a_0}{-1}, \qquad a_2 = 0, \qquad a_3 = \frac{2 \cdot 1a_2}{(3)(5)}, \cdots .$$

The corresponding solution of the differential equation is

$$y = a_0[x^3 + 2].$$

For $m = -1$ the recurrence relation appears as

$$a_{k+1} = \frac{2(3k + 1)a_k}{3(k + 1)(3k + 7)},$$

or

$$a_1 = \frac{(2)(1)a_0}{3(1)(7)}, \qquad a_2 = \frac{(2)(4)a_1}{3(2)(10)}, \qquad a_3 = \frac{(2)(7)a_2}{3(3)(13)}, \cdots ,$$

and the corresponding solution is

$$y = a_0 \left[x^{-1} + \frac{2x^{-4}}{(3)(7)} + \frac{2^2(4)x^{-7}}{3^2(2)(7 \cdot 10)} + \frac{2^3(4 \cdot 7)x^{-10}}{3^3(2 \cdot 3)(7 \cdot 10 \cdot 13)} + \cdots \right] = a_0 y_1(x).$$

Clearly, the two solutions obtained are linearly independent, and the general solution of the differential equation is

$$y = A(x^3 + 2) + By_1(x).$$

Since $a_k x^{m-3k}$ is the general term of the series, the test ratio may be written as

$$\frac{a_{k+1}x^{-3}}{a_k},$$

and by the recurrence relation this becomes

$$\frac{-g(m - 3k)}{f(m - 3k - 3)x^3}.$$

Since $g(m - 3k)$ is of degree one in k while $f(m - 3k - 3)$ is of degree two in k, the test ratio approaches zero as k approaches infinity for every x excepting $x = 0$. For $x = 0$ the series is obviously divergent.

Exercises

1. Integrate in series:

    (a) $y'' - xy' + 2y = 0.$
    (b) $x^2y'' + (x + x^4)y' - y = 0.$

(c) $x^2y'' + (x^3 + 2x)y' + (x^2 - 2)y = 0.$
(d) $x^4y'' + (2x^3 + x)y' - y = 0.$
(e) $x^4y'' + (x - 2x^3)y' + 2y = 0.$
(f) $x^2y'' + 3xy' - 3y = 0.$

2. Adapt the theory of the text to a linear equation of the third order, and solve in series:

(a) $xy''' + 3y'' + xy = 0.$
(b) $x^6y''' + x^2y'' - 2y = 0.$
(c) $x^3y''' + 8x^2y'' - 16y = 0.$

3. Integrate in series:

$$(1 + x^2)y'' + 2xy' = 0.$$

Note that there are two possible solutions, because $f(m)$ and $g(m)$ are each of the second degree. Note also the relation between the two solutions.

4. Integrate in series:

(a) $(x + x^4)y'' + (x^3 - 1)y' - x^2y = 0.$
(b) $(x + x^3)y'' + (2x^2 - 2)y' - 2xy = 0.$

45. Roots of indicial equation equal. If the two roots of the indicial equation are equal, they evidently lead to only one solution in series. In order that the equation may be integrated completely, a second solution, linearly independent of the first, must be obtained. This may be had by employing the one solution in series already obtained and the principle of Exercise 6, Article 25.

As an illustration, consider the equation,

$$x^2y'' - xy' + (x^2 + 1)y = 0.$$

The substitution of (13) yields the indicial equation as $m^2 - 2m + 1 = 0$, with the double root $m = 1$, and the solution obtained is

$$y = A\left(x - \frac{x^3}{2^2} + \frac{x^5}{(2 \cdot 4)^2} - \frac{x^7}{(2 \cdot 4 \cdot 6)^2} + \cdots \right.$$
$$\left. + \frac{(-1)^n x^{2n+1}}{(2 \cdot 4 \cdot 6 \cdots (2n))^2} + \cdots \right) \equiv Ay_1.$$

Now let

$$y = uy_1,$$

and write

$$y' = u'y_1 + u_1', \qquad y'' = u''y_1 + 2u'y_1' + uy_1''.$$

Substituting into the given equation, we obtain

$$x^2 y_1 u'' + [2x^2 y_1' - x y_1] u' = 0$$

since $y = y_1(x)$ satisfies the given equation. In the last equation the variables are separable as

$$\frac{u''}{u'} + \frac{2y_1'}{y_1} - \frac{1}{x} = 0.$$

The solution is clearly

$$\log (u') + 2 \log y_1 - \log x = \log c_1,$$

or

$$u' = \frac{c_1 x}{y_1^2}.$$

Integrating this, we have

$$u = c_1 \int \frac{x \, dx}{y_1^2} + c_2$$

and, finally,

$$y = u y_1 = c_1 y_1(x) \int \frac{x \, dx}{[y_1(x)]^2} + c_2 y_1(x).$$

Exercises

1. Integrate in series:

(a) $x^2 y'' + 5xy' + (4 - 2x^3)y = 0.$
(b) $xy'' + y' - y = 0.$
(c) $x^4 y'' + x^3 y' + y = 0.$
(d) $(x^2 + x)y'' + (1 - x)y' + y = 0.$
(e) $x^3 y'' + (x^2 + x)y' - 2y = 0.$
(f) $x^3 y'' + (1 - x^2)y' + xy = 0.$

46. A coefficient in the series becoming infinite. If the roots of the indicial equation differ by a multiple of s, trouble is found with one of the anticipated series solutions.

To illustrate, consider the equation

$$xy'' - y' + y = 0.$$

The substitution of (13) yields the indicial equation

$$f(m) \equiv m(m - 2) = 0,$$

whose roots are $m = 2$ and $m = 0$. The recurrence relation is

$$a_k + a_{k+1} f(m + k + 1) = 0,$$

or

$$a_{k+1} = \frac{-a_k}{f(m+k+1)} = \frac{-a_k}{(m+k+1)(m+k-1)}.$$

For $m = 2$ this becomes

$$a_{k+1} = \frac{-a_k}{(k+3)(k+1)},$$

$$a_1 = \frac{-a_0}{(1)(3)}, \qquad a_2 = \frac{-a_1}{(2)(4)}, \qquad a_3 = \frac{-a_2}{(3)(5)}, \quad \cdots,$$

and the corresponding series solution is

$$y = y_1(x) = a_0 \left[x^2 - \frac{x^3}{(1)(3)} + \frac{x^4}{(1 \cdot 2)(3 \cdot 4)} - \frac{x^5}{(1 \cdot 2 \cdot 3)(3 \cdot 4 \cdot 5)} + \cdots \right]$$

with a_0 arbitrary.

For $m = 0$ the recurrence relation becomes

$$a_{k+1} = \frac{-a_k}{(k+1)(k-1)},$$

or

$$a_1 = \frac{-a_0}{-1}, \qquad a_2 = \frac{-a_1}{(2)(0)}, \qquad a_3 = \frac{-a_2}{(3)(1)}, \quad \cdots.$$

The indicated value ∞ for a_2 and all subsequent a's evidently cannot be used.

To find a solution linearly independent of $y_1(x)$, let

$$y = u y_1(x),$$
$$y' = u' y_1 + u y_1',$$
$$y'' = u'' y_1 + 2u' y_1' + u y_1'',$$

and obtain

$$x y_1 u'' + (2x y_1' - y_1) u' = 0.$$

Separation of the variables gives

$$\frac{u''}{u'} + \frac{2y_1'}{y_1} - \frac{1}{x} = 0.$$

The solution

$$\log (u') + 2 \log y_1 - \log x = \log c_1$$

leads to the equation

$$u' = \frac{c_1 x}{y_1^2}$$

and the complete solution for u

$$u = c_1 \int \frac{x\,dx}{y_1^2} + c_2.$$

The complete solution of the original equation evidently is given by

$$y = c_1 y_1 \int \frac{x\,dx}{y_1^2} + c_2 y_1.$$

Exercises

1. Solve in series:

    (a) $x^2 y'' + xy' + (x^2 - 1)y = 0.$
    (b) $xy'' - 2y' + y = 0.$
    (c) $x^2 y'' + xy' + (x - 1)y = 0.$
    (d) $x^2 y'' + 2xy' + (x - 2)y = 0.$
    (e) $x^4 y'' + (x^3 + x)y' - x^2 y = 0.$

47. The particular integral. The student will recall that for the non-homogeneous equation

$$P_0 y'' + P_1 y' + P_2 y = Q,$$

the complete solution consists of the sum of the complementary function, *i.e.*, the complete solution of the corresponding homogeneous equation, and of any particular integral. We shall assume that Q is a sum of powers of x and seek to find a particular integral corresponding to a term ax^q of Q. We assume that the substitution of

$$y = x^p$$

into the left-hand member gives the result

$$P_0 y'' + P_1 y' + P_2 y = f(p)x^{p-\alpha} + g(p)x^{p-\alpha+s},$$

where $s \neq 0$ and $f(p)$ is of degree 2 in p. (If $g(p)$ is also of degree 2 in p, then the two functions f and g may be interchanged by changing the sign of s.)

If we now let

$$y = A_0 x^{q+\alpha} + A_1 x^{q+\alpha+s} + \cdots + A_k x^{q+\alpha+ks} + \cdots,$$

we obtain

$$ax^q \equiv A_0 f(q + \alpha)x^q$$
$$+ [A_0 g(q + \alpha) + A_1 f(q + \alpha + s)]x^{q+2}$$
$$+ [A_1 g(q + \alpha + s) + A_2 f(q + \alpha + 2s)]x^{q+2s}$$
$$+ \cdots$$
$$+ [A_k g(q + \alpha + ks) + A_{k+1} f(q + \alpha + ks + s)]x^{q+ks+s}$$
$$+ \cdots .$$

This can be true only if

$$A_0 = \frac{a}{f(q + \alpha)},$$
$$A_{k+1} = \frac{-g(q + \alpha + ks)}{f(q + \alpha + ks + s)} A_k \qquad (k = 0, 1, 2, \cdots).$$

The first of these two equations determines A_0 (unless $f(q + \alpha) = 0$) and the second is a recurrence relation ultimately expressing all $A_k(k > 0)$ in terms of A_0. If $f(q + \alpha + ns) = 0$ for some positive integer n, then at least some one of the A_k becomes infinite. This trouble may be circumvented by resorting to the method of variation of parameters which is available in any linear equation whose complementary function is at hand.

Illustration

To solve the differential equation

$$x^2 y'' + x^3 y' + (x^2 - 2)y = 2x^3 - x,$$

set

$$y = x^p,$$

and find

$$x^2 y'' + x^3 y' + (x^2 - 2)y = (p - 2)(p + 1)x^p + (p + 1)x^{p+2}$$
$$\equiv f(p)x^p + g(p)x^{p+2}.$$

If we substitute the infinite series

$$y = a_0 x^m + a_1 x^{m+2} + a_2 x^{m+4} + \cdots + a_k x^{m+2k} + \cdots ,$$

we obtain in the left-hand side

$$a_0 f(m)x^m + [a_0 g(m) + a_1 f(m + 2)]x^{m+2}$$
$$+ [a_1 g(m + 2) + a_2 f(m + 4)]x^{m+4}$$
$$+ \cdots$$
$$+ [a_k g(m + 2k) + a_{k+1} f(m + 2k + 2)]x^{m+2k+2}$$
$$+ \cdots .$$

If this is to vanish identically, as when finding the complementary function, we must have

$$f(m) = (m - 2)(m + 1) = 0,$$

$m = 2$ or -1 and a_0 arbitrary. If we wish to produce the term $-x$, then $m = 1$ and $a_0 = \dfrac{-1}{f(1)} = \dfrac{1}{2}$. If $2x^3$ is wanted, we set $m = 3$ and $a_0 = \dfrac{2}{f(3)} = \dfrac{2}{4} = \dfrac{1}{2}$.

In all cases we have, from the recurrence relation,

$$a_{k+1} = \frac{-g(m + 2k)a_k}{f(m + 2k + 2)} = \frac{-(m + 2k + 1)a_k}{(m + 2k)(m + 2k + 3)}.$$

For $m = 2$,

$$a_{k+1} = \frac{-(2k + 3)a_k}{(2k + 2)(2k + 5)}, \qquad a_0 = A \ (A \text{ arbitrary})$$

$$a_1 = \frac{-3a_0}{(2)(5)}, \ a_2 = \frac{-5a_1}{(4)(7)}, \qquad a_3 = \frac{-7a_2}{(6)(9)}, \ \cdots,$$

For $m = -1$

$$a_{k+1} = \frac{-2ka_k}{(2k - 1)(2k + 2)}, \qquad a_0 = B \ (B \text{ arbitrary})$$

$$a_1 = 0, \ a_2 = 0, \qquad a_3 = 0, \ \cdots,$$

For $m = 1$

$$a_{k+1} = \frac{-(2k + 2)a_k}{(2k + 1)(2k + 4)}, \qquad a_0 = \frac{1}{2}$$

$$a_1 = \frac{-2a_0}{(1)(4)}, \qquad a_2 = \frac{-4a_1}{(3)(6)}, \qquad a_3 = \frac{-6a_2}{(5)(8)}, \ \cdots,$$

and for $m = 3$

$$a_{k+1} = \frac{-(2k + 4)a_k}{(2k + 3)(2k + 6)}, \qquad a_0 = \frac{1}{2}$$

$$a_1 = \frac{-4a_0}{(3)(6)}, \qquad a_2 = \frac{-6a_1}{(5)(8)}, \qquad a_3 = \frac{-8a_2}{(7)(10)}, \ \cdots.$$

We then have for the complete solution of the given equation

$$y = A \left[x^2 - \frac{3}{(2)(5)} x^4 + \frac{3 \cdot 5}{(2 \cdot 4)(5 \cdot 7)} x^6 - \frac{3 \cdot 5 \cdot 7}{(2 \cdot 4 \cdot 6)(5 \cdot 7 \cdot 9)} x^8 \right.$$
$$\left. + \cdots \right] + Bx^{-1}$$

$$+ \frac{1}{2} \left[x - \frac{2}{(1)(4)} x^3 + \frac{2 \cdot 4}{(1 \cdot 3)(4 \cdot 6)} x^5 - \frac{2 \cdot 4 \cdot 6}{(1 \cdot 3 \cdot 5)(4 \cdot 6 \cdot 8)} x^7 \right.$$
$$\left. + \cdots \right]$$

$$+ \frac{1}{2} \left[x^3 - \frac{4}{(3)(6)} x^5 + \frac{4 \cdot 6}{(3 \cdot 5)(6 \cdot 8)} x^7 - \frac{4 \cdot 6 \cdot 8}{(3 \cdot 5 \cdot 7)(6 \cdot 8 \cdot 10)} x^9 \right.$$
$$\left. + \cdots \right].$$

Exercises

1. Find a particular integral for each of the following equations:

(a) $x^2 y'' + (x^3 + 2x)y' - 2y = 2x^4$.

(b) $x^3 y'' + (4x^2 + x^5)y' + x^4 y = x^2 - 1$.

(c) $x^5 y'' + (x^4 + x^2)y' + xy = 2x^2 - 1$.

2. Find a particular integral of the equation

$$xy'' + (x - 2)y' + 2y = 2.$$

Hint: Let the complementary function be $c_1 y_1 + c_2 y_2$ where y_1 and y_2 are linearly independent. By the method of variation of parameters find the general solution of the given equation to be

$$y = c_1 y_1 + c_2 y_2 + 2y_1 \int \frac{y_2 \, dx}{x(y_1' y_2 - y_2' y_1)} - 2y_2 \int \frac{y_1 \, dx}{x(y_1' y_2 - y_2' y_1)}.$$

3. Find the particular integral of:

(a) $x^2 y'' + x^3 y' + (x^2 - 2)y = \dfrac{2}{x^3}.$

(b) $x^2 y'' + (x^2 + x)y' + (x - 1)y = \dfrac{1}{x^2}.$

48. The Legendre equation.   In the remaining sections of this chapter we shall consider certain homogeneous linear differential equations whose solutions are of particular interest in pure and applied mathematics.

First, let us take the Legendre equation*

$$(1 - x^2)y'' - 2xy' + n(n + 1)y = 0. \qquad (18)$$

The substitution $y = x^p$ in the left-hand member of (18) yields

$$(n - p)(p + n + 1)x^p + p(p - 1)x^{p-2}.$$

If we wish for descending power series solutions of (18), the indicial equation

$$(p - n)(p + n + 1) = 0$$

indicates that one series $u(x)$ will begin with the term x^n while the other series $v(x)$ will start with the term x^{-n-1}. The complete solution of the differential equation is thus found to be

$$y = Au + Bv,$$

where

$$u \equiv x^n - \frac{n(n - 1)}{2(2n - 1)} x^{n-2} + \frac{n(n - 1)(n - 2)(n - 3)}{2 \cdot 4(2n - 1)(2n - 3)} x^{n-4}$$
$$- \frac{n(n - 1)(n - 2)(n - 3)(n - 4)(n - 5)}{2 \cdot 4 \cdot 6(2n - 1)(2n - 3)(2n - 5)} x^{n-6} + \cdots$$

and

$$v \equiv x^{-n-1}$$
$$+ \frac{(n + 1)(n + 2)}{2(2n + 3)} x^{-n-3} + \frac{(n + 1)(n + 2)(n + 3)(n + 4)}{2 \cdot 4(2n + 3)(2n + 5)} x^{-n-5}$$
$$+ \frac{(n + 1)(n + 2)(n + 3)(n + 4)(n + 5)(n + 6)}{2 \cdot 4 \cdot 6(2n + 3)(2n + 5)(2n + 7)} x^{-n-7} + \cdots.$$

The student may further satisfy himself that each series converges for values of x outside the interval from -1 to 1. Particular interest attaches to the function u, which obviously reduces to a polynomial whenever n is a positive integer or zero. If we denote by $u_m(x)$ the value of $u(x)$ for $n = m$, we have

$$u_0(x) \equiv 1, \qquad u_1(x) \equiv x, \qquad u_2(x) \equiv x^2 - \frac{1}{3}, \text{ etc.}$$

Instead of the set of functions $u_m(x)$, we shall consider the set $P_m(x)$ defined by

$$P_m(x) \equiv \frac{(2m)!}{2^m(m!)^2} u_m(x) \qquad (m = 0, 1, 2, \cdots) \qquad (19)$$

---

* Named after the celebrated French mathematician, Adrian Marie Legendre (1752–1833).

so that

$$P_0(x) \equiv u_0(x) \equiv 1,$$
$$P_1(x) \equiv u_1(x) \equiv x,$$
$$P_2(x) \equiv \frac{1 \cdot 3}{2!} u_2(x) \equiv \frac{3}{2} x^2 - \frac{1}{2},$$
$$P_3(x) \equiv \frac{1 \cdot 3 \cdot 5}{3!} u_3(x) \equiv \frac{5}{2} x^3 - \frac{3}{2} x,$$
$$P_4(x) \equiv \frac{1 \cdot 3 \cdot 5 \cdot 7}{4!} u_4(x) \equiv \frac{5 \cdot 7}{2 \cdot 4} x^4 - 2 \frac{3 \cdot 5}{2 \cdot 4} x^2 + \frac{1 \cdot 3}{2 \cdot 4},$$
$$P_5(x) \equiv \frac{1 \cdot 3 \cdot 5 \cdot 7 \cdot 9}{5!} u_5(x) \equiv \frac{7 \cdot 9}{2 \cdot 4} x^5 - 2 \frac{5 \cdot 7}{2 \cdot 4} x^3 + \frac{3 \cdot 5}{2 \cdot 4} x,$$
$$P_6(x) \equiv \frac{1 \cdot 3 \cdot 5 \cdot 7 \cdot 9 \cdot 11}{6!} u_6(x) \equiv \frac{7 \cdot 9 \cdot 11}{2 \cdot 4 \cdot 6} x^6 - 3 \frac{5 \cdot 7 \cdot 9}{2 \cdot 4 \cdot 6} x^4$$
$$+ 3 \frac{3 \cdot 5 \cdot 7}{2 \cdot 4 \cdot 6} x^2 - \frac{1 \cdot 3 \cdot 5}{2 \cdot 4 \cdot 6}, \text{ etc.}$$

These functions (19) are called *Legendre polynomials* (also *Legendre coefficients;* also *zonal harmonics*). Evidently, they are solutions of the Legendre equation in which n has been set equal to m. They have the further property

$$P_m(1) = 1 \ (m = 0, 1, 2, \cdots). \tag{20}$$

The student will do well to verify (20) for various integral values of m. He will be asked to prove it in one of the exercises below.

From the list displayed above, we get

$$1 \equiv P_0(x),$$
$$x \equiv P_1(x),$$
$$x^2 \equiv \left[P_2(x) + \frac{1}{2} \right] \cdot \frac{2}{3} \equiv \frac{2}{3} P_2(x) + \frac{1}{3} P_0(x),$$
$$x^3 \equiv \left[P_3(x) + \frac{3}{2} x \right] \cdot \frac{2}{5} \equiv \frac{2}{5} P_2(x) + \frac{3}{5} P_1(x), \text{ etc.,}$$

which makes it evident that for any positive integer k

$$x^k \equiv a_0 P_k(x) + a_1 P_{k-1}(x) + \cdots + a_k P_0(x),$$

the coefficients a_i being unique and not all zero ($i = 0, 1, 2, \cdots, k$). Let us now rewrite (18) in the equivalent form

$$\frac{d}{dx} [(1 - x^2)y'] + n(n + 1)y = 0 \tag{21}$$

and obtain from it an important theorem on Legendre polynomials.

If $P_r(x)$ and $P_s(x)$ are two such polynomials, we have

$$\frac{d}{dx}[(1 - x^2)P_r'] + r(r + 1)P_r \equiv 0,$$

$$\frac{d}{dx}[(1 - x^2)P_s'] + s(s + 1)P_s \equiv 0.$$

Multiplying the upper equation by P_s, the lower by P_r, and subtracting, we get

$$P_s\frac{d}{dx}[(1 - x^2)P_r'] - P_r\frac{d}{dx}[(1 - x^2)P_s'] + (r - s)(r + s + 1)P_rP_s$$

$$\equiv 0.$$

Integrating this equation between -1 and 1, we have

$$\int_{-1}^{+1} P_s\frac{d}{dx}[(1 - x^2)P_r']dx - \int_{-1}^{+1} P_r\frac{d}{dx}[(1 - x^2)P_s']\,dx$$

$$+ (r - s)(r + s + 1)\int_{-1}^{+1} P_rP_s\,dx = 0.$$

Integrating each of the first two by parts, we find

$$\left[(P_sP_r' - P_rP_s')(1 - x^2)\right]_{-1}^{+1} + (r - s)(r + s + 1)\int_{-1}^{+1} P_rP_s\,dx = 0,$$

whence

$$(r - s)(r + s + 1)\int_{-1}^{+1} P_rP_s\,dx = 0,$$

or

$$\int_{-1}^{+1} P_rP_s\,dx = 0 \qquad (r \neq s), \tag{22}$$

the theorem we wished to prove. A set of functions $f_n(x)$ ($n = 0$, $1, 2, \cdots$), continuous in the interval from $x = a$ to $x = b$ and having the property

$$\int_a^b f_r(x)f_s(x)\,dx = 0 \qquad (r \neq s)$$

is said to be a set of *orthogonal* functions (orthogonal in that interval). By (22), the Legendre polynomials are such a set in the interval $x = -1$ to $x = 1$.

We now prove the following:

THEOREM. $P_m(x)$ *is the coefficient of* h^m *in the expansion of* $(1 - 2xh + h^2)^{-\frac{1}{2}}$ *as a power series in* h, *i. e.,*

$$(1 - 2xh + h^2)^{-\frac{1}{2}} = P_0(x) + hP_1(x) + h^2P_2(x) + \cdots$$
$$+ h^mP_m(x) + \cdots , \quad (23)$$

for all values of h *and* x *for which both* members are defined.

Proof

$$(1 - u)^{-\frac{1}{2}} \equiv 1 + \frac{1}{2}u + \frac{1 \cdot 3}{2 \cdot 4}u^2 + \frac{1 \cdot 3 \cdot 5}{2 \cdot 4 \cdot 6}u^3 + \cdots$$
$$+ \frac{1 \cdot 3 \cdots (2m - 1)}{2 \cdot 4 \cdots (2m)}u^m + \cdots ,$$

whence

$$(1 - 2xh + h^2)^{-\frac{1}{2}} \equiv 1 + \frac{1}{2}(2xh - h^2) + \frac{1 \cdot 3}{2 \cdot 4}(2xh - h^2)^2 + \cdots$$
$$+ \frac{1 \cdot 3 \cdots (2m - 1)}{2 \cdot 4 \cdots (2m)}(2xh - h^2)^m + \cdots$$
$$\equiv 1 + hx + h^2\left(\frac{3}{2}x^2 - \frac{1}{2}\right)$$
$$+ h^3\left(\frac{5}{2}x^3 - \frac{3}{2}x\right) + \cdots .$$

For the lower powers of h, the truth of the theorem is apparent at once. For any m whatever, it is seen that h^m will arise:

(a) In the first term of the expansion of $(2xh - h^2)^m$, and with the coefficient

$$\frac{1 \cdot 3 \cdots (2m - 1)}{2 \cdot 4 \cdots (2m)} \cdot 2^m \cdot x^m \equiv \frac{1 \cdot 3 \cdots (2m - 1)}{m!}x^m;$$

(b) In the second term of the expansion of $(2xh - h^2)^{m-1}$, and with the coefficient

$$\frac{1 \cdot 3 \cdots (2m - 3)}{2 \cdot 4 \cdots (2m - 2)} \cdot (m - 1) \cdot 2^{m-2} \cdot x^{m-2}$$
$$\equiv -\frac{1 \cdot 3 \cdots (2m - 3)}{2(m - 2)!}x^{m-2};$$

(c) In the third term of the expansion of $(2xh - h^2)^{m-2}$, and with the coefficient

$$\frac{1 \cdot 3 \cdots (2m - 5)}{2 \cdot 4 \cdots (2m - 4)} \cdot \frac{(m - 2)(m - 3)}{2} \cdot 2^{m-4} \cdot x^{m-4}$$
$$\equiv \frac{1 \cdot 3 \cdots (2m - 5)}{2 \cdot 4(m - 4)!}x^{m-4}, \text{ etc.}$$

The sum of these coefficients is

$$\frac{1 \cdot 3 \cdot 5 \cdots (2m - 1)}{m!} \left[x^m - \frac{m(m - 1)}{2(2m - 1)} x^{m-2} \right.$$

$$\left. + \frac{m(m - 1)(m - 2)(m - 3)}{2 \cdot 4(2m - 1)(2m - 3)} x^{m-4} - \cdots \right] \equiv P_m(x) \quad \text{[by (19)]},$$

which proves the theorem.

We apply the theorem now to the evaluation of an important definite integral. By (23),

$$\frac{1}{1 - 2xh + h^2} \equiv P_0^2(x) + h^2 P_1^2(x) + h^4 P_2^2(x) + \cdots + h^{2m} P_m^2(x)$$

$$+ \cdots + 2 \sum_{\substack{r, s=0 \\ r \neq s}}^{\infty} h^r h^s P_r(x) P_s(x).$$

Hence,

$$\int_{-1}^{1} \frac{1}{1 - 2xh + h^2} \, dx \equiv \int_{-1}^{1} P_0^2(x) \, dx + h^2 \int_{-1}^{1} P_1^2(x) \, dx + \cdots$$

$$+ h^{2m} \int_{-1}^{1} P_m^2(x) \, dx + \cdots + 2 \sum_{\substack{r, s=0 \\ r \neq s}}^{\infty} h^{r+s} \int_{-1}^{1} P_r(x) P_s(x) \, dx,$$

and the integrals under the last summation sign are all zero, by (22). Carrying out the integration, we find, on the left side of the equation,

$$-\frac{1}{2h} \log (1 - 2xh + h^2) \Big]_{-1}^{1} \equiv -\frac{1}{2h} \log \frac{(1 - h)^2}{(1 + h)^2}$$

$$\equiv \frac{1}{h} [\log (1 + h) - \log (1 - h)]$$

$$\equiv 2 \left(1 + \frac{h^2}{3} + \frac{h^4}{5} + \frac{h^6}{7} + \cdots + \frac{h^{2m}}{2m + 1} + \cdots \right),$$

whence, equating the coefficients of like powers of h on both sides of the equation, we find that

$$\int_{-1}^{1} P_m^2(x) \, dx = \frac{2}{2m + 1} \quad (m = 0, 1, 2, \cdots).$$

Exercises

1. Prove that any polynomial $Q(x)$ of degree l can be expressed as

$$Q(x) \equiv b_0 P_l(x) + b_1 P_{l-1}(x) + \cdots + b_l P_0(x),$$

the constants b_i being unique and not all zero $(i = 0, 1, 2, \cdots, l)$.

2. Prove that if $Q(x)$ is a polynomial of degree $l < r$,

$$\int_{-1}^{1} P_r(x)Q(x)\,dx = 0.$$

3. Prove that:

(a) $P_{2m}(-x) \equiv P_{2m}(x)$.

(b) $P_{2m+1}(-x) \equiv -P_{2m+1}(x)$.

(c) $P_{2m}(0) = (-1)^m \dfrac{1 \cdot 3 \cdot 5 \cdots (2m-1)}{2 \cdot 4 \cdot 6 \cdots (2m)}$.

(d) $P_{2m+1}(0) = 0$.

4. Prove that $P_m(1) = 1$ $(m = 0, 1, 2, \cdots)$.   *Hint:* Put $x = 1$ in (23).

5. Prove that $y = \dfrac{d^n}{dx^n}(x^2-1)^n$ is a solution of the Legendre equation. *Hint:* Set $z = (x^2-1)^n$. Differentiate and obtain $(x^2-1)z' = 2nxz$. Take the $(n+1)^{\text{st}}$ derivative of each member of this equation, and obtain

$$(x^2-1)\frac{d^{n+2}z}{dx^{n+2}} + 2x(n+1)\frac{d^{n+1}z}{dx^{n+1}} + (n+1)n\frac{d^n z}{dx^n}$$

$$= 2nx\frac{d^{n+1}z}{dx^{n+1}} + 2n(n+1)\frac{dz^n}{dx^n}.$$

The result will follow promptly.

6. Explain why $\dfrac{d^n}{dx^n}(x^2-1)^n$ (see Exercise 5) must be a constant multiple of $P_n(x)$. Verify for sundry values of n that $P_n(x) \equiv \dfrac{1}{n!2^n}\dfrac{d^n}{dx^n}(x^2-1)^n$.

7. Show that if $f(x)$ can be expanded, in the interval from -1 to 1, into

$$f(x) \equiv a_0 P_0(x) + a_1 P_1(x) + a_2 P_2(x) + \cdots$$

then, assuming that the series obtained by multiplying the above right-hand member by $P_m(x)$ may be integrated term by term,

$$a_m = \frac{2m+1}{2}\int_{-1}^{1} f(x)P_m(x)\,dx \quad (m = 0, 1, 2, \cdots).$$

8. Verify the result of Exercise 7 for

$$f(x) \equiv x^2 + 1.$$

9. Show that if $f(x)$ can be expanded as in Exercise 7, the expansion is unique. *Hint:* Assume $f(x) \equiv b_0 P_0(x) + b_1 P_1(x) + \cdots$ and show that $a_m - b_m = 0$ $(m = 0, 1, 2, \cdots)$.

10. Prove that

$$(n + 1)P_{n+1}(x) - (2n + 1)xP_n(x) + nP_{n-1}(x) \equiv 0$$
$$(n = 0, 1, 2, \cdots).$$

Hint: Put

$$s \equiv (1 - 2xh + h^2)^{-1/2} \equiv P_0(x) + hP_1(x) + h^2P_2(x) + \cdots$$

and obtain

$$\frac{\partial s}{\partial h} \cdot (1 - 2hx + h^2) \equiv s \cdot (x - h).$$

Use (23) and equate coefficients of h^n on both sides of the resulting equation.

11. Prove that

$$xP_n'(x) - P_{n-1}'(x) \equiv nP_n(x).$$

Hint: Obtain $(x - h)\dfrac{\partial s}{\partial x} \equiv h\dfrac{\partial s}{\partial h}$ (s as in Exercise 10). Expand by (23), and equate coefficients of h.

12. *Prove:* $(1 - x^2)P_n'(x) = nP_{n-1}(x) - nxP_n(x)$.

13. Prove that a function of n and x, which satisfies the properties of Exercises 11 and 12, satisfies the Legendre Equation.

49. The Bessel equation.   The equation

$$x^2 y'' + xy' + (x^2 - n^2)y = 0 \tag{24}$$

is called the Bessel equation.* We leave it to the student to obtain its solutions in series as

$$y = u \equiv x^n \Bigg[1 - \frac{x^2}{4 \cdot 1(1 + n)} + \frac{x^4}{4^2 \cdot 2!(1 + n)(2 + n)}$$
$$- \frac{x^6}{4^3 \cdot 3!(1 + n)(2 + n)(3 + n)} + \cdots$$
$$+ (-1)^k \frac{x^{2k}}{4^k \cdot k!(1 + n)(2 + n) \cdots (k + n)} + \cdots \Bigg]$$

---

* After Friedrich Wilhelm Bessel (1784–1846), an astronomer who earned a place of prominence in mathematics by the study of an important class of functions which bear his name.

$$y = v \equiv x^{-n} \left[1 - \frac{x^2}{4 \cdot 1(1 - n)} + \frac{x^4}{4^2 \cdot 2!(1 - n)(2 - n)} \right.$$
$$- \frac{x^6}{4^3 \cdot 3!(1 - n)(2 - n)(3 - n)} + \cdots$$
$$\left. + (-1)^k \frac{x^{2k}}{4^k \cdot k!(1 - n)(2 - n) \cdots (k - n)} + \cdots \right],$$

and hence its complete solution as

$$y = Au + Bv, \tag{25}$$

provided u and v are linearly independent and are both defined, which is the case when n is not zero or an integer. For $n = 0$, u and v are identical, and recourse must be had to the method of Section 45 of this chapter to obtain a second solution. When n is a positive integer, u is defined but v is not, since from a certain term on, the coefficients of v become infinite; when n is a negative integer, the coefficients of u become infinite, while v is defined. In either case, it is necessary to resort to the method of Section 46 to obtain a second independent solution.

If, as in Section 48, we denote by $u_m(x)$ the value of $u(x)$ corresponding to $n = m$, the Bessel Functions of the first kind are defined by

$$\begin{cases} J_m(x) \equiv \dfrac{u_m(x)}{2^m \cdot m!} & (m \text{ a positive integer}), \\ J_0(x) \equiv u_0(x), \end{cases} \tag{26}$$

in other words,

$$J_m(x) \equiv \frac{x^m}{2^m \cdot m!} \left[1 - \frac{x^2}{4 \cdot 1(1 + m)} + \frac{x^4}{4^2 \cdot 2!(1 + m)(2 + m)} \right.$$
$$\left. - \frac{x^6}{4^3 \cdot 3!(1 + m)(2 + m)(3 + m)} + \cdots \right]$$
$$\equiv \sum_{k=0}^{\infty} (-1)^k \frac{x^{2k+m}}{2^{2k+m} \cdot k!(k + m)!},$$

where $m = 0, 1, 2, \cdots$ and $0! = 1$. Note now that

$$x^m J_m(x) \equiv \sum_{k=0}^{\infty} (-1)^k \frac{x^{2k+2m}}{2^{2k+m} \cdot k!(k + m)!},$$

and hence,

$$\frac{d}{dx}\left[x^m J_m(x)\right] = \sum_{k=0}^{\infty} (-1)^k \cdot \frac{(2k+2m)x^{2k+2m-1}}{2^{2k+m} \cdot k!(k+m)!}$$

$$\equiv \sum_{k=0}^{\infty} (-1)^k \cdot x^m \frac{x^{2k+m-1}}{2^{2k+m-1} \cdot k!(k+m-1)!}.$$

In other words

$$\frac{d}{dx}\left[x^m J_m(x)\right] \equiv x^m \cdot J_{m-1}(x). \tag{27}$$

Likewise, the student may derive

$$\frac{d}{dx}\left[x^{-m} J_m(x)\right] \equiv -x^{-m} \cdot J_{m+1}(x). \tag{28}$$

The last two formulas may be rewritten as

$$x^m \frac{d}{dx}\left[J_m(x)\right] + mx^{m-1}J_m(x) \equiv x_m \cdot J_{m-1}(x),$$

$$x^{-m} \frac{d}{dx}\left[J_m(x)\right] - mx^{-m-1}J_m(x) \equiv -x^{-m}J_{m+1}(x),$$

whence,

$$J_{m-1}(x) - J_{m+1}(x) \equiv 2\frac{d}{dx}\left[J_m(x)\right] \tag{29}$$

and

$$J_{m-1}(x) + J_{m+1}(x) \equiv \frac{2m}{x} J_m(x). \tag{30}$$

We now define Bessel's Functions of the first kind for negative integral values of m by imposing the condition that (30) hold for every integral m. We thus obtain

(setting $m = 0$)

$$J_{-1}(x) + J_1(x) \equiv 0, \therefore J_{-1}(x) \equiv -J_1(x);$$

(setting $m = 1$)

$$J_0(x) + J_2(x) \equiv \frac{2}{x} J_1(x)$$

(setting $m = -1$)

$$J_{-2}(x) + J_0(x) \equiv -\frac{2}{x} J_{-1}(x)$$

$$\left.\begin{array}{c} \\ \\ \\ \end{array}\right\} \therefore J_{-2}(x) \equiv J_2(x);$$

(setting $m = 2$)

$$J_1(x) + J_3(x) \equiv \frac{4}{x} J_2(x)$$

(setting $m = -2$)

$$J_{-3}(x) + J_{-1}(x) \equiv -\frac{4}{x} J_{-2}(x)$$

$$\therefore J_{-3}(x) \equiv -J_3(x).$$

Continuing in this vein, we obtain

$$J_{-m}(x) \equiv (-1)^m \cdot J_m(x) \quad (m = 1, 2, 3, \cdots).$$

It is easy to verify that (27), (28), and (29) will also hold for negative integral values of m. Thus, for $m = -p$ (p a positive integer), we have

$$\frac{d}{dx}[x^{-p} \cdot J_{-p}(x)] \equiv \frac{d}{dx}[x^{-p} \cdot (-1)^p \cdot J_p(x)] \equiv (-1)^p \cdot -x^{-p} \cdot J_{p+1}(x)$$
$$\equiv (-1)^{p+1} \cdot x^{-p} \cdot J_{p+1}(x) \equiv x^{-p} \cdot J_{-p-1}(x),$$

which verifies (27). When m is fractional, the symbol $m!$ is meaningless, and the Bessel Function of order m of the first kind is defined as

$$J_m(x) \equiv \frac{u_m(x)}{2^m \cdot \Gamma(m+1)}.^* \tag{31}$$

Again, $u_m(x)$ and $v_m(x)$ are now both defined, they are independent, and $J_{-m}(x)$ is defined directly by

$$J_{-m}(x) \equiv \frac{v_m(x)}{2^{-m}\Gamma(-m+1)}. \tag{32}$$

Formulas (27) to (30) can be verified to hold also for the Bessel Functions of fractional order.

We close this section by proving the following:

Theorem. *In the expansion of* $e^{\frac{x}{2}\left(h - \frac{1}{h}\right)}$ *in integral powers of* h,

of the form $\displaystyle\sum_{m=-\infty}^{\infty} C_m \cdot h^m$, $C_m \equiv J_m(x)$, *i. e.*,

$$e^{\frac{x}{2}\left(h-\frac{1}{h}\right)} \equiv J_0(x) + h \cdot J_1(x) + h^2 J_2(x) + h^3 J_3(x) + \cdots$$
$$+ h^{-1}J_{-1}(x) + h^{-2}J_{-2}(x) + h^{-3}J_{-3}(x) + \cdots. \tag{33}$$

---

* The Gamma Function of m is defined as $\Gamma(m) \equiv \displaystyle\int_0^\infty x^{m-1}e^{-x}dx$. For integral values of m, it is proved $\Gamma(m+1) \equiv m!$. See Wilson, p. 378.

Proof

$$e^{\frac{x}{2}\left(h-\frac{1}{h}\right)} \equiv e^{xh/2} \cdot e^{-x/2h} \equiv \left(1 + \frac{xh}{2} + \frac{x^2h^2}{4 \cdot 2!} + \frac{x^3h^3}{8 \cdot 3!} + \cdots\right)$$

$$\left(1 - \frac{x}{2h} + \frac{x^2}{4h^2 \cdot 2!} - \frac{x^3}{8h^3 \cdot 3!} + \cdots\right).$$

Hence, the coefficient of h^m in the product is

$$\frac{x^m}{2^m \cdot m!} - \frac{x^{m+1}}{2^{m+1}(m+1)!} \cdot \frac{x}{2} + \frac{x^{m+2}}{2^{m+2}(m+2)!} \cdot \frac{x^2}{4 \cdot 2!}$$

$$- \frac{x^{m+3}}{2^{m+3}(m+3)!} \cdot \frac{x^3}{8 \cdot 3!} + \cdots$$

$$\equiv \frac{x^m}{2^m \cdot m!}\left[1 - \frac{x^2}{4(1+m)} + \frac{x^4}{4^2 \cdot 2!(1+m)(2+m)}\right.$$

$$\left. - \frac{x^6}{4^3 \cdot 3!(1+m)(2+m)(3+m)} + \cdots\right]$$

$$\equiv \frac{u_m(x)}{2^m \cdot m!} \equiv J_m(x).$$

Likewise, h^{-m} enters in the product with the coefficient

$$(-1)^m\left[\frac{x^m}{2^m \cdot m!} - \frac{x^{m+1}}{2^{m+1}(m+1)!} \cdot \frac{x}{2}\right.$$

$$\left. + \frac{x^{m+2}}{2^{m+2}(m+2)!} \cdot \frac{x^2}{4 \cdot 2!} - \cdots\right] \equiv (-1)^m \cdot J_m(x) \equiv J_{-m}(x).$$

Exercises

1. Show that:

(a) $y = x^{-n}J_n(x)$ is a solution of the equation
$$xy'' + (1 + 2n)y' + xy = 0.$$

(b) $y = x^n J_n(x)$ is a solution of the equation
$$xy'' + (1 - 2n)y' + xy = 0.$$

(c) $y = x^{-n/2}J_n(2\sqrt{x})$ is a solution of the equation
$$xy'' + (1 + n)y' + y = 0.$$

(d) $y = J_n(e^x)$ is a solution of the equation
$$y'' + (e^{2x} - n^2)y = 0.$$

(e) $y = J_0(ax)$ is a solution of the equation
$$xy'' + y' + a^2xy = 0.$$

(f) $y = \sqrt{x} \cdot J_n(ax)$ is a solution of the equation
$$4x^2y'' + (4a^2x^2 - 4n^2 + 1)y = 0.$$

2. Prove:

(a) $\dfrac{d}{dx} J_0(x) \equiv -J_1(x)$.

(b) $\dfrac{d}{dx} [x^n J_n(hx)] \equiv hx^n J_{n-1}(hx)$.

(c) $\dfrac{d^2}{dx^2} [J_n(x)] \equiv \dfrac{1}{4} [J_{n-2}(x) - 2J_n(x) + J_{n+2}(x)]$.

3. Prove:

$$(b^2 - a^2) \int_0^x x \cdot J_n(ax) \cdot J_n(bx)\, dx$$
$$\equiv x[aJ_n(bx) \cdot J_n'(ax) - bJ_n(ax) \cdot J_n'(bx)].$$

Hint: Set $u = \sqrt{x} \cdot J_n(ax)$, $v = \sqrt{x} \cdot J_n(bx)$.   By Exercise 1(f),

$$4x^2 u'' + (4a^2 x^2 - 4n^2 + 1)u = 0,$$
$$4x^2 v'' + (4b^2 x^2 - 4n^2 + 1)v = 0.$$

Multiply these by v and $-u$, respectively, add, and then integrate.

4. If $a_1, a_2, a_3, \cdots$ are the positive roots of $J_n(x) = 0$ (it can be shown that the number of such roots is infinite), show that the functions

$$\sqrt{x} \cdot J_n(a_1 x), \quad \sqrt{x} \cdot J_n(a_2 x), \quad \sqrt{x} \cdot J_n(a_3 x), \quad \cdots$$

are orthogonal in the interval from $x = 0$ to $x = 1$, *i. e.*, that

$$\int_0^1 \sqrt{x} \cdot J_n(a_r x) \cdot \sqrt{x} \cdot J_n(a_s x)\, dx = 0 \qquad (r \neq s).$$

Hint: Use the formula in Exercise 3.

5. If a_i are as in Exercise 4 ($i = 1, 2, 3, \cdots$), prove that

$$\int_0^1 x \cdot [J_n(a_r x)]^2\, dx = \frac{1}{2} [J_n'(a_r)]^2.$$

Hint: Differentiate the formula of Exercise 3 partially with respect to b, then set $b = a$.

6. (a) Derive a formula alternative to the one in Exercise 3, *viz.*,

$$(b^2 - a^2) \int_0^x x \cdot J_n(ax) \cdot J_n(bx)\, dx$$
$$\equiv x[bJ_n(ax)J_{n+1}(bx) - aJ_n(bx)J_{n+1}(ax)].$$

(b) From this establish a formula alternative to the one in Exercise 5, *viz.*,

$$\int_0^1 x \cdot [J_n(a_r x)]^2 \, dx = -\frac{1}{2} J_n'(a_r) \cdot J_{n+1}(a_r) = \frac{1}{2} [J_{n+1}(a_r)]^2.$$

7. Show that if $f(x)$ can be developed into a series

$$f(x) \equiv c_1 J_n(a_1 x) + c_2 J_n(a_2 x) + \cdots + c_r J_n(a_r x) + \cdots$$

(where a_i have the same meaning as in Exercise 4), and if the series multiplied by $x \cdot J_n(a_k x)$ may be integrated term by term, then

$$c_k = \frac{2 \int_0^1 x f(x) \cdot J_n(a_k x) \, dx}{[J_{n+1}(a_k)]^2}.$$

8. Prove that

$$J_{\frac{1}{2}}(x) \equiv \sqrt{\frac{2}{\pi x}} \cdot \sin x.$$

Hint: Use (31). Make use of the fact that

$$\Gamma(n+1) \equiv n\Gamma(n) \text{ and } \Gamma\left(\frac{1}{2}\right) = \sqrt{\pi}.$$

9. Prove that

$$J_{-\frac{1}{2}}(x) \equiv \sqrt{\frac{2}{\pi x}} \cdot \cos x.$$

Hint: Use (32).

10. By repeated use of (30), prove:

$$J_{n-1}(x) \equiv \frac{2}{x} [nJ_n(x) - (n+2)J_{n+2}(x) + (n+4)J_{n+4}(x)$$
$$- (n+6)J_{n+6}(x) + \cdots].$$

Note that

$$\lim_{n \to \infty} J_n(x) = 0.$$

11. By means of (33) prove:

$$\text{(a) } J_n(x+y) \equiv \sum_{k=-\infty}^{\infty} J_k(x) \cdot J_{n-k}(y),$$

where n is an integer.

(b) $J_0(x) + 2J_2(x) + 2J_4(x) + 2J_6(x) + \cdots \equiv 1.$

(c) $J_1(x) + 3J_3(x) + 5J_5(x) + 7J_7(x) + \cdots \equiv \dfrac{x}{2}.$

12. Show that a function of m and x, which has the properties (27) and (28) of the text, satisfies the Bessel Equation.

50. The Gauss equation.   The equation

$$(x^2 - x)y'' + [(\alpha + \beta + 1)x - \gamma]y' + \alpha\beta y = 0 \qquad (34)$$

is called the Gauss equation, after Karl Friedrich Gauss (1777–1855), an outstanding name in the history of mathematics.

We leave it to the student to obtain the complete solution of the Gauss equation in each of the forms

$$y = Au + Bv$$

and

$$y = Cu_1 + Dv_1,$$

where

$$u \equiv 1 + \frac{\alpha \cdot \beta}{1!\gamma} x + \frac{\alpha(\alpha + 1) \cdot \beta(\beta + 1)}{2!\gamma(\gamma + 1)} x^2$$
$$+ \frac{\alpha(\alpha + 1)(\alpha + 2) \cdot \beta(\beta + 1)(\beta + 2)}{3!\gamma(\gamma + 1)(\gamma + 2)} x^3 + \cdots,$$

$$v \equiv x^{1-\gamma}\left[1 + \frac{(1 + \alpha - \gamma) \cdot (1 + \beta - \gamma)}{1!(2 - \gamma)} x\right.$$
$$+ \frac{(1 + \alpha - \gamma)(2 + \alpha - \gamma) \cdot (1 + \beta - \gamma)(2 + \beta - \gamma)}{2!(2 - \gamma)(3 - \gamma)} x^2$$
$$+ \frac{(1+\alpha-\gamma)(2+\alpha-\gamma)(3+\alpha-\gamma) \cdot (1+\beta-\gamma)(2+\beta-\gamma)(3+\beta-\gamma)}{3!(2 - \gamma)(3 - \gamma)(4 - \gamma)} x^3$$
$$\left. + \cdots \right],$$

$$u_1 \equiv x^{-\alpha}\left[1 + \frac{\alpha \cdot (1 + \alpha - \gamma)}{1!(1 + \alpha - \beta)} \cdot \frac{1}{x}\right.$$
$$+ \frac{\alpha(\alpha + 1) \cdot (1 + \alpha - \gamma)(2 + \alpha - \gamma)}{2!(1 + \alpha - \beta)(2 + \alpha - \beta)} \cdot \frac{1}{x^2}$$
$$+ \frac{\alpha(\alpha + 1)(\alpha + 2) \cdot (1 + \alpha - \gamma)(2 + \alpha - \gamma)(3 + \alpha - \gamma)}{3!(1 + \alpha - \beta)(2 + \alpha - \beta)(3 + \alpha - \beta)} \cdot \frac{1}{x^3}$$
$$\left. + \cdots \right],$$

$$v_1 \equiv x^{-\beta} \left[1 + \frac{\beta \cdot (1 + \beta - \gamma)}{1!(1 + \beta - \alpha)} \cdot \frac{1}{x} \right.$$

$$+ \frac{\beta(\beta + 1) \cdot (1 + \beta - \gamma)(2 + \beta - \gamma)}{2!(1 + \beta - \alpha)(2 + \beta - \alpha)} \cdot \frac{1}{x^2}$$

$$+ \frac{\beta(\beta + 1)(\beta + 2) \cdot (1 + \beta - \gamma)(2 + \beta - \gamma)(3 + \beta - \gamma)}{3!(1 + \beta - \alpha)(2 + \beta - \alpha)(3 + \beta - \alpha)} \cdot \frac{1}{x^3}$$

$$\left. + \cdots \right].$$

We now define as the hypergeometric series a series of the form

$$1 + \frac{\alpha \cdot \beta}{1!\gamma} z + \frac{\alpha(\alpha + 1) \cdot \beta(\beta + 1)}{2!\gamma(\gamma + 1)} z^2$$

$$+ \frac{\alpha(\alpha + 1)(\alpha + 2) \cdot \beta(\beta + 1)(\beta + 2)}{3!\gamma(\gamma + 1)(\gamma + 2)} z^3$$

$$+ \cdots \quad (35)$$

and denote it, as is customary, by $F(\alpha, \beta, \gamma, z)$. It is seen that the four series which arise as solutions of the Gauss equation are each of this type (the equation itself is frequently called the hypergeometric equation, on that account), and can be designated as

$$u \equiv F(\alpha, \beta, \gamma, x),$$
$$v \equiv x^{1-\gamma} \cdot F(1 + \alpha - \gamma, 1 + \beta - \gamma, 2 - \gamma, x),$$
$$u_1 \equiv x^{-\alpha} \cdot F\left(\alpha, 1 + \alpha - \gamma, 1 + \alpha - \beta, \frac{1}{x}\right),$$
$$v_1 \equiv x^{-\beta} \cdot F\left(\beta, 1 + \beta - \gamma, 1 + \beta - \alpha, \frac{1}{x}\right).$$

A variety of special cases arises, depending on the values of α, β, γ. Thus, when $\gamma = 1$, u and v are identical, and to obtain a second solution independent of u, it is necessary to resort to the method of Section 45 of this chapter. However, u_1 and v_1 are not in that case identical, except when $\alpha = \beta$, and the complete solution of (34) is available in the second form written above, viz., $y = Cu_1 + Dv_1$. Again, if γ is a negative integer (or zero), the coefficients in u presently become infinite, and a second solution, independent of v, must be sought by the method of Section 46 of this chapter. This situation, however, is modified if either α or β is a negative integer of lesser numerical value than γ, so that u reduces to a polynomial. In any event, again in this case, the second form of the complete solution may be available.

Other possibilities for the values of α, β, γ which lead to the exceptional cases that are wont to arise in integration by series, will readily occur to the student.

The hypergeometric series (35) converges for $|z| < 1$, and diverges for $|z| > 1$, whatever the values of α, β, γ.* For $z = 1$, it converges when, and only when, $\alpha + \beta < \gamma$. For $z = -1$, it converges when, and only when, $\alpha + \beta < \gamma + 1$. (For proof of these statements, the student may turn to Section 29 in Pierpont's *Functions of a Complex Variable*.)

It is of interest to note the great variety of functions that can be expressed as hypergeometric series. Thus

(a) $\log (1 + x) \equiv x - \dfrac{x^2}{2} + \dfrac{x^3}{3} - \dfrac{x^4}{4} + \dfrac{x^5}{5} - \cdots$

$$\equiv x \left[1 - \frac{1}{2}x + \frac{1}{3}x^2 - \frac{1}{4}x^3 + \frac{1}{5}x^4 - \cdots \right]$$

$$\equiv x \left[1 - \frac{1 \cdot 1}{1! \, 2}x + \frac{1 \cdot 2 \cdot 1 \cdot 2}{2! \, 2 \cdot 3}x^2 \right.$$
$$\left. - \frac{1 \cdot 2 \cdot 3 \cdot 1 \cdot 2 \cdot 3}{3! \, 2 \cdot 3 \cdot 4}x^3 + \cdots \right]$$

$$\equiv x \cdot F(1, 1, 2, -x).$$

The function converges for $|x| < 1$, and diverges for $|x| > 1$. For $-x = 1 (\therefore x = -1)$ it diverges, since $\alpha + \beta \not< \gamma$. For $-x = -1$ $(\therefore x = 1)$ it converges, since $\alpha + \beta < \gamma + 1$,

(b) $(1 + x)^n \equiv 1 + nx + \dfrac{n(n - 1)}{2!}x^2 + \dfrac{n(n - 1)(n - 2)}{3!}x^3$
$$+ \cdots$$

$$\equiv 1 + \frac{(-n)(-x)}{1!} + \frac{(-n)(-n + 1)}{2!}(-x)^2$$
$$+ \frac{(-n)(-n + 1)(-n + 2)}{3!}(-x)^3 + \cdots$$

$$\equiv F(-n, \beta, \beta, -x),$$

where β is any constant. The function converges for $|x| < 1$, and diverges for $|x| > 1$. For $-x = 1 (\therefore x = -1)$ it converges when, and only when, $-n + \beta < \beta (\therefore n > 0)$. For $-x = -1 (\therefore x = 1)$

---

* Except, of course, when the number of terms is finite, in which case the series converges for all finite values of z.

it converges when, and only when, $-n + \beta < \beta + 1 (\therefore n > -1)$,

$$(c) \qquad \cos x \equiv 1 - \frac{x^2}{2!} + \frac{x^4}{4!} - \frac{x^6}{6!} + \cdots$$

$$\equiv 1 + \frac{\alpha \cdot \beta}{1! \frac{1}{2}}\left(-\frac{x^2}{4\alpha\beta}\right) + \lim_{\substack{\alpha \to \infty \\ \beta \to \infty}} \frac{\alpha(\alpha+1) \cdot \beta(\beta+1)}{2! \frac{1}{2} \cdot \frac{3}{2}}\left(-\frac{x^2}{4\alpha\beta}\right)^2$$

$$+ \lim_{\substack{\alpha \to \infty \\ \beta \to \infty}} \frac{\alpha(\alpha+1)(\alpha+2) \cdot \beta(\beta+1)(\beta+2)}{3! \frac{1}{2} \cdot \frac{3}{2} \cdot \frac{5}{2}}\left(-\frac{x^2}{4\alpha\beta}\right)^3 + \cdots$$

$$\equiv \lim_{\substack{\alpha \to \infty \\ \beta \to \infty}} F\left(\alpha, \beta, \tfrac{1}{2}, -\frac{x^2}{4\alpha\beta}\right).$$

Exercises

1. Express as hypergeometric series:

    (a) $(1 + x)^n + (1 - x)^n$.

    (b) $(1 + x)^n - (1 - x)^n$.

    (c) $\log \dfrac{1 + x}{1 - x}$.

    (d) $\dfrac{1}{1 + x}$.   Examine for convergence.

    (e) $\dfrac{1}{1 - x}$.   Examine for convergence.

    (f) $\sin x$.

    (g) e^x.

2. Solve the following equations:

    (a) $(x^2 - x)y'' + (4x - 3)y' + 2y = 0$.

    (b) $(x^2 - x)y'' + (2x - 1)y' - 2y = 0$.

3. Examine the following series for convergence:

    (a) $F\left(2, 3, 1, \dfrac{5 - x}{3}\right)$.

    (b) $F\left(1, -1, \tfrac{1}{2}, \dfrac{x - 2}{2}\right)$.

4. Prove:

    (a) $(\beta - \alpha) \cdot F(\alpha, \beta, \gamma, x) + \alpha \cdot F(\alpha + 1, \beta, \gamma, x) - \beta \cdot F(\alpha, \beta + 1, \gamma, x) \equiv 0$.

    (b) $(\gamma - \alpha - \beta) \cdot F(\alpha, \beta, \gamma, x) + \alpha(1 - x) \cdot F(\alpha + 1, \beta, \gamma, x) + (\beta - \gamma) \cdot F(\alpha, \beta - 1, \gamma, x) \equiv 0$.

5. Write down the Gauss equation of which

$$y = F(\alpha, \beta, \gamma, -x)$$

is a solution.

6. By making use of the expression as a hypergeometric series for $\log (1 + x)$, write down the Gauss equation of which

$$y = \frac{\log (1 + x)}{x}$$

is a solution.

7. Express $\dfrac{d^m}{dx^m} F(\alpha, \beta, \gamma, x)$ as a hypergeometric series.

8. Reduce the equation

$$(Ax^2 + Bx + C)y'' + (Dx + E)y' + Fy = 0$$

to a Gauss equation. *Hint:* Set $x = lz + m$ in the given equation. l and m will be determined by $\begin{cases} Am^2 + Bm + C = 0 \\ -Al = 2Am + B \end{cases}$, to the effect of yielding a Gauss equation in z.

9. Solve the equation

$$(2x^2 - 8)y'' + (x + 1)y' - 10y = 0$$

by the method of Exercise 8.

51. Miscellaneous exercises on Chapter VI.

1. Integrate in series:

    (a) $x^2y'' + x^2y' - 2y = 0$.
    (b) $(1 - x^2)y'' + 2xy' + y = 0$.
    (c) $x^2y'' - xy' + (x^2 + 1)y = 0$.
    (d) $(1 + x^2)y'' + xy' - 9y = 0$.
    (e) $xy'' - 3y' + x^2y = 0$.
    (f) $x^4y'' + (x - 2x^3)y' + y = 4x + 5$.
    (g) $x^2y'' + (x^3 + x)y' = \dfrac{1}{x} + 9y$.

2. Prove:

    (a) $(1 - x^2)P_n'(x) \equiv (n + 1)[xP_n(x) - P_{n+1}(x)]$.
    (b) $P_{n+1}'(x) - P_{n-1}'(x) \equiv (2n + 1)P_n(x)$.

3. Prove that if $-\frac{1}{2} + \sqrt{k^2 + \frac{1}{4}}$ is an integer n, then the equation $\dfrac{d^2y}{dx^2} + \cot x \dfrac{dy}{dx} + k^2y = 0$ is satisfied by $y = P_n (\cos x)$.

4. Show that:

(a) $y = x^{n/2} \cdot J_n(2 \sqrt{x})$ is a solution of the equation $xy'' + (1 - n)y' + y = 0$.

(b) $x[J_n(x) + J_{n+2}(x)] \equiv 2(n + 1)J_{n+1}(x)$.

5. Verify that $y = \dfrac{1}{x} J_2(2 \sqrt{x})$ is a solution of $xy'' + 3y' + y = 0$.

6. Show that:

(a) $J_{3/2}(x) \equiv \sqrt{\dfrac{2}{\pi x}} \left(\dfrac{\sin x}{x} - \cos x \right).$

Hint: Use (30), with $m = \frac{1}{2}$; also Exercises 8 and 9 of Section 49.

(b) $J_{-3/2}(x) \equiv \sqrt{\dfrac{2}{\pi x}} \left(-\dfrac{\cos x}{x} - \sin x \right).$

(c) $J_{5/2}(x) \equiv \sqrt{\dfrac{2}{\pi x}} \left[\sin x \left(\dfrac{3}{x^2} - 1 \right) - \dfrac{3 \cos x}{x} \right].$

7. By formula (29) and Exercise 10 of Section 49 prove:

$$\dfrac{d}{dx} J_n(x) \equiv \dfrac{2}{x} \left[\dfrac{n}{2} J_n(x) - (n + 2)J_{n+2}(x) + (n + 4)J_{n+4}(x) \right.$$

$$\left. - (n + 6)J_{n+6}(x) + \cdots \right].$$

8. By formula (33), prove:

(a) $\cos (x \sin \varphi) \equiv J_0(x) + 2J_2(x) \cdot \cos 2\varphi + 2J_4(x) \cdot \cos 4\varphi + 2J_6(x) \cdot \cos 6\varphi + \cdots.$

(b) $\sin (x \sin \varphi) \equiv 2J_1(x) \cdot \sin \varphi + 2J_3(x) \cdot \sin 3\varphi + 2J_5(x) \cdot \sin 5\varphi + \cdots.$

Hint: In (33), set $h = e^{i\varphi} \left(\therefore \dfrac{1}{h} = e^{-i\varphi} \right).$ Make use of the formula $[e^{i\varphi}]^m \equiv e^{mi\varphi} \equiv \cos m\varphi + i \sin m\varphi.$ After substituting, equate the real and imaginary parts on each side of (33).

9. From the formula in Exercise 8(a), obtain

(a) $J_0(x) \equiv \dfrac{1}{\pi} \int_0^\pi \cos (x \sin \varphi) \, d\varphi.$

Obtain also an alternative formula

$$\text{(b)} \quad J_0(x) \equiv \frac{1}{\pi} \int_0^\pi \cos\,(x \cos\,\varphi)\,d\varphi.$$

10. Express as hypergeometric series:

    (a) $\sin^{-1} x$.   (b) $\tan^{-1} x$.   (c) $\cosh x$.

11. Prove:

$$(\gamma - \alpha - 1) \cdot F(\alpha, \beta, \gamma, x) + \alpha \cdot F(\alpha + 1, \beta, \gamma, x) + (1 - \gamma) \cdot$$
$$F(\alpha, \beta, \gamma - 1, x) \equiv 0.$$

12. By making use of the expression as a hypergeometric series for $(1 + x)^n$, write down a Gauss equation of which $y = (1 + x)^n$ is a solution.

13. On the basis of Exercise 10, prove:

$$\theta \equiv \sin\,\theta \cdot F(\tfrac{1}{2}, \tfrac{1}{2}, \tfrac{3}{2}, \sin^2\,\theta)$$
$$\equiv \tan\,\theta \cdot F(\tfrac{1}{2}, 1, \tfrac{3}{2}, -\tan^2\,\theta).$$

14. Solve the equation

$$(1 - x^2)\,\frac{d^2y}{dx^2} + (2 - x)\,\frac{dy}{dx} + 4y = 0$$

by converting it to a Gauss Equation.

CHAPTER VII

Ordinary Differential Equations in More Than Two Variables

52. Total differential equations; introductory remarks. In books on calculus* it is proved that the differential of a function $u = f(x, y, z, \cdots)$ is given by the formula

$$du = f_x \, dx + f_y \, dy + f_z \, dz + \cdots,$$

provided, of course, that the partial derivatives $f_x, f_y, f_z, \cdots$ exist and are continuous.

If we take the differential of each side of the equation

$$x^2 y - e^x + \cos z = 7, \qquad (1)$$

we obtain

$$(2xy - e^x) \, dx + x^2 \, dy - \sin z \, dz = 0. \qquad (2)$$

An equation such as (2)† is called a *total differential equation*, and an equality, like (1), which identically satisfies it, is called a *solution*. Obviously, the relation (1) would still satisfy (2) if the constant 7 in the right-hand member were changed to any other; so the equation

$$x^2 y - e^x + \cos z = c,$$

where c is an arbitrary constant, is a solution, and will be called the *general* solution.

Before going into the question of the solvability of total differential equations, let us look at the example

$$x^2 y - e^{x^3 z} = c.$$

It is at once noticeable that the factor x may be removed from the corresponding differential equation

$$(2xy - 3x^2 z e^{x^3 z}) \, dx + x^2 \, dy - x^3 e^{x^3 z} \, dz = 0,$$

---

* Wilson's *Advanced Calculus*, page 93.

† More generally, a total differential equation is one of the form $P(x, y, z, t, \cdots) \, dx + Q(x, y, z, t, \cdots) \, dy + R(x, y, z, t, \cdots) \, dz + S(x, y, z, t, \cdots) \, dt + \cdots = 0$,

producing the equation

$$(2y - 3xze^{x^3z})\, dx + x\, dy - x^2 e^{x^3z}\, dz = 0.$$

If one were confronted with this equation to solve, he would find it expedient first to multiply by the *integrating factor* x, thus rendering the equation *exact*.

53. Condition for exactness. Let us study the differential equation

$$P\, dx + Q\, dy + R\, dz = 0, \tag{3}$$

where P, Q, and R are continuous functions of x, y, and z, having continuous first partial derivatives. We shall first suppose equation (3) to be exact, that is, that there exists a function $\varphi(x, y, z)$ which is continuous and has continuous first and second partial derivatives such that

$$\varphi_x \equiv P,\ \varphi_y \equiv Q,\ \varphi_z \equiv R. \tag{4}$$

In this case we find, by further differentiation, that

$$\varphi_{xy} \equiv P_y \equiv Q_x,\ \varphi_{xz} \equiv P_z \equiv R_x,\ \varphi_{yz} \equiv Q_z \equiv R_y,$$

from which we draw the necessary condition

$$P_y \equiv Q_x,\ R_x \equiv P_z,\ Q_z \equiv R_y. \tag{5}$$

Let us now discard the assumption that such a function φ exists, and assume instead that the relations (5) hold. With this hypothesis we seek to prove the existence of a function φ for which the relations (4) are true. To prove this we follow the style of Section 9, Chapter II, and set up the function

$$\varphi(x, y, z) \equiv \int_a^x P(x, y, z)\, dx + \int_b^y Q(a, y, z)\, dy + \int R(a, b, z)\, dz,$$

where each integral is to be evaluated with all variables in its integrand, other than the variable of integration, held constant, and a and b are any constants for which the integrals exist. Forming the partial derivatives, φ_x, φ_y, and φ_z, we obtain

$$\varphi_x \equiv P(x, y, z),$$
$$\varphi_y \equiv \frac{\partial}{\partial y} \int_a^x P(x, y, z)\, dx + Q(a, y, z)$$
$$\equiv \int_a^x P_y(x, y, z)\, dx + Q(a, y, z)$$

$$\equiv \int_a^x Q_x(x, y, z)dx + Q(a, y, z)$$

$$\equiv Q(x, y, z) \Big|_{x=a}^{x=x} + Q(a, y, z)$$

$$\equiv Q(x, y, z),$$

$$\varphi_z \equiv \frac{\partial}{\partial z}\left[\int_a^x P(x, y, z)dx + \int_b^y Q(a, y, z)dy \right] + R(a, b, z)$$

$$\equiv \int_a^x P_z(x, y, z)dx + \int_b^y Q_z(a, y, z)dy + R(a, b, z)$$

$$\equiv \int_a^x R_x(x, y, z)dx + \int_b^y R_y(a, y, z)dy + R(a, b, z)$$

$$\equiv R(x, y, z) \Big|_{x=a}^{x=x} + R(a, y, z) \Big|_{y=b}^{y=y} + R(a, b, z)$$

$$\equiv R(x, y, z).$$

Thus we see that this function φ has the desired properties, and that the conditions (5) are sufficient for the exactness of the given equation (3). These conditions for exactness can easily be remembered if one notes that they consist of the three conditions for the exactness of the three differential equations $P\,dx + Q\,dy = 0$, $P\,dx + R\,dz = 0$, and $Q\,dy + R\,dz = 0$ obtained from (3) by supposing, first, $z = c$, then $y = c$, then $x = c$.

54. Conditions for integrability. If the differential equation (3) is not exact, it may be possible to make it so by use of an integrating factor $\mu(x, y, z)$, which gives the equation

$$\mu P\,dx + \mu Q\,dy + \mu R\,dz = 0.$$

For this equation to be exact, it is necessary and sufficient that the relations (5) hold, with μP, μQ, μR replacing P, Q, and R, respectively. In this form the relations (5) become

$$\begin{aligned} \mu P_y + P\mu_y &\equiv \mu Q_x + Q\mu_x, \\ \mu R_x + R\mu_x &\equiv \mu P_z + P\mu_z, \\ \mu Q_z + Q\mu_z &\equiv \mu R_y + R\mu_y. \end{aligned} \qquad (6)$$

Now this system of partial differential equations (6) may or may not have a solution $\mu(x, y, z)$. If it has no solution, then the given total differential equation (3) has no solution. Furthermore, if (3) has no solution, we should like to have a test by which we could determine the fact, and so avoid a vain attempt to set up the solution. Relation (6) may be considered to furnish such a test, inasmuch as (4) has a solution if, and only if, the system (6) has a solution.   To solve the system (6) for μ might be very difficult in some cases.   However, it happens that if we multiply the first of these equations by R, the second by Q, and the third by P, add the three results, and divide by μ, we obtain

$$P(Q_z - R_y) + Q(R_x - P_z) + R(P_y - Q_x) \equiv 0.$$

This relation does not contain μ, and so may be used as a test upon the functions P, Q, and R appearing in any equation of the form (3).   It may be shown to be sufficient for the existence of an integrating factor μ of (3), and is called the *condition of integrability* of that equation.   This condition is easily remembered by noting that PQR, QRP, and RPQ, appearing, respectively, in the first, second, and third terms, are all in the cyclic* order PQR, while the small letters run *zyxzyx*.

55. Total differential equations which are integrable.   If a total differential equation is found to be exact, it may be integrated at once as in the example

$$(2x + y + z)dx + (2y + x + z)dy + (x + y + 2z)dz = 0,$$

which has the general solution

$$x^2 + y^2 + z^2 + xy + yz + zx = c.$$

If an equation is integrable but not exact, it may be possible to find an integrating factor by inspection.   For example, the equation

$$x\,dx + y\,dy - \sqrt{1 - x^2 - y^2}\,dz = 0$$

is integrable but not exact.   We note that the variable z is not present in P, Q, or R, and hence division by $\sqrt{1 - x^2 - y^2}$ isolates the variable z.   The resulting equation,

$$\frac{x\,dx + y\,dy}{\sqrt{1 - x^2 - y^2}} - dz = 0,$$

is exact and has the general solution

$$\sqrt{1 - x^2 - y^2} + z = c.$$

If the student is unable to discover an integrating factor by inspection, he may proceed as in the example

$$\left(2 - \frac{2y}{x} + \frac{z^3}{x}\right)dx - 2dy + 3z^2\,dz = 0. \tag{7}$$

---

* By *cyclic order* is meant the order in which one may read off the letters if they are arranged around a circle, with the first letter succeeding the last one.

Assume, for the present, that x is a constant and, hence, that $dx = 0$. The resulting equation

$$-2dy + 3z^2\, dz = 0 \tag{8}$$

has the solution

$$-2y + z^3 = f(x). \tag{9}$$

Here, since we are holding x constant, we replace the constant of integration by an arbitrary function of x. If the quantity x had appeared in (8), we would have solved it, regarding x as a constant. We shall now evaluate the function $f(x)$ in (9) in such a way that (9) will be a solution of the given equation (7), the quantity x being allowed to vary. If we take the differential of both sides of (9), we obtain

$$-2dy + 3z^2\, dz = f'(x)\, dx.$$

Now note that the term

$$\left(2 + \frac{-2y + z^3}{x}\right) dx$$

in (7) may be written

$$\left(2 + \frac{f(x)}{x}\right) dx$$

in view of (9), and so equation (7) takes the form

$$\left(2 + \frac{f}{x} + f'\right) dx = 0,$$

which can be written

$$\left(2 + \frac{f}{x}\right) dx + df = 0,$$

and solved by the use of the integrating factor x. The solution

$$f = \frac{c - x^2}{x}$$

may be substituted in (9) to yield the result

$$-2y + z^3 = \frac{c - x^2}{x}$$

as the complete solution of (7).

Exercises

1. Test the following equations for exactness. Find an integrating factor by inspection if the equation is not exact. Solve all equations.

(a) $(2xy - 1)dx + (x^2 + \cos z)dy - (y \sin z + 2z)dz = 0.$

(b) $[x(x^2 + y^2) - y]dx + [y(x^2 + y^2) + x]dy +$
$$(x^2 + y^2)dz = 0.$$

(c) $z(2xz + 1)dx + 2yz^2\, dy + (z - x)dz = 0.$

(d) $(y + a)^2\, dx + z\, dy - (y + a)dz = 0.$

(e) $(x - 1)dx - \sqrt{4 - z^2 - (x - 1)^2}\, dy + z\, dz = 0.$

(f) $\left(\dfrac{e^{xy}}{z} + \dfrac{e^{xz}}{y}\right)\dfrac{dx}{x} + \left(\dfrac{e^{xy}}{z} + \dfrac{e^{yz}}{x}\right)\dfrac{dy}{y} + \left(\dfrac{e^{xz}}{y} + \dfrac{e^{yz}}{x}\right)\dfrac{dz}{z} = 0.$

(g) $(\sinh y + z \cosh x)dx + (\sinh z + x \cosh y)dy +$
$(\sinh x + y \cosh z)dz = 0.$

2. Test the following equations for integrability, and solve those which are integrable:

(a) $(x + z)dx + zx^2\, dy + (yx^2 - x)dz = 0.$

(b) $(x + y + z + 1)dx + dy + dz = 0.$

(c) $x\, dy - y\, dx + z\, dz = 0.$

(d) $(y - xz)dx - (z - \sin^{-1} x)\sqrt{1 - x^2}\, dy + (1 - x^2$
$- y\sqrt{1 - x^2})\, dz = 0.$

(e) $(y^3 - xy^2)dx + x^2y\, dy + 2z\, dz = 0.$

(f) $dx + (x \tan y + z \sec y - \tan y)\, dy + \sin y\, dz = 0.$

3. If P, Q, and R are homogeneous functions of x, y, and z, of the same degree, show that the substitution $x = uz$, $y = vz$ in the equation $P\, dx + Q\, dy + R\, dz = 0$ will separate the variable z from the variables u and v. For the definition of homogeneous functions, see Section 11, Chapter II.

4. Solve the following homogeneous total differential equations, using a substitution of the type of Exercise 3:

(a) $(2yz + 3xy + 4x^2)dx + (xz + x^2)dy + xy\, dz = 0.$

(b) $(y^3 + 2xyz)dx + (4xy^2 + 2x^2z)dy + x^2y\, dz = 0.$

(c) $y^2z^2\, dx + (2xyz^2 \log x - 2xyz^2 \log z - 3xy^2z)dy - (xzy^2 - xy^3)dz = 0.$

(d) $y\, dx - (x + z)dy + y\, dz = 0.$

5. Show that if the equation $P\, dx + Q\, dy + R\, dz = 0$ is exact and homogeneous, of degree not -1, its solution is $xP + yQ + zR = c$. *Hint:* See footnote to Exercise 8, page 32.

6. Solve the following exercises, using the proposition of Exercise 5:

(a) $\dfrac{dx + dz}{y^2} - \dfrac{2(x + z)}{y^3}\, dy = 0.$

(b) $\dfrac{4dx}{x^5} + \dfrac{dy}{z^5} - \dfrac{5y\,dz}{z^6} = 0.$

(c) $(4x^3 + y^2z)dx + 2xyz\,dy + (y^2x + z^3)dz = 0.$

7. Prove that if the variables x, y, and z in the integrable differential equation $P\,dx + Q\,dy + R\,dz = 0$ are replaced by the substitution $x = X(r,\,s,\,t)$, $y = Y(r,\,s,\,t)$, $z = Z(r,\,s,\,t)$, where X, Y, and Z are continuous functions of r, s, and t, having continuous first and second partial derivatives, then the resulting equation is integrable.

8. Find conditions necessary for the exactness of the equation $P\,dx + Q\,dy + R\,dz + S\,dt = 0$, and prove that those conditions are sufficient. *Hint:* To find the necessary conditions, suppose x, y, z, and t to be constant in pairs, and write down the conditions that the equations in two variables thus obtained be exact. To prove the conditions sufficient, suppose that they hold, and set up a function $\varphi(x,\,y,\,z,\,t)$, as in the text, page 181.

9. Test the following equations for exactness, and solve those which are exact:

(a) $(t + y)dx + (x + z)dy + (y + t)dz + (z + x)dt = 0.$
(b) $y\,dx + z\,dy + t\,dz + x\,dt = 0.$
(c) $3x^2y^2\,dx + (2x^3y + 2z)dy + (2y + t)dz + z\,dt = 0.$

10. The following equations are not exact, but integrable. Find the general solution.

(a) $(2xy + 2x^2z - 2xt + z)dx + dy + x\,dz - dt = 0.$
(b) $t^2\,dx + 2xyt^2\,dy + xt^2\,dz + x\,dt + xt^2\,du + 2xt^2v\,dv$
$\qquad\qquad\qquad\qquad\qquad\qquad\qquad = 0.$

11. Prove that if the equation $P\,dx + Q\,dy + R\,dz + S\,dt = 0$ is exact and homogeneous, and of degree not -1, then the solution is

$$xP + yQ + zR + tS = c.$$

Hint: See hint of Exercise 5, above.

12. Use the proposition of Exercise 11 to write down the solution of

$(4x^3 + 3x^2y + 2xyz + yzt)dx + (x^3 + x^2z + xzt)dy$
$\qquad\qquad\qquad + (x^2y + xyt)dz + xyz\,dt = 0.$

13. By following a method similar to that of Section 54 of this chapter, show that if the equation

$$P \, dx + Q \, dy + R \, dz + S \, dt = 0$$

is integrable, the relations

$$P(Q_z - R_y) + Q(R_x - P_z) + R(P_y - Q_x) \equiv 0,$$
$$P(Q_t - S_y) + Q(S_x - P_t) + S(P_y - Q_x) \equiv 0,$$
$$P(R_t - S_z) + R(S_x - P_t) + S(P_z - R_x) \equiv 0,$$
$$Q(R_t - S_z) + R(S_y - Q_t) + S(Q_z - R_y) \equiv 0,$$

hold. Show also that if any three of these relations hold, then the fourth one holds.

56. Geometric significance.

For the sake of clarity, geometric nomenclature will be employed occasionally in the discussions which are to follow. If the set of variables (x, y, z) are taken as the rectangular coördinates of a point in space, then a relation among them, such as $x^2y - e^x + \cos z = 3$, represents a surface. Two equations, considered as simultaneous, represent a curve which is the curve of intersection of the two surfaces represented by the two equations, considered separately. The differentials dx, dy, and dz determine a line through the point (x, y, z) and the point $(x + dx, y + dy, z + dz)$ having the direction ratios $dx:dy:dz$. If we think of x, y, and z as fixed coördinates of a point, and dx, dy, and dz as variables in a differential equation

$$P \, dx + Q \, dy + R \, dz = 0, \tag{3}$$

we may assign the quantities dy and dz arbitrarily, and solve* for dx. This freedom makes it possible to satisfy (3), with x, y, and z fixed, by an infinite number of directions $dx:dy:dz$. If we consider P, Q, and R as direction ratios, we see that (3) is satisfied by any direction $dx:dy:dz$ which is perpendicular to the direction $P:Q:R$. Hence, these directions $dx:dy:dz$, satisfying (3) with x, y, and z fixed, while infinite in number, are all in a plane.†

57. Pairs of total differential equations.

Let us consider simultaneously two equations

$$P_1 \, dx + Q_1 \, dy + R_1 \, dz = 0, \tag{10}$$
$$P_2 \, dx + Q_2 \, dy + R_2 \, dz = 0.$$

---

* Assuming $P \neq 0$.

† This plane is unique for every point (x, y, z), excepting those points for which $P = Q = R = 0$. At such points the direction $P:Q:R$ is indeterminate, and equation (3) is satisfied by every direction $dx:dy:dz$.

Geometrically, (10_1) is satisfied at each point (x, y, z) by the direction $dx:dy:dz$ of any line in a plane π_1, while (10_2) is satisfied at each point by the direction $dx:dy:dz$ of any line in another* plane π_2. Then both of the equations (10) are satisfied by at least one direction, *viz.*, that of any line common to the planes π_1 and π_2.   In other words, we expect equations (10) to determine a direction $dx:dy:dz$ unique for every point $P(x, y, z)$ of space, excepting at those points for which

$$P_1:Q_1:R_1 = P_2:Q_2:R_2.$$

If we eliminate dz between (10_1) and (10_2), we obtain

$$(R_1P_2 - R_2P_1)dx = (Q_1R_2 - Q_2R_1)dy,$$

or

$$\frac{dx}{Q_1R_2 - Q_2R_1} = \frac{dy}{R_1P_2 - R_2P_1}.$$

If we eliminate dx, we obtain

$$\frac{dy}{R_1P_2 - R_2P_1} = \frac{dz}{P_1Q_2 - P_2Q_1}.$$

These two equations may be written in the form

$$\frac{dx}{P} = \frac{dy}{Q} = \frac{dz}{R}, \tag{11}$$

where $P \equiv \lambda(Q_1R_2 - Q_2R_1)$, $Q \equiv \lambda(R_1P_2 - R_2P_1)$, $R \equiv \lambda(P_1Q_2 - P_2Q_1)$, $\lambda \not\equiv 0$.   Equations (11) are said to be the *symmetric* form of equations (10), and show that the direction $dx:dy:dz$ which the equations define for the point (x, y, z), if unique, is that given by the ratios $P:Q:R$.

58. Solutions of a pair of total differential equations in three variables.   We have seen that a pair of total differential equations of the form (10) define a direction through each point (x, y, z). Another method of representing a direction through each point of space is to give the equations of two one-parameter families of surfaces such that through each point (x, y, z) passes one surface of each family.   The two, being distinct surfaces,† determine a curve

---

* This plane π_2 will coincide with π_1 only in case $P_1:Q_1:R_1 = P_2:Q_2:R_2$, at (x, y, z).

† If the surfaces of the family $u(x, y, z) = C$ coincide with the surfaces of the family $v(x, y, z) = c$, then u is a function of v, and the functions u and v are dependent.   A discussion of dependence of functions appears in Section 61.

through the point, the tangent to which provides a direction. We are thus led intuitively to expect the solution of the pair of equations (10) to be a pair of relations

$$f(x, y, z, c_1) = 0, \quad g(x, y, z, c_2) = 0. \tag{12}$$

In the event that each of the equations (10) is separately integrable, we have (12) immediately by taking the solution of (10_1) as (12_1) and the solution of (10_2) as (12_2). For example, the equations

$$\begin{cases} y^2 \, dx + z \, dy - y \, dz = 0, \\ (2y - 3z)dx + (z - 2x)dy + (3x - y)dz = 0, \end{cases} \tag{13}$$

are each integrable. The complete solution of (13_1) is

$$(x + c_1)y - z = 0, \tag{14_1}$$

while the complete solution of (13_2) is

$$2x - z + c_2(2y - 3z) = 0. \tag{14_2}$$

These two equations (14), considered simultaneously, form the solution to (13) considered simultaneously, since every curve on a surface of (14_1) has a direction satisfying (13_1), and every curve on a surface of (14_2) has a direction satisfying (13_2). Every curve of intersection (14), being on both types of surfaces, has a direction satisfying both equations (13).

If only one of equations (10), say (10_1), is integrable, let its solution be (12_1). We may employ (10_1), (10_2), and (12_1) to eliminate one variable and its differential, obtaining a differential equation in the other two variables. Its solution may be called (12_2). For example, consider

$$\begin{cases} (2x + z + y)dx + (1 - z)dy + (7 - y)dz = 0, \\ (z + y)dx + dy + dz = 0. \end{cases} \tag{15}$$

The first equation is not integrable, but the second one is, and has as solution

$$e^x y + e^x z = c_1. \tag{16}$$

If we eliminate dz between the two equations (15) by subtracting $(7 - y)$ times the second one from the first, we obtain

$$(2x - 6y - 6z + y^2 + yz)dx + (y - 6 - z)dy = 0. \tag{17}$$

From (16) we have the result that

$$z = c_1 e^{-x} - y,$$

which we may substitute in (17) to obtain

$$(2x - 6c_1 e^{-x} + c_1 y e^{-x})dx + (2y - 6 - c_1 e^{-x})dy = 0.$$

This equation is exact and has as solution

$$x^2 + 6c_1 e^{-x} - c_1 y e^{-x} + y^2 - 6y = c_2. \tag{18}$$

We may then consider (16) and (18) simultaneously as the solution of (15). If we substitute the value $(y + z)e^x$ of c_1 from (16) into (18), the latter reduces to

$$x^2 - yz + 6z = c_2, \tag{19}$$

which is not only simpler, but is free of c_1. Equations (16) and (18), or (16) and (19), furnish the desired solution of (15).

By ratio and proportion we may pass from (11) to the relation

$$\frac{dx}{P} = \frac{dy}{Q} = \frac{dz}{R} = \frac{l\,dx + m\,dy + n\,dz}{lP + mQ + nR},$$

where l, m, and n are any quantities whatever. It may be possible that the denominator $lP + mQ + nR$ is identically zero. Then the numerator must vanish, and if the resulting equation

$$l\,dx + m\,dy + n\,dz = 0$$

is integrable, we can find a solution. For example, if in the equations

$$\frac{dx}{x^2 + z^2 - 2yz} = \frac{dy}{2yz - 2xy} = \frac{dz}{2xy - x^2 - z^2} \tag{20}$$

we use the multipliers 1, 1, 1, we have the result

$$\frac{dx}{x^2 + z^2 - 2yz} = \frac{dy}{2yz - 2xy} = \frac{dz}{2xy - x^2 - z^2} = \frac{dx + dy + dz}{0}$$

or

$$dx + dy + dz = 0.$$

This equation is exact and has the solution

$$x + y + z = c_1. \tag{21}$$

Substitution of this into (20) gives

$$\frac{dx}{2x^2 + 4xy + 3y^2 - 2c_1x - 4c_1y + c_1^2} = \frac{dy}{2c_1y - 4xy - 2y^2},$$

or

$$(2c_1y - 4xy - 2y^2)dx - (2x^2 + 4xy + 3y^2 - 2c_1x - 4c_1y + c_1^2)dy = 0.$$

This equation is exact and has as solution

$$2c_1xy - 2x^2y - 2xy^2 - y^3 + 2c_1y^2 - c_1^2y = c_2.$$

If we substitute $c_1 = x + y + z$ into this, upon simplification we have

$$x^2y + yz^2 = c_2. \tag{22}$$

We may note that (22) could be obtained directly by taking the multipliers $l = 2xy$, $m = x^2 + z^2$, $n = 2yz$, which makes the members of (20) equal to

$$\frac{2xy\, dx + (x^2 + z^2)dy + 2yz\, dz}{2xy(x^2+z^2) - 4xy^2z + 2x^2yz + 2yz^3 - 2xy(x^2+z^2) + 4xy^2z - 2x^2yz - 2yz^3}$$

of which the denominator is identically zero, and gives

$$2xy\, dx + (x^2 + z^2)dy + 2yz\, dz = 0,$$

which is exact and has (22) as its solution.

Exercises

1. Solve the following pairs of integrable equations:

(a) $\begin{cases} y\, dx + (x + 2yz)dy + y^2\, dz = 0, \\ 3x^2yz\, dx + x^3z\, dy - x^3y\, dz = 0. \end{cases}$

(b) $\dfrac{2x^3\, dx}{yz} = \dfrac{y\, dy}{x^2z} = \dfrac{dz}{y}.$

(c) $\begin{cases} z\, dx + (xz - y^2 - 2y)dy + x\, dz = 0, \\ yz^2\, dx - z(xz + y^2)dy + y^3\, dz = 0. \end{cases}$

(d) $\dfrac{dx}{-2x^3y^3z} = \dfrac{dy}{z} = \dfrac{dz}{2y^3}.$

(e) $\begin{cases} x\, dx + y\, dy + z\, dz = 0, \\ (y + z)dx + (z + x)dy + (x + y)dz = 0. \end{cases}$

(f) $\dfrac{dx}{y^2} = \dfrac{dy}{x^2} = \dfrac{dz}{x^2y^2e^z}.$

2. Solve the following pairs of equations, in each of which one equation is integrable:

(a) $\dfrac{dx}{y} = \dfrac{dy}{x} = \dfrac{dz}{z}.$

(b) $\begin{cases} (2xy + z^2)dx + (2yz + x^2)dy + (2xz + y^2)dz = 0, \\ (2xy - z^2)dx + (2yz + x^2)dy - (2xz - y^2)dz = 0. \end{cases}$

(c) $\dfrac{dx}{x^2z^2 - 4y^2z^2 - 1} = \dfrac{dy}{xyz^2} = \dfrac{dz}{-2xz^3}.$

(d) $-\dfrac{dx}{y} = \dfrac{dy}{x} = \dfrac{dz}{\sqrt{1 - z^2}}.$

(e) $\dfrac{du}{uz} = -\dfrac{dv}{vz} = \dfrac{dz}{2u}.$

(f) $\begin{cases} 2(z - 2x)dx = (z - 3x)dz, \\ (z - x)dy = (xz - x^2 + yz - xy + 3x - z)(dz - dx). \end{cases}$

(g) $\dfrac{x - y}{dx} = \dfrac{x + y - 10}{dy} = \dfrac{0}{dz}.$

(h) $\dfrac{dx}{3x(y - 2x)} = \dfrac{dy}{3y(2y - x)} = \dfrac{dz}{z(x - y)}.$

3. Solve the following pairs of equations by use of multipliers l, m, and n, as on page 190:

(a) $\dfrac{dx}{6(y - z)} = \dfrac{2dy}{3(z - x)} = \dfrac{3dz}{2(x - y)}.$

(b) $\dfrac{dx}{9y - 3z} = \dfrac{dy}{4x + 6y} = \dfrac{dz}{12x + 6z}.$

(c) $\dfrac{dx}{x(3y - 4z)} = \dfrac{dy}{y(4z - 2x)} = \dfrac{dz}{z(2x - 3y)}.$

(d) $\dfrac{dx}{3yz} = -\dfrac{dy}{3xz} = \dfrac{dz}{xy}.$

(e) $\dfrac{dx}{x(4y^2 - z^2)} = \dfrac{-dy}{y(z^2 + 9x^2)} = \dfrac{dz}{z(9x^2 + 4y^2)}.$

(f) $\dfrac{dx}{x(y^3 - z^3)} = \dfrac{dy}{y(z^3 - x^3)} = \dfrac{dz}{z(x^3 - y^3)}.$

4. Show that a system of equations of the form

$$\frac{dx}{P} = \frac{dy}{Q} = \frac{dz}{R} \tag{11}$$

can be reduced to a linear equation of order 2 in two variables.

Hint: Solve (11) for $\dfrac{dy}{dx}$ and $\dfrac{dz}{dx}$ to obtain

$$\frac{dy}{dx} = \frac{Q}{P} \tag{23}$$

and

$$\frac{dz}{dx} = \frac{R}{P}. \tag{24}$$

Differentiate (23) with respect to x, replacing $\dfrac{dz}{dx}$ by $\dfrac{R}{P}$ from (24) whenever it appears, to obtain

$$\frac{d^2y}{dx^2} = \frac{PQ_y - QP_y}{P^2} \cdot \frac{dy}{dx} + \frac{RPQ_z - QRP_z + P^2Q_x - PQP_x}{P^3}. \tag{25}$$

Now eliminate z between (23) and (25) if it appears in the former. If it is not in (23), it will not be in (25).

5. Solve the following systems of equations by first reducing each system to a linear equation, as in Exercise 4:

(a) $\dfrac{dx}{1} = \dfrac{dy}{4y - z} = \dfrac{dz}{3y - x}.$

Hint: The method of Exercise 4 gives the linear equation

$$\frac{d^2y}{dx^2} - 4\frac{dy}{dx} + 3y = x,$$

of which

$$y = c_1 e^x + c_2 e^{3x} + \frac{x}{3} + \frac{4}{9} \tag{26}$$

is the general solution. If from the given equation we draw the equation

$$\frac{dy}{dx} = 4y - z,$$

which is free of dz, we may solve for z to obtain

$$z = 4y - \frac{dy}{dx},$$

$$z = 4\left(c_1 e^x + c_2 e^{3x} + \frac{x}{3} + \frac{4}{9}\right) - \left(c_1 e^x + 3c_2 e^{3x} + \frac{1}{3}\right),$$

$$z = 3c_1 e^x + c_2 e^{3x} + \frac{4x}{3} + \frac{13}{9}. \tag{27}$$

The relations (26) and (27) furnish the general solution. They may be solved for c_1 and c_2 to obtain

$$\begin{cases} e^{-x}(z - y - x - 1) = 2c_1, \\ e^{-3x}(27y - 9z + 3x + 1) = 18c_2, \end{cases}$$

or

$$\begin{cases} z - y - x - 1 = c_1 e^{x}, \\ 27y - 9z + 3x + 1 = c_2 e^{3x}, \end{cases}$$

where $2c_1$ has been called c_1 and $18c_2$ has been called c_2.

(b) $\dfrac{dy}{dx} = 6y - 2z, \dfrac{dz}{dx} = 2y + 2z.$

(c) $\begin{cases} (15y + 9z)dx + 3dy + dz = 0, \\ (12y + 3z)dx + 6dy - dz = 0. \end{cases}$

(d) $\dfrac{dx}{1} = \dfrac{dy}{-5y + z + e^{x}} = \dfrac{dz}{2y - 6z + 2e^{2x}}.$

(e) $\dfrac{dx}{1} = \dfrac{dy}{y + 4z + \sin x} = \dfrac{dz}{y + 4z + \cos x}.$

(f) $\dfrac{dx}{1} = \dfrac{dy}{3y + z + 12e^{2x}} = \dfrac{dz}{-y + z + 6xe^{2x}}.$

(g) $\dfrac{dx}{1} = \dfrac{dy}{ay + bz + f(x)} = \dfrac{dz}{cy + gz + \varphi(x)}.$

6. Solve the system of equations

$$\frac{dy}{dx} + X_0 \cdot (a_1 y + b_1 z) = X_1,$$

$$\frac{dz}{dx} + X_0 \cdot (a_2 y + b_2 z) = X_2,$$

where X_0, X_1, and X_2 are functions of x. By multiplying the second equation by m and adding it to the first, we obtain

$$\frac{dy}{dx} + m\frac{dz}{dx} + X_0[(a_1 + ma_2)y + (b_1 + mb_2)z] = X_1 + mX_2.$$

It is noticeable that the first two terms can be written as $\dfrac{d}{dx}(y + mz)$. If we select m so that $[(a_1 + ma_2)y + (b_1 + mb_2)z]$ is a constant multiple of $(y + mz)$, the equation becomes linear in the two variables $y + mz$, and x. This requires that $\dfrac{a_1 + ma_2}{b_1 + mb_2} = \dfrac{1}{m}$, or that m be a solution of the quadratic equation

$$a_2 m^2 + (a_1 - b_2)m - b_1 = 0.$$

7. Solve by the method of Exercise 6:

(a)
$$\begin{cases} \dfrac{dy}{dx} + x^2(4y + 2z) = e^{x^3}, \\[2mm] \dfrac{dz}{dx} + x^2(y + 5z) = 3x^2 e^{x^3}. \end{cases}$$

(b)
$$\begin{cases} \dfrac{dy}{dx} + \dfrac{3}{x}(2y - z) = x^2 - \dfrac{3}{x}, \\[2mm] \dfrac{dz}{dx} + \dfrac{1}{x}(y + 2z) = x^2 - \dfrac{1}{x}. \end{cases}$$

(c)
$$\begin{cases} \dfrac{dy}{dx} - 2(y - 3z) = \sinh x, \\[2mm] \dfrac{dz}{dx} + y + z = \cosh x. \end{cases}$$

(d)
$$\begin{cases} \dfrac{dy}{dx} + \tan x \cdot 8z = \sec x, \\[2mm] \dfrac{dz}{dx} + \tan x \cdot (y + z) = \sec^2 x. \end{cases}$$

8. If $f(x, y, z) = c_1$ and $g(x, y, z) = c_2$ furnish a solution of the pair of differential equations $\dfrac{dx}{P} = \dfrac{dy}{Q} = \dfrac{dz}{R}$, show that $f(x, y, z) + \lambda g(x, y, z) = c_1$ and $f(x, y, z) + kg(x, y, z) = c_2$ are a solution, where λ and k are different constants.   Explain geometrically.

9. Test each equation in the system below for integrability. Find the solution of each equation, and draw your conclusions about the number of relations in four variables which can satisfy three ordinary differential equations simultaneously.

$$\begin{cases} (y + w)dx + (w + x)dy + 2z\,dz + (x + y)dw = 0, \\ y(z - w)dx - x(x - w)dy + y^2\,dz - y^2\,dw = 0, \\ (5x^3 + 4x^2y + 3xz^2 + 2w^3)dx + x^3\,dy + 2x^2z\,dz + 3xw^2\,dw = 0. \end{cases}$$

59. Non-integrable equations.   We have seen that a differential equation

$$P\,dx + Q\,dy + R\,dz = 0 \tag{3}$$

may be non-integrable, while a pair of equations such as

$$\begin{aligned} P_1\,dx + Q_1\,dy + R_1\,dz = 0, \\ P_2\,dx + Q_2\,dy + R_2\,dz = 0, \end{aligned} \tag{10}$$

is always integrable as a pair. This suggests the expedient of annexing, to a non-integrable equation of the form (3), an arbitrary equation such as

$$P' \, dx + Q' \, dy + R' \, dz = 0 \qquad (28)$$

and solving (3) and (28) simultaneously as a pair. For convenience, one may choose (28) as an equation which is integrable and whose solution is known to satisfy any desired condition. Geometrically, this means that while we can find no surface such that every direction on the surface satisfies (3) at each point, we may find curves on an arbitrary surface, such that the direction of each curve satisfies (3).

Exercises

In each of the following, find the equations of the curves which lie on the surface defined by relation (b) and which satisfy the differential equation (a):

1. (a) $2y \, dx - 3x \, dy + z \, dz = 0$,
    (b) $x^2 + y^2 + z^2 = c$.

2. (a) $aby \, dx + abx \, dy - c(ax + by + cz)dz = 0$,
    (b) $ax + by + cz = d$.

3. (a) $x(a \cos^2 y + b \sin^2 y)dx + x^2(b^2 - a^2) \sin y \cos y \, dy + (1 - x^2)^{1/2}dz = 0$,
    (b) $x^2 + z^2 = 1$.

4. (a) $x \, dy - y \, dx + z \, dz = 0$,
    (b) $x = c$.

5. (a) $(y^3 - xy^2)dx + x^2y \, dy + 2z \, dz = 0$,
    (b) $2z^2 = x^2y^2$.

6. (a) $dx = z \, dy + dz$,
    (b) $z = f(y)$.

60. Dependence and functional determinants. Let us consider n functions

$$u'(x_1, \cdots, x_n), \, u''(x_1, \cdots, x_n), \, \cdots, \, u^{(n)}(x_1, \cdots, x_n)$$

of the same n independent variables $x_1, \cdots, x_n$, which have continuous first partial derivatives $u_{x_i}^{(j)}$. If there exists a function $\varphi(u', u'', \cdots, u^{(n)})$ of the n arguments $u', \cdots, u^{(n)}$ having first partial derivatives $\varphi_{u^{(j)}}(j = 1, \cdots, n)$ such that the relation

$$\varphi(u', u'', \cdots, u^{(n)}) \equiv 0 \qquad (29)$$

is satisfied, the functions $u^{(j)}$ are said to be *dependent*. If no such function exists, the functions $u^{(j)}$ are called *independent*.

To find a criterion for the dependence of a set of functions, let us assume that (29) holds, with φ and the $u^{(j)}$ subject to the restrictions cited above. Taking the first partial derivative of each side of (29) with respect to each variable x_i, we obtain thus the n relations

$$\begin{cases} \varphi_{u'} \, u'_{x_1} + \varphi_{u''} \, u''_{x_1} + \cdots + \varphi_{u^{(n)}} \, u^{(n)}_{x_1} \equiv 0, \\ \varphi_{u'} \, u'_{x_2} + \varphi_{u''} \, u''_{x_2} + \cdots + \varphi_{u^{(n)}} \, u^{(n)}_{x_2} \equiv 0, \\ \cdots \cdots \cdots \cdots \cdots \cdots \cdots \cdots \cdots \\ \cdots \cdots \cdots \cdots \cdots \cdots \cdots \cdots \cdots \\ \varphi_{u'} \, u'_{x_n} + \varphi_{u''} \, u''_{x_n} + \cdots + \varphi_{u^{(n)}} \cdot u^{(n)}_{x_n} \equiv 0. \end{cases}$$

In order that these n linear equations in the n derivatives $\varphi_{u^{(j)}}$ hold simultaneously, with $\varphi_{u^{(j)}}$ not all zero, it is necessary and sufficient that the determinant of the coefficients vanish identically, *i. e.*,

$$\begin{vmatrix} u'_{x_1} & u''_{x_1} & \cdots & u^{(n)}_{x_1} \\ u'_{x_2} & u''_{x_2} & \cdots & u^{(n)}_{x_2} \\ \cdot & \cdot & \cdots & \cdot \\ \cdot & \cdot & \cdots & \cdot \\ u'_{x_n} & u''_{x_n} & \cdots & u^{(n)}_{x_n} \end{vmatrix} \equiv 0.$$

This determinant is met with very frequently in mathematics, and is known as the *functional determinant* of the functions involved. It is also called their *Jacobian*, in honor of the German mathematician Jacobi (1804–1851), who made important contributions to many branches of pure and applied mathematics.

From the results above, we draw

THEOREM I.   *If* $u^{(j)}(j = 1, \cdots, n)$ *are* n *dependent functions of* n *independent variables* $x_i(i = 1, \cdots, n)$ *having continuous first partial derivatives* $u^{(j)}_{x_i}$, *the Jacobian of the* u's *vanishes identically.*

It can be shown,* conversely, that, if the Jacobian of the u's vanishes identically, the functions are dependent.

In an entirely similar manner we define n functions

$$u', u'', \cdots, u^{(n)}$$

in more than n variables $x_i(i = 1, \cdots, n + t)$, having continuous first partial derivatives $u^{(j)}_{x_i}$, to be *dependent* if there exists a function φ of n arguments, having first partial derivatives with

---

* Wilson's *Advanced Calculus*, page 129 ff.

respect to those arguments, such that (29) holds. Under these circumstances we may form the system

$$
\begin{cases}
\varphi_{u'} \, u'_{x_1} + \cdots + \varphi_{u^{(n)}} \, u^{(n)}_{x_1} \equiv 0, \\
\cdots \cdots \cdots \cdots \cdots \cdots \\
\varphi_{u'} \, u'_{x_m} + \cdots + \varphi_{u^{(n)}} \, u^{(n)}_{x_m} \equiv 0 \qquad (m = n + t),
\end{cases}
$$

of m equations in n functions $\varphi_{u^{(j)}}$. Since $m > n$, we can find solutions* with $\varphi_{u^{(j)}}$ not all zero if, and only if, the matrix of coefficients

$$
\begin{pmatrix}
u'_{x_1} & \cdots & u^{(n)}_{x_1}, \\
\cdots & \cdots & \cdots \\
u'_{x_m} & \cdots & u^{(n)}_{x_m},
\end{pmatrix}
\tag{30}
$$

has a rank† less than n, and this is therefore a necessary condition for the dependence of the functions $u^{(j)}$. We shall employ this result without the formality of stating it in a theorem.

The converse of the above proposition is also true, as can be established by adjoining to the matrix (30) $m - n$ new columns

$$
\begin{matrix}
u^{(n+1)}_{x_1} & \cdots & u^{(m)}_{x_1} \\
\cdots & \cdots & \cdots \\
u^{(n+1)}_{x_m} & \cdots & u^{(m)}_{x_m},
\end{matrix}
$$

where $u^{(n+1)}, \cdots, u^{(m)}$ are arbitrary functions, and then applying the converse of Theorem 1.

61. Determinate systems involving several variables. Let us consider n simultaneous equations

$$
u^{(j)} = c_j \qquad (j = 1, \cdots, n), \quad (31)
$$

where the $u^{(j)}$ are n independent functions of the variables $z, x_1, \cdots, x_n$, as the *solution* of the system of ordinary differential equations

$$
\begin{cases}
u'_z \, dz + u'_{x_1} \, dx_1 + \cdots + u'_{x_n} \, dx_n = 0, \\
u''_z \, dz + u''_{x_1} \, dx_1 + \cdots + u''_{x_n} \, dx_n = 0, \\
\cdots \cdots \cdots \cdots \cdots \cdots \cdots \cdots \cdots \\
\cdots \cdots \cdots \cdots \cdots \cdots \cdots \cdots \cdots \\
u^{(n)}_z \, dz + u^{(n)}_{x_1} \, dx_1 + \cdots + u^{(n)}_{x_n} \, dx_n = 0.
\end{cases}
\tag{32}
$$

---

* Bocher's *Higher Algebra*, page 47, Theorem 3.

† If at least one r-rowed determinant of a matrix is not zero (identically), while every determinant of order higher than r is zero (identically), the matrix is said to have the *rank r*.

We can solve this system for the ratios of the differentials, and obtain

$$\frac{dz}{X_0} = \frac{dx_1}{X_1} = \frac{dx_2}{X_2} = \cdots = \frac{dx_n}{X_n}, \tag{33}$$

where

$$
\begin{aligned}
X_0 &\equiv |u_{x_1}^{(j)} \, u_{x_2}^{(j)} \, u_{x_3}^{(j)} \cdots u_{x_n}^{(j)}|, \\
X_1 &\equiv - |u_z^{(j)} \, u_{x_2}^{(j)} \, u_{x_3}^{(j)} \cdots u_{x_n}^{(j)}|, \\
X_2 &\equiv |u_z^{(j)} \, u_{x_1}^{(j)} \, u_{x_3}^{(j)} \cdots u_{x_n}^{(j)}|, \\
&\; \cdots \cdots \cdots \cdots \cdots \cdots \cdots \cdots \\
X_n &\equiv (-1)^n |u_z^{(j)} \, u_{x_1}^{(j)} \, u_{x_2}^{(j)} \cdots u_{x_{n-1}}^{(j)}|,
\end{aligned}
\tag{34}
$$

the symbols on the right representing determinants, of which the jth row is displayed. The functions $X_i(i = 0, \cdots, n)$ cannot all be zero, since in that case the n-rowed matrix whose j^{th} row is

$$(u_z^{(j)} \, u_{x_1}^{(j)} \, u_{x_2}^{(j)} \, u_{x_3}^{(j)} \cdots u_{x_n}^{(j)}) \tag{35}$$

would have a rank less than n, and the functions $u^{(i)}$ would be dependent, which is contrary to the hypothesis. In the event that $X_i \equiv 0$ for $i = i_0, i_1, \cdots, i_p$ and $X_i \not\equiv 0$ for $i = i_{p+1}, \cdots, i_n$ we shall understand (33) to mean

$$
\begin{aligned}
dx_{i_e} &= 0 \qquad\qquad\qquad (e = 0, \cdots, p), \\
\frac{dx_{i_{p+1}}}{X_{i_{p+1}}} &= \frac{dx_{i_{p+2}}}{X_{i_{p+2}}} = \cdots = \frac{dx_{i_n}}{X_{i_n}},
\end{aligned}
$$

where z is denoted by x_0.

The n simultaneous equations (31) define a system of *curves* in space of $n + 1$ *dimensions*. The ratios $dz:dx_1:dx_2: \cdots :dx_n$ are uniquely determined for every *point* $(z, x_1, \cdots, x_n)$ for which the X_i do not all vanish, and are said to define a *direction*. The curves defined by (31) are called the *characteristics* of the system (32). A single characteristic is, thus, the locus of points which satisfy all of the equations (31) with a set of particular values assigned to the n arbitrary constants c_j. The coördinates of any fixed point $(\zeta, \xi_1, \xi_2, \cdots, \xi_n)$ satisfy all equations (31) with $c_j = u^{(i)}(\zeta, \xi_1, \cdots, \xi_n)$, and hence there is one, and only one, characteristic through each point.

If, now, we set up n independent functions $v^{(j)}(j = 1, \cdots, n)$ of the u's of (31) and form the n equations

$$v^{(j)} = d_j \qquad (j = 1, \cdots, n) \tag{36}$$

and form from (36) the system

$$\frac{dz}{Y_0} = \frac{dx_1}{Y_1} = \frac{dx_2}{Y_2} = \cdots = \frac{dx_n}{Y_n} \tag{37}$$

Corresponding to (33), we have

$$Y_0 \equiv \left| v_{x_1}^{(j)} \, v_{x_2}^{(j)} \, \cdots \, v_{x_n}^{(j)} \right|,$$
$$Y_1 \equiv - \left| v_z^{(j)} \, v_{x_2}^{(j)} \, \cdots \, v_{x_n}^{(j)} \right|,$$
$$\cdot \quad \cdot \quad \cdot \quad \cdot \quad \cdot \quad \cdot \quad \cdot \quad \cdot$$
$$Y_n \equiv (-1)^n \left| v_z^{(j)} \, v_{x_1}^{(j)} \, \cdots \, v_{x_{n-1}}^{(j)} \right|.$$

Now, since

$$v_{x_i}^{(j)} = v_{u'}^{(j)} \, u'_{x_i} + v_{u''}^{(j)} \, u''_{x_i} + \cdots + v_{u^{(n)}}^{(j)} \, u_{x_i}^{(n)},$$

the element in the jth row and i^{th} column of the determinant

$$\left| v_{x_1}^{(j)} \, v_{x_2}^{(j)} \, \cdots \, v_{x_n}^{(j)} \right|$$

defining Y_0, is the sum of the products of the corresponding elements from the jth row of

$$\Delta \equiv \left| v_{u'}^{(j)} \, v_{u''}^{(j)} \, \cdots \, v_{u^{(n)}}^{(j)} \right|$$

and the ith column of

$$X_0 \equiv \left| u_{x_1}^{(j)} \, u_{x_2}^{(j)} \, \cdots \, u_{x_n}^{(j)} \right|.$$

Thus, by the rule for the product of determinants,

$$Y_0 \equiv \Delta X_0.$$

Similarly,

$$Y_i \equiv \Delta X_i \qquad\qquad (i = 1, \cdots, n),$$

and since the functions $v^{(j)}$ are independent, their Jacobian Δ is not zero, and we may reduce (37) to (33) by multiplying its members by Δ.

Let us now note that all points on the characteristic passing through $(\zeta, \xi_1 \cdots, \xi_n)$ satisfy all equations

$$u^{(j)} = u^{(j)}(\zeta, \xi_1, \cdots, \xi_n) = C_j \quad (j = 1, \cdots, n).$$

They therefore satisfy all equations

$$v^{(j)} = v^{(j)}(C_1, C_2, \cdots, C_n) \quad (j = 1, \cdots, n),$$

and hence the characteristics can be defined by the simultaneous equations (36).

In the light of the above discussions, we may conclude that any function ϕ of a set of one or more functions $u^{(j)}$, where $u^{(j)} = C_j$ is a solution of (33) for every j, may be used to form the relation

$$\phi(u', u'', \cdots, u^{(n)}) = 0, \tag{38}$$

which will, in turn, be a solution of (33). Lagrange called the relation (38) the general solution of (33) if the $u^{(j)}$ were independent.

We have seen that (38) always provides a solution.   Now, if

$$w(z, x_1, \cdots, x_n) = 0$$

is a solution, then the equation

$$w_z \, dz + w_{x_1} \, dx_1 + \cdots + w_{x_n} \, dx_n = 0$$

is satisfied by the values of the differentials dz, dx_i, which satisfy (32).   Then, since not all these are zero, the determinant of the coefficients

$$\begin{vmatrix} w_z & w_{x_1} & \cdots & w_{x_n} \\ u'_z & u'_{x_1} & \cdots & u'_{x_n} \\ \cdot & \cdot & \cdots & \cdot \\ \cdot & \cdot & \cdots & \cdot \\ u_z^{(n)} & u_{x_1}^{(n)} & \cdots & u_{x_n}^{(n)} \end{vmatrix}$$

vanishes.   But this is the Jacobian of the $n + 1$ functions w, $u^{(j)}$, which are therefore dependent.   Hence, w is a function of the $u^{(j)}$, and the solution $w = 0$ is included in the general solution of (38).

Now every point on the characteristic through the point $(\zeta, \xi_1, \cdots, \xi_n)$ satisfies the equations

$$u^{(j)} = u^{(j)}(\zeta, \xi_1, \cdots, \xi_n) = C_j \quad (j = 1, \cdots, n)$$

and hence satisfies

$$\phi(u', \cdots, u^{(n)}) = \phi(C_1, \cdots, C_n),$$

so that any solution of (33) is seen to be a locus of characteristics. It can be shown, conversely, that every locus of characteristics of (33) is a solution.

62. Jacobi's multipliers.   An interesting generalization of the notion of an integrating factor is afforded by Jacobi's multipliers. Notice that if the equation

$$X \, dy - Y \, dx = 0 \tag{39}$$

is exact, then

$$X_x \equiv -Y_y$$

Notice that (39) may be written

$$\frac{dx}{X} = \frac{dy}{Y},$$

and that the test for exactness of (39) may be written

$$X_x + Y_y \equiv 0. \tag{40}$$

If this condition holds, there exists a function u such that

$$u_x \equiv Y \text{ and } u_y \equiv -X,$$

and the equation may be written

$$\frac{dy}{u_x} = \frac{dx}{-u_y}.$$

Note, now, that Y is obtained by striking out the first column from the matrix

$$(u_y \; u_x),$$

and that X is obtained by striking out the second column of the same matrix and changing the sign. In an entirely analogous manner the X_0 of (33) is the determinant obtained by striking the first column from the matrix (35), X_1 is obtained by striking out the second column and changing the sign of the determinant remaining, and so on. If a set of n independent functions $u^{(i)}$ exists, by means of which the X's of a given system of the form (33) can be obtained, the system is said to have the property of *generalized exactness*. In seeking a test for this generalized exactness, let us study an example.

Take as the functions

$$u' \equiv x + y + z,$$
$$u'' \equiv x^2 y.$$

Then the system analogous to (33) determined by

$$u' = c_1,$$
$$u'' = c_2,$$

is

$$\frac{dz}{X_0} = \frac{dx_1}{X_1} = \frac{dx_2}{X_2},$$

where

$$X_0 \equiv x^2 - 2xy,$$
$$X_1 \equiv -x^2,$$
$$X_2 \equiv 2xy.$$

Let us form, as a possible generalization of (40), the condition

$$\frac{\partial X_0}{\partial z} + \frac{\partial X_1}{\partial x_1} + \frac{\partial X_2}{\partial x_2} = 0$$

We note that it is satisfied identically in this case. To generalize this we shall establish

THEOREM II. *If a set of functions* $u^{(j)}(j = 1, \cdots, n)$ *exists such that* X_i $(i = 0, \cdots, n)$ *are defined as in* (34), *then*

$$\frac{\partial X_0}{\partial z} + \frac{\partial X_1}{\partial x_1} + \cdots + \frac{\partial X_n}{\partial x_n} \equiv 0. \qquad (41)$$

The X_i in (41) can be thought of as replaced by their values given by (34), and if we denote z by x_0, we can say that the partial derivative $u_{x_i x_l}^{(j)}$ comes only from the jth rows of the determinants, forming the X's and the columns containing $u_{x_i}^{(j)}$ or $u_{x_l}^{(j)}$. To obtain the terms in $u_{x_0 x_1}^{(j)}$, write

$$\frac{\partial X_0}{\partial x_0} \equiv \frac{\partial}{\partial x_0} \left| u_{x_1}^{(j)} \ u_{x_2}^{(j)} \cdots u_{x_n}^{(j)} \right|,$$

$$\frac{\partial X_1}{\partial x_1} \equiv - \frac{\partial}{\partial x_1} \left| u_{x_0}^{(j)} \ u_{x_2}^{(j)} \cdots u_{x_n}^{(j)} \right|,$$

and expand according to the elements in the jth row, to obtain

$$(-1)^{j-1} \frac{\partial X_0}{\partial x_0} \equiv \frac{\partial}{\partial x_0} \left[u_{x_1}^{(j)} \left| u_{x_2}^{(l)} \cdots u_{x_n}^{(l)} \right| + \cdots \right], \qquad (l \neq j)$$

$$(-1)^{j-1} \frac{\partial X_1}{\partial x_1} \equiv - \frac{\partial}{\partial x_1} \left[u_{x_0}^{(j)} \left| u_{x_2}^{(l)} \cdots u_{x_n}^{(l)} \right| + \cdots \right], \qquad (l \neq j)$$

then the term

$$u_{x_0 x_1}^{(j)}$$

drops out of the sum (41). Similarly for every term $u_{x_i x_k}^{(j)}$, with $i \neq k$. Since X_i contains no derivative $u_{x_i}^{(j)}$, no terms of the type $u_{x_i x_i}^{(j)}$ enter into (41). Hence Theorem II.

The theorem just proved is true conversely in the form of

THEOREM III. *If* X_i $(i = 0, \cdots, n)$ *are* n + 1 *functions of* z, x_1, $\cdots$, x_n *such that*

$$\frac{\partial X_0}{\partial z} + \frac{\partial X_1}{\partial x_1} + \frac{\partial X_2}{\partial x_2} + \cdots + \frac{\partial X_n}{\partial x_n} \equiv 0, \qquad (41)$$

there exist functions u′, u″, $\cdots$, $u^{(n)}$ *of the variables* z, x_1, $\cdots$, x_n *such that the* X_i *are given by* (34).

To prove this we shall assume* that

$$v^{(j)}(z, \ x_1, \cdots, x_n) \qquad (j = 1, \cdots, n)$$

are n independent functions such that

$$v^{(j)} = c_j$$

_____

*To show that such solutions exist is beyond the scope of this book.

furnish the solution to the system

$$\frac{dz}{X_0} = \frac{dx_1}{X_1} = \cdots = \frac{dx_n}{X_n}. \tag{42}$$

Then, as we have seen before,

$$\begin{aligned}
Y_0 &\equiv \left| v_{x_1}^{(j)} \, v_{x_2}^{(j)} \, \cdots \, v_{x_n}^{(j)} \right| &&\equiv \Delta X_0, \\
Y_1 &\equiv - \left| v_z^{(j)} \, v_{x_2}^{(j)} \, \cdots \, v_{x_n}^{(j)} \right| &&\equiv \Delta X_1,
\end{aligned}$$

$$\cdots\cdots\cdots\cdots\cdots\cdots\cdots\cdots\cdots$$

$$Y_n \equiv (-1)^n \left| v_z^{(j)} \, v_{x_1}^{(j)} \, \cdots \, v_{x_{n-1}}^{(j)} \right| \equiv \Delta X_n,$$

$$\Delta \not\equiv 0.$$

Let us employ the notation

$$X(y) \equiv X_0 y_z + X_1 y_{x_1} + \cdots + X_n y_{x_n}.$$

Then,

$$\begin{aligned}
\Delta \cdot X(y) &\equiv \Delta X_0 y_z + \Delta X_1 y_{x_1} + \cdots + \Delta X_n y_{x_n} \\
&\equiv Y_0 y_z + Y_1 y_{x_1} + \cdots + Y_n y_{x_n},
\end{aligned}$$

or

$$\Delta \cdot X(y) \equiv \begin{vmatrix} y_z & y_{x_1} & \cdots & y_{x_n} \\ v_z' & v_{x_1}' & \cdots & v_{x_n}' \\ \cdots & \cdots & \cdots & \cdots \\ v_z^{(n)} & v_{x_1}^{(n)} & \cdots & v_{x_n}^{(n)} \end{vmatrix}. \tag{43}$$

Now, from Theorem II we see that

$$\frac{\partial}{\partial z}(Y_0) + \frac{\partial}{\partial x_1}(Y_1) + \frac{\partial}{\partial x_2}(Y_2) + \cdots + \frac{\partial}{\partial x_n}(Y_n) \equiv 0,$$

and, since

$$Y_i \equiv \Delta X_i \qquad (i = 0, 1, \cdots, n),$$

$$X_0 \frac{\partial \Delta}{\partial z} + X_1 \frac{\partial \Delta}{\partial x_1} + \cdots + X_n \frac{\partial \Delta}{\partial x_n}$$

$$+ \Delta \left(\frac{\partial X_0}{\partial z} + \frac{\partial X_1}{\partial x_1} + \cdots + \frac{\partial X_n}{\partial x_n} \right) \equiv 0$$

or

$$X(\Delta) \equiv 0,$$

because the principal hypothesis of this theorem states that the coefficient of Δ in this equation vanishes identically. Let us now employ the multipliers $\Delta_z, \Delta_{x_1}, \cdots, \Delta_{x_n}$ upon the system (42) to obtain

$$\frac{dz}{X_0} = \frac{dx_1}{X_1} = \cdots = \frac{dx_n}{X_n} = \frac{\Delta_z\, dz + \Delta_{x_1}\, dx_1 + \cdots + \Delta_{x_n}\, dx_n}{X_0 \Delta_z + X_1 \Delta_{x_1} + \cdots + X_n \Delta_{x_n}}.$$

The last denominator is $X(\Delta)$, and has been shown to be zero; therefore the numerator is zero and

$$\Delta = 0$$

is a solution of the system (42). Then, by Section 61, Δ is a function of the $v^{(j)}$, say

$$\Delta \equiv \phi(v', v'', \cdots, v^{(n)}).$$

Now let us define a function $V^{(n)}$ by the quadrature

$$V^{(n)} \equiv \int \frac{dv^{(n)}}{\phi(v', \cdots, v^{(n)})},$$

evaluated with $v', v'', \cdots, v^{(n-1)}$ held constant, or

$$\frac{1}{\Delta} \equiv \frac{1}{\phi(v', v'', \cdots, v^{(n)})} \tag{44}$$

$$\equiv \frac{\partial V^{(n)}}{\partial v^{(n)}} \equiv \begin{vmatrix} 1 & 0 & 0 & \cdots & 0 & 0 \\ 0 & 1 & 0 & \cdots & 0 & 0 \\ 0 & 0 & 1 & \cdots & 0 & 0 \\ \cdots & \cdots & \cdots & \cdots & \cdots & \cdots \\ \cdots & \cdots & \cdots & \cdots & \cdots & \cdots \\ 0 & 0 & 0 & \cdots & 1 & 0 \\ V^{(n)}_y & V^{(n)}_{v'} & V^{(n)}_{v''} & \cdots & V^{(n)}_{v^{(n-1)}} & V^{(n)}_{v^{(n)}} \end{vmatrix}.$$

Upon multiplying (43) by (44), we have

$$X(y) \equiv \begin{vmatrix} 1 & 0 & 0 & \cdots & 0 & 0 \\ 0 & 1 & 0 & \cdots & 0 & 0 \\ 0 & 0 & 1 & \cdots & 0 & 0 \\ \cdots & \cdots & \cdots & \cdots & \cdots & \cdots \\ \cdots & \cdots & \cdots & \cdots & \cdots & \cdots \\ 0 & 0 & 0 & \cdots & 1 & 0 \\ V^{(n)}_y & V^{(n)}_{v'} & V^{(n)}_{v''} & \cdots & V^{(n)}_{v^{(n-1)}} & V^{(n)}_{v^{(n)}} \end{vmatrix} \cdot \begin{vmatrix} y_z & y_{x_1} & y_{x_2} & \cdots & y_{x_n} \\ v'_z & v'_{x_1} & v'_{x_2} & \cdots & v'_{x_n} \\ v''_z & v''_{x_1} & v''_{x_2} & \cdots & v''_{x_n} \\ \cdots & \cdots & \cdots & \cdots & \cdots \\ v^{(n)}_z & v^{(n)}_{x_1} & v^{(n)}_{x_2} & \cdots & v^{(n)}_{x_n} \end{vmatrix}$$

$$\equiv \begin{vmatrix} y_z & y_{x_1} & \cdots & y_{x_n} \\ v'_z & v'_{x_1} & \cdots & v'_{x_n} \\ v''_z & v''_{x_1} & \cdots & v''_{x_n} \\ \cdots & \cdots & \cdots & \cdots \\ v^{(n-1)}_z & v^{(n-1)}_{x_1} & \cdots & v^{(n-1)}_{x_n} \\ V^{(n)}_z & V^{(n)}_{x_1} & \cdots & V^{(n)}_{x_n} \end{vmatrix}$$

$$\equiv X_0 y_z + X_1 y_{x_1} + \cdots + X_n y_{x_n},$$

where the X_i are of the form (34), with $u^{(j)}$ replaced by $v^{(j)}$ ($j = 1, \cdots, n - 1$) and $u^{(n)}$ replaced by $V^{(n)}$. Hence Theorem III.

If the X_i in a system such as (42) do not have the property of generalized exactness, but the functions MX_i do have that property, then M is said to be a *multiplier* for the system.

63. Indeterminate systems. We have seen that a system of equations of the form

$$\begin{cases} u_{10}\,dz + u_{11}\,dx_1 + \cdots + u_{1n}\,dx_n = 0, \\ u_{20}\,dz + u_{21}\,dx_1 + \cdots + u_{2n}\,dx_n = 0, \\ \cdots\cdots\cdots\cdots\cdots\cdots\cdots\cdots \\ \cdots\cdots\cdots\cdots\cdots\cdots\cdots\cdots \\ u_{n0}\,dz + u_{n1}\,dx_1 + \cdots + u_{nn}\,dx_n = 0, \end{cases}$$

determines a unique direction

$$dz:dx_1:dx_2: \cdots :dx_n$$

through each point $(z,\ x_1,\ x_2,\ \cdots,\ x_n)$ if the matrix whose j^{th} row is

$$(u_{j0}\ u_{j1}\ \cdots\ u_{jn})$$

has the rank n for the point; and that the system (32) has a complete solution in the form of a system of n relations

$$v^{(j)}(z,\ x_1,\ x_2,\ \cdots,\ x_n) = c_j \quad (j = 1,\ \cdots,\ n).$$

We have also seen that a single equation of the form

$$P\,dx + Q\,dy + R\,dz = 0$$

does not always have a solution, and never determines a unique direction

$$dx:dy:dz.$$

In the same way a system

$$\begin{cases} u_{10}\,dz + u_{11}\,dx_1 + \cdots + u_{1n}\,dx_n = 0, \\ u_{20}\,dz + u_{21}\,dx_1 + \cdots + u_{2n}\,dx_n = 0, \\ \cdots\cdots\cdots\cdots\cdots\cdots\cdots\cdots \\ \cdots\cdots\cdots\cdots\cdots\cdots\cdots\cdots \\ u_{m0}\,dz + u_{m1}\,dx_1 + \cdots + u_{mn}\,dx_n = 0, \end{cases} \quad (0 < m < n), \quad (45)$$

does not determine a unique direction through each point. In fact, if the rank of matrix

$$\begin{vmatrix} u_{10} & u_{11} & \cdots & u_{1n} \\ u_{20} & u_{21} & \cdots & u_{2n} \\ \cdot & \cdot & \cdots & \cdot \\ \cdot & \cdot & \cdots & \cdot \\ u_{m0} & u_{m1} & \cdots & u_{mn} \end{vmatrix} \qquad (46)$$

is r at a given point $(z, x_1, \cdots, x_n)$, then $n + 1 - r$ of the quantities $dz, dx_1, \cdots, dx_n$ may be assigned arbitrarily,* and the remaining r may be expressed linearly in terms of them.   If the matrix (46) has the rank r, the system (45) may be satisfied, in some cases, identically by a system of r relations of the form

$$v^{(j)}(z, x_1, \cdots, x_n) = c_j \qquad (j = 1, \cdots, r),$$

but this will not always be true.   We shall call the system *integrable* in the former case, and *non-integrable* in the latter case.   If the matrix (46) has the rank r, and the system (45) is *nonintegrable*, the system may be augmented by $n - r$ arbitrary equations such that the matrix of the augmented system will have rank n.   The augmented system will be integrable.

64. Exercises.

1. Test the following sets of functions for dependence:

(a) $u' \equiv z + x_1 + x_2 + x_3,\ u'' \equiv z^2 + x_1^2 + x_2^2 + x_3^2,$
$u''' \equiv z(x_1 + x_2 + x_3).$

(b) $u' \equiv zx_1x_2x_3x_4,\ u'' \equiv zx_1,\ u''' \equiv zx_2\ u^{iv} \equiv zx_3x_4.$

(c) $u' \equiv zx_1,\ u'' \equiv zx_1 + x_2,\ u''' \equiv z(x_1 + x_2).$

(d) $u' \equiv ze^{x_1},\ u'' \equiv ze^{x_2},\ u''' \equiv z^2e^{x_1+x_2}.$

(e) $u' \equiv z + x_1 + x_2 + x_3 + x_4,\ u'' \equiv z^2 + x_1^2 + x_2^2 + x_3^2 + x_4^2,\ u''' \equiv z(x_1 + x_2 + x_3 + x_4) + x_1(x_2 + x_3 + x_4) + x_2(x_3 + x_4) + x_3x_4.$

2. For each of the five exercises above, form the system of ordinary differential equations having as solutions the functions displayed in that exercise.   Where possible, put the system in the form

$$\frac{dz}{X_0} = \frac{dx_1}{X_1} = \cdots = \frac{dx_n}{X_n}.$$

3. Test the system

$$\frac{dz}{0} = \frac{dx_1}{-z^2} = \frac{dx_2}{z^2} = \frac{dx_3}{z^2} = \frac{dx_4}{-z^2}$$

for generalized exactness.   If it is exact, find the four functions u', u'', u''', u^{iv} such that

$$X_0 \equiv 0,\ X_1 \equiv -z^2,\ X_2 \equiv z^2,\ X_3 \equiv z^2,\ X_4 \equiv -z^2.$$

---

* Dickson's *First Course* in the Theory of Equations, page 119.

4. Solve the system

$$\frac{dz}{-z} = \frac{dx_1}{2x_1} = \frac{dx_2}{-x_2}, = \frac{dx_3}{0}.$$

5. Solve the system

$$\frac{dx_1}{x_1} = \frac{dx_2}{x_3 + x_4} = \frac{dx_3}{x_2 + x_4} = \frac{dx_4}{x_2 + x_3}.$$

6. Solve the system

$$\frac{dx_1}{x_2 + x_3 + x_4 + x_5} = \frac{dx_2}{x_1 + x_3 + x_4 + x_5} = \frac{dx_3}{x_1 + x_2 + x_4 + x_5}$$
$$= \frac{dx_4}{x_1 + x_2 + x_3 + x_5} = \frac{dx_5}{x_1 + x_2 + x_3 + x_4}.$$

7. Solve the system

$$\frac{dz}{az} = \frac{dx_1}{x_1} . = \frac{dx_2}{x_2} = \frac{dx_3}{x_3}.$$

8. Solve the system

$$\frac{dx_1}{x_1} =: \frac{dx_2}{x_2} = \frac{dx_3}{x_3} = \frac{x_3 \, dx_4}{ax_4 x_3 + x_1 x_2}.$$

9. Find a multiplier for the system

$$\frac{dx}{x(y - z)} = \frac{dy}{y(z - x)} = \frac{dz}{z(x - y)}.$$

10. Find a multiplier for the system

$$\frac{dx}{-x} = \frac{dy}{y} = \frac{dz}{(x - y)\left(2 + \dfrac{z}{x + y}\right)}.$$

11. Prove that if M and N are two multipliers of the system

$$\frac{dx}{X_0} = \frac{dx_1}{X_1} = \cdots = \frac{dx_n}{X_n},$$

where N is not identically equal to M times a constant, then $\dfrac{M}{N} = C$ is a solution of the system.

12. Show that the condition

$$XY(Z_t - T_z) + YZ(T_x - X_t) + ZT(X_y - Y_x) + TX(Y_z - Z_y)$$
$$\equiv 0$$

is necessary for the integrability of the equation

$$X\,dx + Y\,dy + Z\,dz + T\,dt = 0.$$

13. Solve the system

$$\begin{cases} yzw\,dx + xzw\,dy + xyw\,dz + xyz\,dw = 0, \\ (2xy + w^2)dx + (2yz + x^2)dy + (2zw + y^2)dz + (2wx + z^2)dw \\ \qquad = 0, \\ 2xy\,dx + (2yz + x^2 - z)dy + (2zw + y^2 - y)dz + z^2\,dw = 0. \end{cases}$$

14. Solve the system

$$\begin{cases} (yw + zw)dx + w\,dy + w\,dz + (y + z)dw = 0, \\ (1 - yw - zw)dx + (z - w)dy + y\,dz - y\,dw = 0, \\ 2yz\,dx + xz\,dy + xy\,dz = 0. \end{cases}$$

CHAPTER VIII

Partial Differential Equations of the First Order

65. Illustrations and definitions. Let us consider z to be a function of two independent variables x and y, defined by the relation

$$x^2y + az + by = 0. \tag{1}$$

If we differentiate partially with respect to x and y, we obtain the relations

$$\begin{cases} 2xy + a\,z_x = 0, \\ x^2 + a\,z_y + b = 0. \end{cases} \tag{2}$$

We may eliminate a and b from equations (1) and (2) by multiplying (1) by z_x, (2_1) by $yz_y - z$, and (2_2) by $-yz_x$, adding the three resulting equations, and dividing out $2xy$, to obtain a partial differential equation

$$y\,z_y - z = 0, \tag{3}$$

of which (1) is a solution for any constant values of a and b.

If, now, we separate the variables in equation (3), writing the equation in the form

$$\frac{z_y}{z} - \frac{1}{y} = 0,$$

and integrate partially with respect to y, we obtain

$$\log z - \log y = \phi(x),$$

where $\phi(x)$ is an arbitrary function of x. This can be put in the form

$$\frac{z}{y} = e^{\phi(x)},$$

or

$$z = y\,f(x), \tag{4}$$

where $f(x) \equiv e^{\phi(x)}$. Equation (4) is a *solution* of the partial differential equation (3), as we shall see by direct differentiation, and it is what we shall later define as the *general* solution. By differentiating with respect to y, we obtain the equation

$$z_y = f(x),$$

between which and (4), $f(x)$ may be eliminated to give (3). The original equation (1) is a special case of (4), as we can see by solving (1) for z to obtain

$$z = y\left(-\frac{x^2}{a} - \frac{b}{a}\right).$$

We notice that (4) can be written in the form

$$\frac{z}{y} = f(x),$$

where f is an arbitrary function of one argument, and that this equation in turn is equivalent to

$$\phi\left(\frac{z}{y}, x\right) = 0,$$

where ϕ is an arbitrary function of two arguments, since the last equation can be solved for its first argument $\frac{z}{y}$ in terms of its second argument x.

As a generalization of (4) we may take the relation

$$\phi(u, v) = 0, \tag{5}$$

where u and v are known independent functions of x, y, and z, while ϕ denotes an arbitrary function of two arguments. For every choice of the function ϕ, for which $\phi_z \neq 0$, equation (5) defines* a function $z = f(x, y)$, and we may form the partial derivatives z_x and z_y directly from (5), obtaining

$$\begin{cases} \phi_u(u_x + u_z z_x) + \phi_v(v_x + v_z z_x) = 0, \\ \phi_u(u_y + u_z z_y) + \phi_v(v_y + v_z z_y) = 0, \end{cases}$$

from which the quantities ϕ_u and ϕ_v may easily be eliminated to give

$$(v_x + v_z z_x)(u_y + u_z z_y) = (v_y + v_z z_y)(u_x + u_z z_x),$$

or, when coefficients of z_x and z_y are collected,

$$z_x(u_y v_z - u_z v_y) + z_y(u_z v_x - u_x v_z) - (u_x v_y - u_y v_x) = 0.$$

_____

* Wilson's *Advanced Calculus*, page 123.

The functions u and v and their derivatives being known functions, we write the above equation in the form

$$P Z_x + Q Z_y = R, \tag{6}$$

known as a *linear* partial differential equation, where

$$
\begin{aligned}
P &\equiv \lambda(u_y v_z - u_z v_y), \\
Q &\equiv \lambda(u_z v_x - u_x v_z), \\
R &\equiv \lambda(u_x v_y - u_y v_x), \\
\lambda &\not\equiv 0.
\end{aligned}
$$

By substitution we can verify that $u = c$ satisfies (6), as does $v = c$. A relation $u = 0$, where u is a known function of x, y, and z having $u_z \not\equiv 0$, which satisfies (6) identically, is called a *particular solution* of (6). An arbitrary functional relationship between u and v, such as (5), is called the *general solution* of (6) if $u = 0$ and $v = 0$ are particular solutions, while u and v are independent functions. A relation such as

$$f(x, y, z, a, b) = 0,$$

which has two arbitrary constants and has $f_z \not\equiv 0$ and which satisfies (6) for all values of those constants, is called a *complete solution* of (6).

66. Lagrange's equations. In Section 66 we employed two independent functions u and v of three variables x, y, and z, to build up equation

$$P Z_x + Q Z_y = R, \tag{6}$$

whose general solution is

$$\phi(u, v) = 0. \tag{5}$$

Let us now employ the same functions u and v to build up a system of ordinary differential equations whose solution is

$$
\begin{cases}
u = c_1, \\
v = c_2.
\end{cases}
$$

Taking the differentials, we obtain

$$
\begin{cases}
u_x \, dx + u_y \, dy + u_z \, dz = 0, \\
v_x \, dx + v_y \, dy + v_z \, dz = 0.
\end{cases}
$$

This system can be put into the symmetric form

$$\frac{dx}{u_y v_z - u_z v_y} = \frac{dy}{u_z v_x - u_x v_z} = \frac{dz}{u_x v_y - u_y v_x},$$

or, if we multiply through by $\frac{1}{\lambda}$, into the form

$$\frac{dx}{P} = \frac{dy}{Q} = \frac{dz}{R},\tag{7}$$

where P, Q, and R are the same functions as in (6).   We shall refer to (7) as the *Lagrange system* corresponding to (6).

Since u and v are independent functions, not all of P, Q, and R are zero, as otherwise the matrix

$$\begin{pmatrix} u_x & u_y & u_z \\ v_x & v_y & v_z \end{pmatrix}$$

would have rank less than 2.   If some of P, Q, and R are zero, we understand the system to mean that the corresponding numerators are zero, as we did in the preceding chapter.

Since we know how to solve a system like (7), it at once occurs that, if we are given an equation of the form (6) to be solved, we may set up the corresponding system (7), may find two solutions, $u = c_1$, $v = c_2$, such that u and v are independent functions, and with these functions u and v we may set up the general solution (5). It is obvious that any two such functions u and v satisfying (7) will determine P, Q, and R uniquely except for a factor, that they will therefore determine (6) uniquely except for a factor, and that, hence, they will furnish the general solution of the form (5).

Illustration

To find the general solution of the linear partial differential equation

$$x\,z_x + y\,z_y = z,\tag{8}$$

note that it is of the form (6), with $P \equiv x$, $Q \equiv y$, and $R \equiv z$, and that the corresponding Lagrange system is

$$\frac{dx}{x} = \frac{dy}{y} = \frac{dz}{z}.\tag{9}$$

An obvious solution of (9) is

$$\frac{z}{x} = a, \frac{z}{y} = b,$$

from which we form the general solution

$$\phi\left(\frac{z}{x}, \frac{z}{y}\right) = 0\tag{10}$$

of the form (5). We may verify directly that (10) will satisfy (8) by differentiating to obtain

$$\begin{cases} \phi_u\left(-\dfrac{z}{x^2}+\dfrac{z_x}{x}\right)+\phi_v\left(\dfrac{z_x}{y}\right)=0, \\[2ex] \phi_u\left(\dfrac{z_y}{x}\right)+\phi_v\left(-\dfrac{z}{y^2}+\dfrac{z_y}{y}\right)=0. \end{cases}$$

From these, eliminate the ratio $\phi_u:\phi_v$, and obtain

$$\frac{z_x z_y}{xy}=\frac{z_x z_y}{xy}-\frac{z z_x}{xy^2}-\frac{z z_y}{x^2 y}+\frac{z^2}{x^2 y^2},$$

or, upon simplifying,

$$x\,z_x+y\,z_y=z.$$

Any other two independent functions u and v, such that $u=a$, $v=b$ furnishes the solution of (9), could have been used just as well in (10).

Exercises

1. Find the general solution of each of the following:

(a) $l\,z_x+m\,z_y=n.$

(b) $x\,z_x+z\,z_y=y.$

(c) $x\,z_x=y.$

(d) $y\,z_x+x\,z_y=5.$

(e) $(ax+by+cz)z_x+(by+cz)z_y=ax.$

(f) $(2z-3y)z_x+(3x-z)z_y=y-2x.$

(g) $(xy+y^2-xz-z^2)z_x+(yz+z^2-yx-x^2)z_y=(zx+x^2-zy-y^2).$

(h) $2yz\,z_x+2xz\,z_y=-xy.$

(i) $\operatorname{ctn} x\,z_x+\operatorname{ctn} y\,z_y=\operatorname{ctn} z.$

(j) $y^2z\,z_x+z^2x\,z_y=-xy^2.$

(k) $3xy\,z_x+z^2 z_y=-yz.$

(l) $(2xy^4-xz^4)z_x+(yz^4-2x^4y)z_y=x^4z-y^4z.$

(m) $x\,z_x+y\,z_y+z=0.$

(n) $x(\operatorname{ctn} z)z_x-y(\operatorname{ctn} z)z_y+1=0.$

2. Find the most general solution of the equation $zz_x-(x+z)z_y=x$ which passes through the point $(1,2,3)$.

3. Find the most general solution of $2z_x-y\,z_y+z=0$ which passes through the point $(0,1,1)$

4. Find the most general solution of $2z_x - y\,z_y + z = 0$ which contains the curve $\begin{cases} x = \log y, \\ y = z \log y. \end{cases}$ *Hint:* If $\begin{cases} u = c_1 \\ v = c_2 \end{cases}$ is the general solution, eliminate x_0, y_0, and z_0 among $u(x, y, z) = u(x_0, y_0, z_0)$, $v(x, y, z) = v(x_0, y_0, z_0)$, $x_0 = \log y_0$, and $y_0 = z_0 \log y_0$.

5. Find the integral surface of

$$(2xy^2 + xz)z_x - (yz + 3x^3y)z_y = 3x^3z - 2y^2z$$

which passes through the parabola $\begin{cases} y^2 = z, \\ x = 2. \end{cases}$

6. Find the integral surface of $4y\,zz_x - z_y + 2y = 0$ which passes through the hyperbola $\begin{cases} x + z = 5, \\ y^2 - z^2 = 9. \end{cases}$

7. Find the integral surfaces of $z_x - y\,z_y + z = 0$ which pass through the curve $\begin{cases} 2(y + z) \cosh x = z^2 + y^2 + 1, \\ 2(y + z) \sinh x = z^2 + y^2 - 1. \end{cases}$

8. Form a linear partial differential equation whose solution is $\phi(z^2 + x^2 + y^2,\ xy\,z) = 0$.

9. Form a linear partial differential equation whose solution is $\phi(x^2e^z,\ ye^z) = 0$.

10. Solve completely $z_x - z_y = 0$.

11. Solve completely $x^2z\,z_x + ye^z\,z_y = 0$.

12. Find the linear partial differential equation of all cylinders not parallel to the z-axis. Write its general solution. *Hint:* Let its elements cut the yz-plane in a curve whose equations are $\begin{cases} x = 0, \\ f(y, z) = 0, \end{cases}$ and let the elements remain parallel to the line $\begin{cases} y = ax, \\ z = bx. \end{cases}$ If $(0, \alpha, \beta)$ are the coördinates of the point where an element cuts the yz-plane, then the equations of the element are $\begin{cases} y = ax + \alpha, \\ z = bx + \beta, \end{cases}$ and (α, β) satisfies the equation $f(\alpha, \beta) = 0$.

13. Find the linear partial differential equation of all cones with vertex at the origin. *Hint:* Let its trace in the plane $x = 1$ be represented by $\begin{cases} x = 1, \\ f(y, z) = 0. \end{cases}$ Write its general solution.

14. Find the linear partial differential equation of all cones with vertex at a given point (a, b, c). Write its general solution.

15. Find the linear partial differential equation of all surfaces of revolution whose axes pass through the origin in a given direction $(\alpha:\beta:\gamma)$, not $(0:0:1)$. *Hint:* Let the axis have equations $\dfrac{x}{\alpha} = \dfrac{y}{\beta} = \dfrac{z}{\gamma}$. Then the plane $\alpha x + \beta y + \gamma z = \delta$, whose distance from $(0, 0, 0)$ is determined by δ, is perpendicular to the axis and meets a sphere with center at the origin in circles whose centers are on the axis.

16. Find the partial differential equation of the surfaces of revolution whose axes go through a given point (a, b, c) in a given direction not parallel to the z-axis.

17. Find the linear partial differential equation of a conoid whose generating line connects a point on the z-axis to a point on the curve $\begin{cases} x = c, \\ f(y, z) = 0, \end{cases}$ and remains parallel to the xy-plane. Write its general solution.

18. Show that the ordinary differential equation $M\,dx + N\,dy = 0$ treated in Chapter II has an infinite number of integrating factors. *Hint:* If μ is an integrating factor of $M\,dx + N\,dy = 0$, then $\dfrac{\partial}{\partial y}(\mu M) = \dfrac{\partial}{\partial x}(\mu N)$, or μ satisfies the partial differential equation $N\mu_x - M\mu_y = \mu(M_y - N_x)$.

19. Find an equation giving all integrating factors of the equation $x\,dy - y\,dx = 0$.

67. Functions of several variables. The results of the preceding sections may be readily extended to the case of a function z of n variables $x_1, \cdots, x_n$. Such a function z may be defined by an equation of the form

$$u(x_1, x_2, \cdots, x_n, z) = 0,$$

where $u_z \not\equiv 0$. If $u', u'', \cdots, u^{(n)}$ are n such functions which are independent, a relation among them such as

$$\phi(u', u'', \cdots, u^{(n)}) = 0 \tag{11}$$

will ordinarily define z as a function of the x's. From (11), we set up by differentiation the system of equations

$$\phi_{u'}(u'_{x_1} + u'_z z_{x_1}) + \phi_{u''}(u''_{x_1} + u''_z z_{x_1}) + \cdots$$
$$+ \phi_{u^{(n)}}(u^{(n)}_{x_1} + u^{(n)}_z z_{x_1}) = 0,$$
$$\phi_{u'}(u'_{x_2} + u'_z z_{x_2}) + \phi_{u''}(u''_{x_2} + u''_z z_{x_2}) + \cdots$$
$$+ \phi_{u^{(n)}}(u^{(n)}_{x_2} + u^{(n)}_z z_{x_2}) = 0,$$
$$\phi_{u'}(u'_{x_n} + u'_z z_{x_n}) + \phi_{u''}(u''_{x_n} + u''_z z_{x_n}) + \cdots$$
$$+ \phi_{u^{(n)}}(u^{(n)}_{x_n} + u^{(n)}_z z_{x_n}) = 0.$$

This system of n linear equations in n variables $\phi_u{}^{(j)}$ can have solutions, not all zero, if, and only if, the determinant of its coefficients vanishes. Hence, we have

$$|u'_{x_1} + u'_z z_{x_1} \ \ u'_{x_2} + u'_z z_{x_2} \ \ u'_{x_3} + u'_z z_{x_3} \cdots u'_{x_n} + u'_z z_{x_n}| = 0,$$

where for brevity we have written only the first column of the determinant, *viz.*, the coefficients of $\phi_{u'}$. The above determinant may be expressed as a sum of determinants, in which case we have the equation

$$0 = |u'_{x_1} u'_{x_2} \cdots u'_{x_n}| + z_{x_1} |u'_z u'_{x_2} u'_{x_3} \cdots u'_{x_n}|$$
$$+ z_{x_2} |u'_{x_1} u'_z u'_{x_3} \cdots u'_{x_n}| + \cdots$$
$$+ z_{x_1} z_{x_2} |u'_z u'_z u'_{x_3} u'_{x_4} \cdots u'_{x_n}| + \cdots$$
$$+ z_{x_1} z_{x_2} z_{x_3} |u'_z u'_z u'_z u'_{x_4} \cdots u'_{x_n}| + \cdots,$$

where the determinants whose coefficients are of degree higher than one in the z_{x_i} are all zero, because two columns are alike. This may be written as

$$X_1 z_{x_1} + X_2 z_{x_2} + \cdots + X_n z_{xn} = X_0, \tag{12}$$

where

$$X_1 \equiv - |u'_z u'_{x_2} u'_{x_3} \cdots u'_{x_n}|,$$
$$X_2 \equiv |u'_z u'_{x_1} u'_{x_3} \cdots u'_{x_n}|,$$
$$X_3 \equiv - |u'_z u'_{x_1} u'_{x_2} u'_{x_4} \cdots u'_{x_n}|,$$
$$\cdots$$
$$X_n \equiv (-1)^n |u'_z u'_{x_1} u'_{x_2} \cdots u'_{x_{n-1}}|,$$
$$X_o \equiv |u'_{x_1} u'_{x_2} u'_{x_3} \cdots u'_{x_n}|.$$

This special form of the X_i suggests minors of a determinant, and we see by inspection that (12) is actually expressible in the form

$$\begin{vmatrix} -1 & z_{x_1} & z_{x_2} & z_{x_3} & \cdots & z_{x_n} \\ u'_z & u'_{x_1} & u'_{x_2} & u'_{x_3} & \cdots & u'_{x_n} \\ u''_z & u''_{x_1} & u''_{x_2} & u''_{x_3} & \cdots & u''_{x_n} \\ \cdots & & & & & \\ \cdots & & & & & \\ u^{(n)}_z & u^{(n)}_{x_1} & u^{(n)}_{x_2} & u^{(n)}_{x_3} & \cdots & u^{(n)}_{x_n} \end{vmatrix} = 0. \tag{13}$$

We may now show that for any j, $u^{(j)} = c$ is a solution, which we shall call a *particular solution*, of (12). By differentiation we have

$$u_{x_i}^{(j)} + u_z^{(j)} z_{x_i} = 0 \qquad (i = 1, \cdots, n),$$

hence, remembering that $u_z^{(j)}$ is not zero,

$$z_{x_i} = - \frac{u_{x_i}^{(j)}}{u_z^{(j)}} \qquad (i = 1, \cdots, n),$$

which we may substitute into (13) to obtain

$$\begin{vmatrix} -1 - \dfrac{u_{x_1}^{(j)}}{u_z^{(j)}} & - \dfrac{u_{x_2}^{(j)}}{u_z^{(j)}} & \cdots & - \dfrac{u_{x_n}^{(j)}}{u_z^{(j)}} \\ u_z' & u_{x_1}' & u_{x_2}' & \cdots & u_{x_n}' \\ u_z'' & u_{x_1}'' & u_{x_2}'' & \cdots & u_{x_n}' \\ \cdots & \cdots & \cdots & \cdots & \cdots \\ \cdots & \cdots & \cdots & \cdots & \cdots \\ u_z^{(n)} & u_{x_1}^{(n)} & u_{x_2}^{(n)} & \cdots & u_{x_n}^{(n)} \end{vmatrix} = 0.$$

Multiplication of the elements of the first row by $u_z^{(j)}$ gives a determinant whose elements in the first row are the negatives of those in the $(j+1)^{st}$ row; hence the determinant vanishes for every value of j. We define (11), where ϕ is an arbitrary function, to be the general solution of (12) if $u^{(j)} = c$ $(j = 1, \cdots, n)$ are n particular solutions such that the n functions u are independent.

68. Lagrange's equations; case of $n + 1$ variables. If we begin with the same functions $u^{(j)}$ which were used in (11), and build up a system of ordinary differential equations as in Chapter VII, we obtain

$$\frac{dz}{X_0} = \frac{dx_1}{X_1} = \cdots = \frac{dx_n}{X_n}, \tag{14}$$

where the X_i are the same as in (12). This system is called *Lagrange's system*, and its solution gives us the solution of the equation (12). As we have seen in Chapter VII, if $v', v'', \cdots, v^{(n)}$ are n independent functions such that

$$v^{(j)} = c_j \qquad (j = 1, \cdots, n)$$

satisfy (14), then any solution of (14) may be written in the form

$$\phi(v', v'', \cdots, v^{(n)}) = 0, \tag{15}$$

and any such relation is a solution. However, a relation of the form (15) is a solution of the partial differential equation (12) only if $\phi_z \not\equiv 0$, since otherwise ϕ is independent of z.

Exercises

1. Find the general solution of

$$(y - z)z_x + (x + y + t)z_y + z_t = x + z + t.$$

2. Find the general solution of

$$m^2n^2(x_2 - x_3)z_{x_1} + n^2l^2(x_3 - x_1)z_{x_2} + l^2m^2(x_1 - x_2)z_{x_3} = 0.$$

3. Find the general solution of

$$(x_2 + x_3 + x_4 + z)z_{x_1} + (x_1 + x_3 + x_4 + z)z_{x_2}$$
$$+ (x_1 + x_2 + x_4 + z)z_{x_3} + (x_1 + x_2 + x_3 + z)z_{x_4}$$
$$= x_1 + x_2 + x_3 + x_4.$$

4. Find the general solution of

$$x_2x_3z\, z_{x_1} + x_1x_3z\, z_{x_2} + x_1x_2z\, z_{x_3} = x_1x_2x_3.$$

5. Find the general solution of

$$x_3\, z_{x_1} + x_2\, z_{x_2} + x_1\, z_{x_3} = 0.$$

69. Equations not of the first degree; Charpit's method. Let us consider now any first order partial differential equation of one dependent variable z and two independent variables x and y. For convenience we shall employ the notation $z_x \equiv p$, $z_y \equiv q$. The equation may be written in the form

$$F(x, y, z, p, q) = 0, \tag{16}$$

and we seek a function $\phi(x, y)$ such that

$$z = \phi(x, y)$$

satisfies (16) identically. That is, we seek a function such that the equations

$$z = \phi(x, y),\ p = \phi_x(x, y),\ q = \phi_y(x, y)$$

satisfy (16) identically.

If the function $\phi(x, y)$ which we seek were defined implicitly by a relation as

$$\psi(x, y, z) = 0,$$

we would have expressions for p and q defined in terms of x, y, and z as

$$p = g(x, y, z),\ q = h(x, y, z),$$

which satisfy (16).   For example, we might choose $g(x, y, z)$ arbitrarily and, after substituting $p = g(x, y, z)$ into (16), solve for q to obtain $q = h(x, y, z)$.   Unless the choice of g was very fortunate, the functions g and h thus obtained would not be such as to render the equation

$$dz = p \, dx + q \, dy \qquad (17)$$

integrable.   However, if a choice of g and h could be made so that (17) was integrable, then a solution of (17) would define z as a function of x and y which would satisfy the given equation (16).

Two equations involving p and q, as

$$F(x, y, z, p, q) = 0 \qquad (16)$$

and

$$f(x, y, z, p, q) = 0, \qquad (18)$$

may be solved for p and q each as a function of x, y, and z, provided the determinant*

$$\begin{vmatrix} F_p & F_q \\ f_p & f_q \end{vmatrix} \equiv \Delta$$

does not vanish identically; and we seek to find a relation of the form (18) such that the functions p and q,

$$p = g(x, y, z),$$
$$q = h(x, y, z),$$

defined by (16) and (18), will render (17) integrable.   To find such a relation (18), let us differentiate (16) and (18) partially with respect to x to obtain

$$F_x + F_p p_x + F_q q_x = 0, \qquad (19)$$
$$f_x + f_p p_x + f_q q_x = 0. \qquad (20)$$

Similarly, differentiating (16) and (18) partially with respect to y, and then z, we have

$$F_y + F_p p_y + F_q q_y = 0, \qquad (21)$$
$$f_y + f_p p_y + f_q q_y = 0, \qquad (22)$$
$$F_z + F_p p_z + F_q q_z = 0, \qquad (23)$$
$$f_z + f_p p_z + f_q q_z = 0. \qquad (24)$$

Between (19) and (20) we may eliminate p_x to obtain

$$\Delta q_x = F_x f_p - F_p f_x. \qquad (25)$$

---

* Wilson's *Advanced Calculus*, page 124.

Similarly, eliminating p_z from (23) and (24), q_y from (21) and (22), and q_z from (23) and (24), we obtain

$$\Delta q_z = F_z f_p - F_p f_z, \tag{26}$$
$$\Delta p_y = -F_y f_q + F_q f_y, \tag{27}$$
$$\Delta p_z = -F_z f_q + F_q f_z. \tag{28}$$

Now, the condition that (17) be integrable reduces to

$$pq_z - qp_z - p_y + q_x \equiv 0.$$

We may multiply this through by Δ, substitute from (25), (26), (27), and (28), and obtain

$$pF_z f_p - pF_p f_z + qF_z f_q - qF_q f_z + F_y f_q - F_q f_y + F_x f_p - F_p f_x = 0.$$

When arranged in terms of derivatives of f, this becomes

$$-F_p f_x - F_q f_y - (pF_p + qF_q)f_z + (F_x + pF_z)f_p + (F_y + qF_z)f_q = 0,$$

which is a linear partial differential equation in f considered as a function of the five independent variables x, y, z, p, and q. The corresponding Lagrange equations are

$$\frac{dx}{-F_p} = \frac{dy}{-F_q} = \frac{dz}{-(pF_p + qF_q)} = \frac{dp}{F_x + pF_z} = \frac{dq}{F_y + qF_z} = \frac{df}{0}.$$

Any solution of this system, involving p or q, or both, and one arbitrary constant, such that $\Delta \neq 0$, may be used with (16) to define p and q. These functions will render (17) integrable, and its complete solution

$$\psi(x, y, z, a, b) = 0 \tag{29}$$

will be the *complete solution* of (16), that is, a solution involving two arbitrary constants.

The relation (29) represents a two-parameter system of surfaces. If this system has an envelope, the equation of the envelope is called the *singular solution*. It may be found by eliminating a and b between (29) and the two derived equations

$$\psi_a(x, y, z, a, b) = 0,$$
$$\psi_b(x, y, z, a, b) = 0.$$

As in the case of one independent variable treated in Chapter III, the eliminant must not be accepted on faith, but its factors must be separately tried in (16). The singular solution may also be found by eliminating p and q from (16) and

$$F_p(x, y, z, p, q) = 0,$$
$$F_q(x, y, z, p, q) = 0,$$

and testing the eliminant by substitution in (16).

If, in the complete solution (29), we choose b as an arbitrary function of a, say $b = f(a)$, we have a one-parameter system of solutions

$$\psi(x, y, z, a, f(a)) = 0. \tag{30}$$

The envelope of this family is obtained by eliminating a between (30) and

$$\psi_a(x, y, z, a, f(a)) + \psi_b(x, y, z, a, f(a))f'(a) = 0.$$

The eliminant will involve an arbitrary function f, and is called the *general solution*. The curves of contact of the surfaces (30) and their envelope are called *characteristics* of the given equation (16) or of the system (29). We see, then, that a general solution is a locus of characteristics.

Illustration

Let us study the differential equation

$$16z^2p^2 + 25z^2q^2 + 9z^2 - 81 = 0. \tag{31}$$

This is of the form (16), with

$$F \equiv 16z^2p^2 + 25z^2q^2 + 9z^2 - 81,$$
$$F_x \equiv 0 \equiv F_y,$$
$$F_z \equiv 32zp^2 + 50zq^2 + 18z,$$
$$F_p \equiv 32z^2p,$$
$$F_q \equiv 50z^2q.$$

We wish to find a new relation

$$f(x, y, z, p, q) = 0 \tag{18}$$

such that the functions of p and q defined by (18) and (31) will make

$$dz = p\, dx + q\, dy \tag{17}$$

integrable. For such a function we look among the solutions of

$$\frac{dx}{-32z^2p} = \frac{dy}{-50z^2q} = \frac{dz}{-32z^2p^2 - 50z^2q^2}$$
$$= \frac{dp}{32zp^3 + 50zpq^2 + 18zp}$$
$$= \frac{dq}{32zqp^2 + 50zq^3 + 18zq} = \frac{df}{0}.$$

We may find a solution by using the multipliers 9, 0, 16p, 16z, 0, 0, which produce the ratio

$$\frac{9dx + 16p\,dz + 16z\,dp}{-288z^2p - 512z^2p^3 - 800z^2pq^2 + 512z^2p^3 + 800z^2pq^2 + 288z^2p}.$$

Since the denominator vanishes identically, we have

$$9dx + 16p\,dz + 16z\,dp = 0,$$

an exact equation having as solution

$$9(x - a) + 16pz = 0, \tag{32}$$

where the arbitrary constant has been called 9a. Solving (32) for p, we obtain

$$p = -\frac{9}{z}\left(\frac{x - a}{16}\right),$$

which we substitute into the given equation (31) to solve for q. We thus obtain

$$q = \pm\frac{9}{5z}\sqrt{1 - \frac{z^2}{9} - \frac{(x - a)^2}{16}}.$$

These two expressions for p and q may be substituted into (17) to obtain

$$dz = -\frac{9(x - a)dx}{16z} \pm \frac{9}{5z}\sqrt{1 - \frac{z^2}{9} - \frac{(x - a)^2}{16}}\,dy.$$

Dividing through by the coefficient of dy, we obtain

$$\pm dy = \frac{5\left\{\dfrac{z\,dz}{9} + \dfrac{x - a}{16}\,dx\right\}}{\sqrt{1 - \dfrac{z^2}{9} - \dfrac{(x - a)^2}{16}}},$$

which has the solution

$$\pm(y - b) = 5\sqrt{1 - \frac{z^2}{9} - \frac{(x - a)^2}{16}}$$

or, upon rationalization,

$$\frac{(x - a)^2}{16} + \frac{(y - b)^2}{25} + \frac{z^2}{9} = 1, \tag{33}$$

the complete solution of (31).

This complete solution represents a two-parameter system of ellipsoids, the parameters a and b defining the center $(a, b, 0)$. The ellipsoids have the over-all measurements of 8 units parallel to the x-axis, 10 units parallel to the y-axis, and 6 units parallel to the z-axis.

The envelope of the system is seen to have the equation $z^2 = 9$, but we shall go through the formal work of determining the singular solution in order to illustrate the methods. With

$$\psi \equiv \frac{(x - a)^2}{16} + \frac{(y - b)^2}{25} + \frac{z^2}{9} - 1$$

we have

$$\psi_a \equiv \frac{-(x - a)}{8}, \; \psi_b \equiv \frac{-2(y - b)}{25},$$

so we eliminate a and b between (33) and the two equations

$$\frac{-(x - a)}{8} = 0, \; \frac{-2(y - b)}{25} = 0.$$

We obtain

$$z^2 - 9 = 0,$$

as predicted.

Also, we may find the singular solution from the given equation (31) and the two equations

$$\begin{cases} 32z^2 p = 0, \\ 50z^2 q = 0, \end{cases}$$

obtained by differentiating (31) partially with respect to p and q. Since $z^2 = 0$ does not satisfy the equation, we reduce the derived equations to $p = 0$, $q = 0$, which, substituted into (31), give $z^2 - 9 = 0$, as before. The student should verify that $z^2 - 9 = 0$ actually satisfies the given differential equation.

If we set b equal to a function of a, say $b = f(a)$, we restrict the centers of the ellipsoids to the curve $y = f(x)$ in the xy-plane, and the ellipsoids thus determined generate a tubular surface whose equation is obtained by eliminating a between

$$\frac{(x - a)^2}{16} + \frac{(y - f(a))^2}{25} + \frac{z^2}{9} - 1 = 0$$

and

$$\frac{-(x - a)}{8} - \frac{2(y - f(a))f'(a)}{25} = 0.$$

This eliminant we have called the general solution of the original differential equation (31).

70. Equations involving several variables; Jacobi's method. Consider a partial differential equation of the first order in n independent variables $x_1, \cdots, x_n$, but free of the dependent variable z, as

$$F_1(x_1, x_2, \cdots, x_n, p_1, p_2, \cdot \quad \cdot, p_n) = 0, \qquad (34)$$

where p_i represents z_{x_i}. The problem of solution becomes that of determining n functions p_i which satisfy it identically, and such that the equation

$$dz = p_1 \, dx_1 + p_2 \, dx_2 + \cdots + p_n \, dx_n \qquad (35)$$

is integrable. This equation is clearly exact if

$$\frac{\partial p_i}{\partial x_k} \equiv \frac{\partial p_k}{\partial x_i} \qquad (i, \, k = 1, \, \cdots, \, n),$$

and, analogous to the above treatment, we shall determine these p_i by means of (34) and $n - 1$ additional equations

$$\begin{cases} F_2(x_1, \, \cdots, \, x_n, \, p_1, \, \cdots, \, p_n) = a_2, \\ \cdots \cdots \cdots \cdots \cdots \cdots \cdots \cdots \\ F_n(x_1, \, \cdots, \, x_n, \, p_1, \, \cdots, \, p_n) = a_n, \end{cases} \qquad (36)$$

where $a_2, \cdots, a_n$ are arbitrary constants. By differentiating (34) and all of the equation (36) partially with respect to x_i, we obtain

$$\begin{cases} \dfrac{\partial F_1}{\partial x_i} + \dfrac{\partial F_1}{\partial p_1} \cdot \dfrac{\partial p_1}{\partial x_i} + \dfrac{\partial F_1}{\partial p_2} \cdot \dfrac{\partial p_2}{\partial x_i} + \cdots + \dfrac{\partial F_1}{\partial p_n} \cdot \dfrac{\partial p_n}{\partial x_i} = 0, \\[2mm] \dfrac{\partial F_2}{\partial x_i} + \dfrac{\partial F_2}{\partial p_1} \cdot \dfrac{\partial p_1}{\partial x_i} + \dfrac{\partial F_2}{\partial p_2} \cdot \dfrac{\partial p_2}{\partial x_i} + \cdots + \dfrac{\partial F_2}{\partial p_n} \cdot \dfrac{\partial p_n}{\partial x_i} = 0, \\[2mm] \cdots \cdots \cdots \cdots \cdots \cdots \cdots \cdots \cdots \cdots \\ \cdots \cdots \cdots \cdots \cdots \cdots \cdots \cdots \cdots \cdots \\ \dfrac{\partial F_n}{\partial x_i} + \dfrac{\partial F_n}{\partial p_1} \cdot \dfrac{\partial p_1}{\partial x_i} + \dfrac{\partial F_n}{\partial p_2} \cdot \dfrac{\partial p_2}{\partial x_i} + \cdots + \dfrac{\partial F_n}{\partial p_n} \cdot \dfrac{\partial p_n}{\partial x_i} = 0. \end{cases}$$

This is a system of n linear equations in the n quantities $\dfrac{\partial p_k}{\partial x_i}$ $(k = 1, \cdots, n)$, whose determinant,

$$\Delta \equiv \left| \frac{\partial F_1}{\partial p_1} \ \frac{\partial F_1}{\partial p_2} \ \cdots \ \frac{\partial F_1}{\partial p_n} \right|^*,$$

---

* Here, as before, we have exhibited only the first row. To obtain the jth row, replace F_1 by F_j.

must not vanish if the n equations (34), (36) are to determine unique values of $p_1, \cdots, p_n$. The system may be solved for $\dfrac{\partial p_k}{\partial x_i}$ to obtain

$$-\Delta \frac{\partial p_k}{\partial x_i} = \left| \frac{\partial F_1}{\partial p_1} \frac{\partial F_1}{\partial p_2} \cdots \frac{\partial F_1}{\partial p_{k-1}} \frac{\partial F_1}{\partial x_i} \frac{\partial F_1}{\partial p_{k+1}} \cdots \frac{\partial F_1}{\partial p_n} \right|.$$

From the conditions for exactness we then have

$$\left| \frac{\partial F_1}{\partial p_1} \cdots \frac{\partial F_1}{\partial p_{k-1}} \frac{\partial F_1}{\partial x_i} \frac{\partial F_1}{\partial p_{k+1}} \cdots \frac{\partial F_1}{\partial p_n} \right|$$
$$\equiv \left| \frac{\partial F_1}{\partial p_1} \cdots \frac{\partial F_1}{\partial p_{i-1}} \frac{\partial F_1}{\partial x_k} \frac{\partial F_1}{\partial p_{i+1}} \cdots \frac{\partial F_1}{\partial p_n} \right|.$$

These determinants differ only in their kth and ith columns, and will certainly be equal if all corresponding two-rowed minors from those columns are equal. Hence, set

$$\left| \begin{matrix} \dfrac{\partial F_1}{\partial p_i} & \dfrac{\partial F_1}{\partial x_i} \\[2mm] \dfrac{\partial F_j}{\partial p_i} & \dfrac{\partial F_j}{\partial x_i} \end{matrix} \right| \equiv \left| \begin{matrix} \dfrac{\partial F_1}{\partial x_k} & \dfrac{\partial F_1}{\partial p_k} \\[2mm] \dfrac{\partial F_j}{\partial x_k} & \dfrac{\partial F_j}{\partial p_k} \end{matrix} \right|,$$

or

$$\frac{\partial F_1}{\partial x_k} \cdot \frac{\partial F_j}{\partial p_k} + \frac{\partial F_1}{\partial x_i} \cdot \frac{\partial F_j}{\partial p_i} - \frac{\partial F_1}{\partial p_i} \cdot \frac{\partial F_j}{\partial x_i} - \frac{\partial F_1}{\partial p_k} \cdot \frac{\partial F_j}{\partial x_k} \equiv 0.$$

This is a linear partial differential equation in the unknown function F_j, and the corresponding Lagrange system of ordinary differential equations is

$$\frac{dx_i}{-\dfrac{\partial F_1}{\partial p_i}} = \frac{dx_k}{-\dfrac{\partial F_1}{\partial p_k}} = \frac{dp_i}{\dfrac{\partial F_1}{\partial x_i}} = \frac{dp_k}{\dfrac{\partial F_1}{\partial x_k}} = \frac{dF_j}{0}.$$

Since the equations hold for all values of i and k, we have

$$\frac{dx_1}{-\dfrac{\partial F_1}{\partial p_1}} = \frac{dx_2}{-\dfrac{\partial F_1}{\partial p_2}} = \cdots = \frac{dx_n}{-\dfrac{\partial F_1}{\partial p_n}} = \frac{dp_1}{\dfrac{\partial F_1}{\partial x_1}} = \frac{dp_2}{\dfrac{\partial F_1}{\partial x_2}} = \cdots = \frac{dp_n}{\dfrac{\partial F_1}{\partial x_n}}$$
$$= \frac{dF_j}{0} \ (j = 2, 3, \cdots, n).$$

Therefore, any $n - 1$ solution of this system of the form

$$\begin{cases} F_2(x_1, \cdots, x_n, p_1, \cdots, p_n) = a_2, \\ \cdots\cdots\cdots\cdots\cdots\cdots\cdots\cdots\cdots\cdots \\ \cdots\cdots\cdots\cdots\cdots\cdots\cdots\cdots\cdots\cdots \\ F_n(x_1, \cdots, x_n, p_1, \cdots, p_n) = a_n, \end{cases}$$

such that $\Delta(F_1, \cdots, F_n) \neq 0$, may be taken as the n functions determining $p_1, \cdots, p_n$, and these p_i will render (35) exact. Its solution introduces one additional arbitrary constant a, giving a relation

$$z = f(x_1, \cdots, x_n, a_1, \cdots, a_n) \qquad (37)$$

as the *complete* solution of (34). As before, we obtain the singular solution, if it exists, by eliminating the constants a_i from (37) and the n equations

$$f_{a_i}(x_1, \cdots, x_n, a_1, \cdots, a_n) = 0 \quad (i = 1, \cdots, n),$$

or by eliminating the p_i from (34) and the n equations

$$\frac{\partial}{\partial p_i} \cdot F_1(x_1, \cdots, x_n, p_1, \cdots, p_n) = 0 \quad (i = 1, \cdots, n).$$

If, in an equation of the first order in n independent variables, the dependent variable z appears the equation can be replaced by another equation containing $n + 1$ independent variables in which the dependent variable does not appear. Let the equation be designated by

$$F(z, x_1, \cdots, x_n, p_1, \cdots, p_n) = 0, \qquad (38)$$

and a solution be

$$y(x_1, \cdots, x_n, z) - a_0 = 0, \qquad (39)$$

By partial differentiation in (39), we obtain

$$y_{x_i} + y_z p_i = 0 \qquad (i = 1, \cdots, n),$$

or

$$p_i = - \frac{y_{x_i}}{y_z} \qquad (i = 1, \cdots, n),$$

which satisfy (38) identically. Then we have

$$F\left(z, x_1, x_2, \cdots, x_n, -\frac{y_{x_1}}{y_z}, \cdots, -\frac{y_{x_n}}{y_z}\right) \equiv 0. \qquad (40)$$

This may be written as

$$F_1(z, x_1, \cdots, x_n, y_z, y_{x_1}, \cdots, y_{x_n}) = 0 \qquad (41)$$

and may be considered as a partial differential equation in $n + 1$ independent variables $z, x_1, \cdots, x_n$, in which the dependent variable y does not appear. By the foregoing methods it may be solved in the form

$$y - a_0 = f(z, x_1, \cdots, x_n, a_1, \cdots, a_n).$$

Since this satisfies (41) identically, it satisfies the other form, (40), identically. But (40) is the result of substituting $y - a_0$ into (38), so $y - a_0 = 0$, or, what is the same thing,

$$f(z, x_1, \cdots, x_n, a_1, \cdots, a_n) = 0,$$

which satisfies (38) identically.

Exercises

Find the complete solution of each of the following:

1. $q^2 = 2p$. *Hint:* If the equation lacks x, y, and z, choose p and q as constants which satisfy the equation, and integrate $dz = p\,dx + q\,dy$. In this case $q \equiv 2a$, $p \equiv 2a^2$, a constant.

2. $p^2 = 2q - 1$.

3. $p^{2/3} + q^{2/3} = 1$

4. $p^2 + q^2 = 4$.

5. $pq = 2p - q$.

6. $p_1 + p_2 + p_3 = 0$. *Hint:* Let $p_3 \equiv a_3$, $p_2 \equiv a_2$, $p_1 \equiv -a_3 - a_2$, and solve $dz = p_1\,dx_1 + p_2\,dx_2 + p_3\,dx_3$.

7. $p_1^2 + p_2^2 + p_3^2 = 1$.

8. $p_1p_2 - p_1p_3 + p_2p_3 = 0$.

9. $p^2z + q^2 = 10$. *Hint:* If the equation is free of x and y, let $z = f(x + ay) \equiv f(s)$; then $p = \dfrac{dz}{ds} \cdot \dfrac{\partial s}{\partial x} = \dfrac{dz}{ds}$, and $q = \dfrac{dz}{ds} \cdot \dfrac{\partial s}{\partial y} = a\dfrac{dz}{ds}$, and the equation becomes an ordinary differential equation in z and s.

10. $p = z(1 - pq)$.

11. $q^2(1 + p) = p(z - 1)$.

12. $p^2 + q^2 = 5z$.

13. $pq(1 - z) = z^2$.

14. $zp^3 - zpq - 3p^2 + 3q = 0$.

15. $q^2y^2 = z(z - px)$. *Hint:* Let $y = e^Y$, $x = e^X$.

16. $z^2pq^2 + p^2z^3 + pq^3 + p^2qz = zq^3 + pqz^2 + p^3z^2 + zp^2q^2$.

17. $p_1^2 + zp_2^2 + z^2p_3^2 = z^3p_1p_2p_3$.

18. $z = p + pq$.

19. $p^4 - q^2z^2 = 0$.

20. $p^3 - 4qz^2 = 0$.

21. $z = q + \sqrt{1 + p^2}$.

22. $p - x^2 = q - y^2$. *Hint:* In equations of the form $f(x, p) = g(y, q)$, set each side equal to the same constant, solve for p and q, and integrate $dz = p\,dx + q\,dy$.

23. $p^3 = q + x$.

24. $zpx - zxy = p^2z$. Is $z = 0$ a solution? Is it a singular solution? A particular solution?

25. $p^2q = x^2y$.

26. $p(q - \sin y) = \sin x$.

27. Prove that the extended Clairaut equation $z = p_1x_1 + p_2x_2 + \cdots + p_nx_n + f(p_1, \cdots, p_n)$ is satisfied by $z = a_1x_1 + a_2x_2 + \cdots + a_nx_n + f(a_1, \cdots, a_n)$.

28. $z = px + qy + 2p + 3q^2$.

29. $z = px + qy + p^2 + q^2 + 1$.

30. $z = px + qy + 5p^3 - 2p - q$.

31. $(z - px - qy)^2 = pq$.

32. $z = p_1x_1 + p_2x_2 + p_3x_3 + p_1p_2p_3$.

33. $z = p_1x_1 + p_2x_2 + p_3x_3 + p_4x_4 + p_1p_2 + p_3p_4$.

34. $z^2p^2 + z^2q^2 - z^2 = 1$.

35. $x^2yp + xy^2q - xyz + zpq = 0$.

36. $p^2x + pq(x + y + z - 1) + q^2y - pq(px + qy) - (p + q)z = 0$.

37. $z^2p^2 - z^2q^2 - z^2 = 1$.

38. $z^2p^2 + 5z^2q^2 - z^2 = 0$.

39. $z = px + qy + \log pq$.

40. $q^2 + 6x^4 + 2x^2p + 2xz = 0$.

41. $z = px + qy + \sqrt{q^{1/2} - p}$.

42. $4z^2q^2 = y + 2zp - 2x$.

43. $2zp_3 + 4z^2p_1^2 + 8z^3p_2^3 = 1.$

44. $p_1^2 - p_2p_3 = zp_2 + zp_3.$

45. $2zp_3 = 4z^2e^{x_3}(p_1e^{-x_1} + p_2e^{-x_2})^2.$

46. $2p_1x_1 + 3p_2x_2 + 6p_3x_3 - 6 = 0.$

47. $x_1p_1 + x_2p_2 + x_3p_3 + x_4p_4 - p_1p_2p_3p_4 = 0.$

48. $x_1p_1 + x_2p_2 + x_3p_3 + x_4p_4 - p_1^2p_2^2p_3^2p_4^2 = 0.$

CHAPTER IX

Linear Partial Differential Equations
with Constant Coefficients

71. Homogeneous linear equations with constant coefficients.
In Chapter IV we made use of an operator $D \equiv \dfrac{d}{dx}$, and in an
entirely analogous manner we shall employ here two operators
$D_1 \equiv \dfrac{\partial}{\partial x}$ and $D_2 \equiv \dfrac{\partial}{\partial y}$. Thus,

$$D_1 z \equiv \frac{\partial z}{\partial x}, \; D_2 z \equiv \frac{\partial z}{\partial y},$$

and

$$f(D_1, D_2)z \equiv \sum_{p, q} a_{pq} \frac{\partial^{p+q} z}{\partial x^p \partial y^q},$$

where p and q are positive integers or zero, a_{pq} are constants, and

$$f(D_1, D_2) \equiv \sum_{p, q} a_{pq} D_1^p D_2^q$$

when D_1 and D_2 are regarded as variables.

We leave it as an exercise for the student to verify that the
addition and multiplication of these operators obey the laws of
algebra, i. e., that

$$\begin{aligned}
[f(D_1, D_2) + g(D_1, D_2)]z &\equiv [g(D_1, D_2) + f(D_1, D_2)]z \\
&\equiv f(D_1, D_2)z + g(D_1, D_2)z, \\
[f(D_1, D_2) \cdot g(D_1, D_2)]z &\equiv [g(D_1, D_2) \cdot f(D_1, D_2)]z \\
&\equiv f(D_1, D_2) [g(D_1, D_2)z],
\end{aligned}$$

if z is a function of x and y that has continuous partial derivatives
of all orders called for by these operators.

By a homogeneous linear partial differential equation of order n
with constant coefficients, we shall mean an equation of the form

$$a_n \frac{\partial^n z}{\partial x^n} + a_{n-1} \frac{\partial^n z}{\partial x^{n-1} \partial y} + \cdots + a_1 \frac{\partial^n z}{\partial x \partial y^{n-1}} + a_0 \frac{\partial^n z}{\partial y^n} = 0,$$

231

where the a's are real constants, not all zero. This can be written as

$$(a_n D_1^n + a_{n-1} D_1^{n-1} D_2 + \cdots + a_1 D_1 D_2^{n-1} + a_0 D_2^n)z = 0. \quad (1)$$

The simplest possible equation of this kind is one of the first order, as

$$(a_1 D_1 + a_0 D_2)z = 0.$$

It can be written in the form

$$a_1 z_x + a_0 z_y = 0.$$

This falls under the treatment of first order partial differential equations given in Chapter VIII, and the general solution is

$$z = F(a_1 y - a_0 x).$$

Since the operator in (1) may be factored into the product of n linear factors of the form

$$\alpha_i D_1 + \beta_i D_2 \qquad (i = 1, \cdots, n),$$

where the α_i and β_i are complex numbers in general, we shall have need of the following

THEOREM I. *If* $z = F(\alpha y - \beta x)$ *is a solution of the differential equation* $\phi(D_1, D_2)z = 0$, *it is a solution of the equation* $[\psi(D_1, D_2) \cdot \phi(D_1, D_2)]z = 0$.

The truth of this theorem is evidently a direct consequence of the property of the operators which asserts that

$$[\psi(D_1, D_2) \cdot \phi(D_1, D_2)]z \equiv \psi(D_1, D_2)[\phi(D_1, D_2)z].$$

We know from algebra that the operator in (1) can be broken up into a product of linear operators in essentially only one way, so that (1) takes the form

$$(\alpha_1 D_1 + \beta_1 D_2)(\alpha_2 D_1 + \beta_2 D_2) \cdots (\alpha_n D_1 + \beta_n D_2)z = 0. \quad (2)$$

Then, by Theorem I, a solution is

$$z = F_n(\alpha_n y - \beta_n x),$$

and, since the order of factors in the operator is immaterial,

$$z = F_i(\alpha_i y - \beta_i x) \qquad (i = 1, \cdots, n - 1)$$

are also solutions. To obtain the general solution, we shall employ

THEOREM II. *If* $z = u(x, y)$ *and* $z = v(x, y)$ *are both solutions of* $f(D_1, D_2)z = 0$, *then* $z = u(x, y) + v(x, y)$ *is also a solution.*

The proof of this theorem comes directly from the properties of the operator, as the student may readily verify.

By use of Theorem II, we now see that

$$z = F_1(\alpha_1 y - \beta_1 x) + F_2(\alpha_2 y - \beta_2 x) + \cdots + F_n(\alpha_n y - \beta_n x) \quad (3)$$

is also a solution of (2), with each function F_i arbitrary in form. If the factors $\alpha_i D_1 + \beta_i D_2$ of the operator are essentially distinct, i. e., if no one of them is a constant multiple of any other, (3) is what we shall call the *general solution* of (1).

In each of the n factors $\alpha_i D_1 + \beta_i D_2$, not both of α_i and β_i are zero, and, for simplicity in notation, we shall assume for the present $\alpha_i \neq 0$ $(i = 1, \cdots, n)$, so that (2) may be written in the form

$$(D_1 - m_1 D_2)(D_1 - m_2 D_2) \cdots (D_1 - m_n D_2)z = 0, \quad (4)$$

while (3) is written

$$z = F_1(y + m_1 x) + F_2(y + m_2 x) + \cdots + F_n(y + m_n x). \quad (5)$$

72. Case of complex roots. Although (5) may be called the general solution of (4), it is not the general *real* solution unless all of the numbers m_i are real. If one of these is complex, its conjugate is also present. That is, if $m_i = a + bi$ (a, b, real), then $m_j = a - bi$ is present among the m's. To find real solutions, consider the equation

$$[D_1^2 - 2a D_1 D_2 + (a^2 + b^2)D_2^2]z = 0. \quad (6)$$

From the above discussion,

$$z = \Phi(y + ax, bx) \equiv F_1(y + ax + ibx) + F_1(y + ax - ibx)$$

and

$$z = \Psi(y + ax, bx) \equiv iF_2(y + ax + ibx) - iF_2(y + ax - ibx)$$

are solutions of (6) by Theorem II, and

$$z = \Phi(y + ax, bx) + \Psi(y + ax, bx) \quad (7)$$

is the desired solution. Since F_1 and F_2 are entirely arbitrary real functions, this solution is general. By means of exponential identities we can easily throw (7), which, in full, is

$$z = F_1(y + ax + ibx) + F_1(y + ax - ibx) \\ + i[F_2(y + ax + ibx) - F_2(y + ax - ibx)],$$

into the form

$$z = c_1 e^{g_1 \cdot (y+ax)} \cos g_1 bx + c_2 e^{g_2 \cdot (y+ax)} \cos g_2 bx + \cdots$$
$$+ d_1 e^{h_1 \cdot (y+ax)} \sin h_1 bx + d_2 e^{h_2 \cdot (y+ax)} \sin h_2 bx + \cdots$$
$$\equiv \sum_{j=1}^{\infty} c_j e^{g_j \cdot (y+ax)} \cos g_j bx + \sum_{j=1}^{\infty} d_j e^{h_j \cdot (y+ax)} \sin h_j bx, \qquad (8)$$

where c_j, d_j, g_j, h_j are any real constants such that

$$2F_1(t) \equiv c_1 e^{g_1 t} + c_2 e^{g_2 t} + c_3 e^{g_3 t} + \cdots$$

and

$$2F_2(t) \equiv d_1 e^{h_1 t} + d_2 e^{h_2 t} + d_3 e^{h_3 t} + \cdots ,$$

but it is easier to verify directly that

$$z = c \cdot e^{g \cdot (y+ax)} \cos gbx$$

and

$$z = d \cdot e^{h \cdot (y+ax)} \sin hbx$$

are solutions of (6) for any constant values of g, h, c, d, and hence apply Theorem II to obtain (8). The student should make this verification.

73. Case of multiple roots. To state our next theorem we shall need the following:

DEFINITION. *The solution*

$$z = F_i(y + m_i x)$$

is said to be the solution of (1) *corresponding to the factor* $D_1 - m_i D_2$ *of the operator in* (1) *if* m_i *is real.*

DEFINITION. *The solution* (7) *or the solution* (8) *is said to be the solution of* (1) *corresponding to the factor* $D_1^2 - 2a D_1 D_2 + (a^2 + b^2) D_2^2$ *of the operator in* (1) *if* a *and* b *are real.*

In this nomenclature we can state

THEOREM III. *If* $z = f(x, y)$ *is the solution of* (1) *corresponding to a factor of the operator of multiplicity* k, *then* $z = xf(x, y), \cdots ,$ $z = x^{k-1}f(x, y)$ *are all solutions.*

To prove this, take the equation

$$(D_1 - mD_2)^k z = 0, \qquad (9)$$

where m is real, write it

$$(D_1 - mD_2)^{k-1}(D_1 - mD_2)z = 0,$$

and compute $(D_1 - mD_2)z$ with

$$z \equiv x^p F(y + mx). \tag{10}$$

We have

$$D_1 z \equiv px^{p-1}F(y + mx) + mx^p F'(y + mx)$$

and

$$D_2 z \equiv x^p F'(y + mx),$$

hence

$$(D_1 - mD_2)z \equiv px^{p-1}F(y + mx).$$

The equation (9) is satisfied by (10) if, and only if,

$$(D_1 - mD_2)^{k-2}(D_1 - mD_2)[px^{p-1}F(y + mx)] \equiv 0.$$

The operation $(D_1 - mD_2)[px^{p-1}F(y + mx)]$ reduces to

$$p(p - 1)x^{p-2}F(y + mx).$$

The equation (9) is now satisfied if, and only if,

$$(D_1 - mD_2)^{k-3}(D_1 - mD_2)[p(p - 1)x^{p-2}F(y + mx)] \equiv 0.$$

Continuing in this manner, we arrive finally at the equation

$$p(p - 1)(p - 2) \cdots (p - k + 1)x^{p-k}F(y + mx) \equiv 0.$$

which is immediately seen to be true if $p = 0, 1, 2, \cdots, k - 1$.

For the case of a factor which is a power of $[D_1^2 - 2aD_1D_2 + (a^2 + b^2)D_2^2]$, consider the equation

$$[D_1^2 - 2aD_1D_2 + (a^2 + b^2)D_2^2]^k z = 0. \tag{11}$$

Let

$$z \equiv x^p \sum_i c_i e^{g_i \cdot (y+ax)} \cos g_i bx + x^p \sum_i d_i e^{h_i \cdot (y+ax)} \sin h_i bx, \tag{12}$$

where the sums are either finite or infinite.* In evaluating the operation

$$[D_1^2 - 2aD_1D_2 + (a^2 + b^2)D_2^2]z,$$

we obtain

$$p(p - 1)x^{p-2} \left\{ \sum_i c_i e^{g_i \cdot (y+ax)} \cos g_i bx + \sum_i d_i e^{h_i \cdot (y+ax)} \sin h_i bx \right\}$$

$$- 2bpx^{p-1} \sum_i \{g_i c_i e^{g_i \cdot (y+ax)} \sin g_i bx - h_i d_i e^{h_i \cdot (y+ax)} \cos h_i bx\}.$$

---

* The condition that a series of differentiable functions, which converges to a function $F(x)$ in an interval, be differentiable term by term, in the interval, is shown in the Theory of Functions of a Real Variable to be, that the derived series converge uniformly in the interval.

This is seen to consist of two terms of the type of the proposed solution (12), in one of which a coefficient is p, and in the other of which a coefficient is $p(p-1)$. If the process is repeated k times, the number of terms becomes $k+1$, with the coefficients $p(p-1)$ $\cdots (p-k+1)$, $p(p-1) \cdots (p-k)$, $\cdots$, $p(p-1) \cdots$ $(p-2k+1)$, all of which vanish if $p = 0, 1, 2, \cdots, k-1$. The student may show, in an entirely similar manner, that

$$z = x^p\{\Phi(y+ax, bx) + \Psi(y+ax, bx)\}$$

is a solution of (11) if Φ and Ψ are defined as in (7), and $p = 0$, $1, \cdots, k-1$.

Exercises

Find the general solution of each of the following:

1. $(D_1^2 - 7D_1D_2 + 10D_2^2)z = 0$.

2. $(D_1^2 - 2D_1D_2 - 3D_2^2)z = 0$.

3. $(D_1^3 - 6D_1^2D_2 + 11D_1D_2^2 - 6D_2^3)z = 0$.

4. $(D_1^3 + 2D_1^2D_2 - D_1D_2^2 - 2D_2^3)z = 0$.

5. $(D_1^4 - 5D_1^2D_2^2 + 4D_2^4)z = 0$.

6. $(D_1^4 + 2D_1^3D_2 - 5D_1^2D_2^2 - 6D_1D_2^3)z = 0$.

7. $(D_1^2 - 2D_1D_2 - 2D_2^2)z = 0$.

8. $(D_1^2 + 4D_1D_2 - 6D_2^2)z = 0$.

9. $(D_1^3 + D_1^2D_2 - 10D_1D_2^2 - 6D_2^3)z = 0$.

10. $(D_1^3 - 4D_1^2D_2 - 5D_1D_2^2 + 14D_2^3)z = 0$.

11. $(D_1^4 + 2D_1^3D_2 - 10D_1^2D_2^2 - 20D_1D_2^3 - 8D_2^4)z = 0$.   *Hint:* $D_1^2 - 2D_1D_2 - 4D_2^2$ is a factor of the operator.

12. $(D_1^2 + 6D_1D_2 + D_2^2)(D_1^2 - 6D_1D_2 - 5D_2^2)z = 0$.

13. $(D_1^2 + 4D_1D_2 + 4D_2^2)z = 0$.

14. $(4D_1^2 - 12D_1D_2 + 9D_2^2)z = 0$.

15. $(D_1^3 + 3D_1^2D_2 + 3D_1D_2^2 + D_2^3)z = 0$.

16. $(8D_1^3 - 12D_1^2D_2 + 6D_1D_2^2 - D_2^3)z = 0$.

17. $(2D_1^4 - 13D_1^3D_2 + 25D_1^2D_2^2 - 8D_1D_2^3 - 12D_2^4)z = 0$.

18. $(2D_1 - D_2)^2(2D_1 - 3D_2)^2z = 0$.

19. $(D_1^2 - 2D_1D_2 + 2D_2^2)z = 0$.

20. $(9D_1^2 - 6D_1D_2 + 5D_2^2)z = 0.$

21. $(3D_1^3 + 11D_1^2D_2 + 20D_1D_2^2 - 8D_2^3)z = 0.$

22. $(-2D_1^3 - 3D_1^2D_2 - 18D_1D_2^2 + 10D_2^3)z = 0.$

23. $(D_1^2 + 2D_1D_2 + 2D_2^2)^2z = 0.$

24. $(2D_1^2 - 6D_1D_2 + 5D_2^2)^2z = 0.$

74. Right-hand member not zero. We now study the case of an equation of the form

$$f(D_1, D_2)z = \phi(x, y), \tag{13}$$

where $f(D_1, D_2)$ is a homogeneous polynomial of degree n in D_1, D_2. This case is analogous to linear equations with one independent variable, treated in Chapter IV, and hence the general solution of (13) consists of the general solution of the *reduced* equation

$$f(D_1, D_2)z = 0,$$

which solution we shall call the *complementary function*, plus any particular solution of the complete equation. The problem at hand becomes, therefore, the problem of finding a particular solution of (13).

75. Special cases. Before attacking the problem in general, let us consider a few special forms of the function $\phi(x, y)$ which can be expediently handled by special methods. If, for example, z is a homogeneous polynomial of degree m, $f(D_1, D_2)z$ is a homogeneous polynomial of degree $m - n$; hence we state

NOTE I. *If $\phi(x, y)$ is a homogeneous polynomial of degree* m, *assume a particular solution of the form* $z = A_0 x^{m+n} + A_1 x^{m+n-1} y + \cdots + A_{m+n} y^{m+n}$, *operate on* z *by* f(D_1, D_2), *equate coefficients of corresponding terms in* f(D_1, D_2)z *and* $\phi(x, y)$ *and solve for the coefficients.*

If z is $\sin\left(\dfrac{n\pi}{2} + ay + bx\right) + \cos\left(\dfrac{n\pi}{2} + ay + bx\right)$, the homogeneous operator $f(D_1, D_2)$ of degree n reduces z to

$$f(-a, -b)\{\sin(ay + bx) + \cos(ay + bx)\}$$

and hence we deduce

NOTE II. *If* $\phi(x, y) \equiv c \cos(ay + bx) + d \cdot \sin(ay + bx)$, *assume a particular integral of the form*

$$z = A \cos(ay + bx) + B \sin(ay + bx),$$

operate on z by f(D_1, D_2), *equate* f(D_1, D_2)z *identically to* $\phi(x, y)$, *and solve for* A *and* B.   (See Exercises 8 and 9 below for exception.)

If $z = e^{ax+by}$, the homogeneous operator $f(D_1, D_2)$ reduces z to $f(a, b)e^{ax+by}$, and hence

NOTE III.   *If* $\phi(x, y) \equiv ce^{ax+by}$, *assume a particular solution of the form*

$$z = Ae^{ax+by},$$

operate on z by f(D_1, D_2), *equate the result identically to* $\phi(x, y)$, *and solve for* A.   (See Exercise 15 for exception.)

Exercises

Solve completely:

1. $(D_1^2 - 7D_1D_2 + 10D_2^2)z = 12x^2y + y^3$.

2. $(D_1^2 - 2D_1D_2 - 2D_2^2)z = x^3y^4$.

3. $(D_1^3 + D_1^2D_2 - 10D_1D_2^2 - 6D_2^3)z = x + y^2$.   *Hint:* Add the particular solutions obtained for $\phi(x, y) \equiv x$ to the particular solution obtained for $\phi(x, y) \equiv y^2$.

4. $(D_1^2 + 4D_1D_2 + 2D_2^2)(D_1^2 - 2D_1D_2 - 4D_2^2)z = x^2 + x^2y^2$.

5. $(D_1^2 - 2D_1D_2 - 3D_2^2)z = 20 \cos (y + 2x)$.

6. $(D_1^4 + 2D_1^3D_2 - 5D_1^2D_2^2 - 6D_1D_2^3)z = 5 \cos (2y + 3x) - \sin (2y + 3x)$.

7. $(4D_1^2 - 12D_1D_2 + 9D_2^2)z = \cos (x + y) + \cos (2x - y)$.

8. $(D_1^2 - 5D_1D_2 + 6D_2^2)z = \cos (y + 2x)$.   *Hint:* The method of the Note would be to try

$$z = A \cos (\pi + y + 2x) \equiv -A \cos (y + 2x),$$

but this must fail since

$$z = -A \cos (y + 2x)$$

is an instance of

$$z = F_1(y + 2x) + F_2(y + 3x),$$

which is the general solution of the reduced equation

$$(D_1^2 - 5D_1D_2 + 6D_2^2)z = 0.$$

Try

$$z = Ax \sin (y + 2x).$$

9. $(D_1^2 - 4D_1D_2 + 4D_2^2)z = \cos (y + 2x)$.   *Hint:* Try $z = Ax^2 \cos (y + 2x) + Bx^2 \sin (y + 2x)$ for the particular integral.

10. $(D_1^2 - 5D_1D_2) + 6D_2^2)z = \sin(y + 2x)$.

11. $(D_1^2 - 5D_1D_2 + 6D_2^2)z = 3\sin(y + 2x) + \cos(y + 3x)$.

12. $(D_1 + 2D_2)^3z = \cos x + \sin(y - 2x)$.

13. $(D_1^2 + 4D_1D_2 + 4D_2^2)z = 5e^{2x+3y}$.

14. $(D_1^3 - 4D_1^2D_2 - 5D_1D_2^2 + 24D_2^3)z = e^{3x-y}$.

15. $(D_1^2 - 7D_1D_2 + 10D_2^2)z = e^{y+2x}$.   *Hint:* The method of the Note fails, because $z = Ae^{y+2x}$ is a part of the complementary function.   Try $z = Axe^{y+2x}$.

16. $(D_1^3 + 6D_1^2D_2 + 12D_1D_2^2 + 8D_2^3)z = e^{y-2x}$.

17. $(D_1^3 - 4D_1^2D_2 + 5D_1D_2^2 - 2D_2^3)z = e^{y+x} + e^{y+2x} + e^{y+3x}$.

76. Inverse operators; factoring.   If we were to treat the operator $f(D_1, D_2)$ as an algebraic quantity, the equation

$$f(D_1, D_2)z = \phi(x, y) \tag{13}$$

would reduce to

$$z = \frac{1}{f(D_1, D_2)} \phi(x, y). \tag{14}$$

No such operator as $\dfrac{1}{f(D_1, D_2)}$ has been defined, but it is clear that if equation (14) is to mean the same as (13), then

$$f(D_1, D_2)z = f(D_1, D_2) \cdot \frac{1}{f(D_1, D_2)} \phi(x, y) \equiv \phi(x, y).$$

Now if

$$f(D_1, D_2) \equiv (D_1 - m_1D_2)(D_1 - m_2D_2) \cdots (D_1 - m_nD_2)$$
$$\equiv \prod_{i=1}^{n} (D_1 - m_iD_2),*$$

then

$$z = \frac{1}{\prod\limits_{i=1}^{n} (D_1 - m_iD_2)} \phi(x, y),$$

---

* The symbol Π stands for repeated multiplication; thus, $\prod\limits_{i=1}^{4} x_i \equiv x_1 x_2 x_3 x_4$.

As used here, the index runs from 1 to n, unless it appears as $\prod\limits_{i \neq r}$, when it runs from 1 to n, excepting the value r.

and this can be written as

$$z = \frac{1}{\prod\limits^{i \neq n} (D_1 - m_i D_2)} \left[\frac{1}{D_1 - m_n D_2} \cdot \phi(x, y) \right],$$

since

$$f(D_1, D_2) \equiv (D_1 - m_n D_2) \left[\overset{i \neq n}{\prod} (D_1 - m_i D_2) \right];$$

and hence

$$f(D_1, D_2)z \equiv (D_1 - m_n D_2) \left[\overset{i \neq n}{\prod} (D_1 - m_i D_2) \cdot \frac{1}{\prod\limits^{i \neq n} (D_1 - m_i D_2)} \right.$$

$$\left. \left\{ \frac{1}{(D_1 - m_n D_2)} \cdot \phi(x, y) \right\} \right]$$

$$\equiv (D_1 - m_n D_2) \left[\frac{1}{D_1 - m_n D_2} \cdot \phi(x, y) \right] \equiv \phi(x, y).$$

Then we may evaluate the expression $\dfrac{1}{f(D_1, D_2)} \phi(x, y)$ by factoring the operator and applying one factor at a time; this gives

$$\frac{1}{D_1 - m_1 D_2} \left[\frac{1}{D_1 - m_2 D_2} \left[\frac{1}{D_1 - m_3 D_2} \left[\cdots \right. \right. \right.$$

$$\left. \left. \left. \left[\frac{1}{D_1 - m_n D_2} \cdot \phi(x, y) \right] \cdots \right] \right] \right].$$

For example, consider the equation

$$(D_1^3 - D_1^2 D_2 - 4D_1 D_2^2 + 4D_2^3)z = \cos(3y + 2x),$$

or

$$(D_1 - D_2)(D_1 - 2D_2)(D_1 + 2D_2)z = \cos(3y + 2x).$$

The general solution is expressible as

$$z = F_1(y + x) + F_2(y + 2x) + F_3(y - 2x)$$

$$+ \frac{1}{D_1 - D_2} \left[\frac{1}{D_1 - 2D_2} \left\{ \frac{1}{D_1 + 2D_2} \cos(3y + 2x) \right\} \right], \quad (15)$$

where $F_1(y + x) + F_2(y + 2x) + F_3(y - 2x)$ is the complementary function, $i.$ $e.,$ the solution of $(D_1 - D_2)(D_1 - 2D_2)(D_1 + 2D_2)z = 0.$

To effect the operation $\dfrac{1}{D_1 + 2D_2} \cdot \cos(3y + 2x)$, call the result u, and write

$$(D_1 + 2D_2)u = \cos(3y + 2x).$$

This can be put into the form

$$u_x + 2u_y = \cos (3y + 2x),$$

and the corresponding Lagrange system is

$$\frac{dx}{1} = \frac{dy}{2} = \frac{du}{\cos (3y + 2x)}. \tag{16}$$

A solution of (16) is $y - 2x = a$, and if we substitute $a + 2x$ for y, the system (16) gives

$$\frac{dx}{1} = \frac{du}{\cos (8x + 3a)},$$

a solution of which is $u = \frac{1}{8} \sin (8x + 3a)$.   When a is replaced by $y - 2x$, this becomes

$$u = \frac{1}{8} \sin (3y + 2x).$$

The solution (15) now takes the form

$$z = F_1(y + x) + F_2(y + 2x) + F_3(y - 2x)$$
$$+ \frac{1}{D_1 - D_2} \left[\frac{1}{D_1 - 2D_2} \cdot \frac{1}{8} \sin (3y + 2x) \right].$$

Evaluation of the quantity $\dfrac{1}{D_1 - 2D_2} \cdot \dfrac{1}{8} \sin (3y + 2x)$ reduces the solution to

$$z = F_1(y + x) + F_2(y + 2x) + F_3(y - 2x)$$
$$+ \frac{1}{D_1 - D_2} \cdot \frac{1}{32} \cos (3y + 2x).$$

This, finally, reduces to

$$z = F_1(y + x) + F_2(y + 2x) + F_3(y - 2x) - \frac{1}{32} \sin (3y + 2x).$$

77. Partial fractions.   We may write

$$\frac{1}{f(D_1, D_2)} \equiv \frac{1}{D_2^n} \cdot \left[\frac{1}{\displaystyle\prod_{i=1}^{n} \left(\frac{D_1}{D_2} - m_i \right)} \right], \tag{17}$$

and resolve the second factor into partial fractions such that

$$
\frac{1}{\prod\limits_{i=1}^{n}\left(\dfrac{D_1}{D_2}-m_i\right)} \equiv \frac{A_1}{\dfrac{D_1}{D_2}-m_1} + \frac{A_2}{\dfrac{D_1}{D_2}-m_2} + \cdots + \frac{A_n}{\dfrac{D_1}{D_2}-m_n}
$$

$$
\equiv \sum_{i=1}^{n} \frac{A_i}{\dfrac{D_1}{D_2}-m_i},
$$

where the A_i are constants such that

$$
\sum_{i=1}^{n}\left[A_i \overset{j\neq i}{\prod}\left(\frac{D_1}{D_2}-m_j\right)\right] \equiv 1,
$$

when $\dfrac{D_1}{D_2}$ is considered as a variable. This can be written

$$
\sum_{i=1}^{n} A_i \overset{j\neq i}{\prod}(D_1 - m_j D_2) \equiv D_2^{n-1}.
$$

To show that the operator $\dfrac{1}{f(D_1, D_2)}$ may be replaced by this sum of partial operators, form the expression

$$
\left\{\frac{1}{D_2^n}\sum_{i=1}^{n}\left[\frac{A_i}{\dfrac{D_1}{D_2}-m_i}\right]\right\}\phi(x, y) \equiv \frac{1}{D_2^{n-1}}\sum_{i=1}^{n}\left[\frac{A_i}{D_1 - m_i D_2}\cdot\phi(x, y)\right],
$$

and operate on it by $f(D_1, D_2)$, obtaining

$$
f(D_1, D_2)\cdot\frac{1}{D_2^{n-1}}\sum_{i=1}^{n}\left[\frac{A_i}{D_1 - m_i D_2}\cdot\phi(x, y)\right]
$$

$$
\equiv \frac{1}{D_2^{n-1}}\sum_{i=1}^{n} f(D_1, D_2)\cdot\left[\frac{A_i}{D_1 - m_i D_2}\cdot\phi(x, y)\right]
$$

$$
\equiv \frac{1}{D_2^{n-1}}\sum_{i=1}^{n}\left[A_i \overset{j\neq i}{\prod}(D_1 - m_j D_2)\right]\cdot\phi(x, y)
$$

$$
\equiv \left[\frac{1}{D_2^{n-1}}\cdot D_2^{n-1}\right]\phi(x, y) \equiv \phi(x, y).
$$

In the example just demonstrated we have

$$\frac{1}{(D_1 - D_2)(D_1 - 2D_2)(D_1 + 2D_2)} \cos{(3y + 2x)}$$

$$\equiv \frac{1}{D_2^3} \cdot \frac{1}{\left(\dfrac{D_1}{D_2} - 1\right)\left(\dfrac{D_1}{D_2} - 2\right)\left(\dfrac{D_1}{D_2} + 2\right)} \cdot \cos{(3y + 2x)}$$

$$\equiv \frac{1}{D_2^3} \left[\frac{-\tfrac{1}{3}}{\dfrac{D_1}{D_2} - 1} + \frac{\tfrac{1}{4}}{\dfrac{D_1}{D_2} - 2} + \frac{\tfrac{1}{12}}{\dfrac{D_1}{D_2} + 2}\right] \cos{(3y + 2x)}$$

$$\equiv \frac{1}{D_2^2} \left[\frac{1}{-3D_1 + 3D_2} + \frac{1}{4D_1 - 8D_2} + \frac{1}{12D_1 + 24D_2}\right] \cos{(3y + 2x)}$$

$$\equiv \frac{1}{D_2^2} \left[\frac{1}{3} \sin{(3y + 2x)} - \frac{1}{16} \sin{(3y + 2x)} + \frac{1}{96} \sin{(3y + 2x)}\right]$$

$$\equiv \frac{1}{D_2^2} \left[\frac{9}{32} \sin{(3y + 2x)}\right] \equiv \frac{1}{D_2}\left[-\frac{3}{32} \cos{(3y + 2x)}\right]$$

$$\equiv -\frac{1}{32} \sin{(3y + 2x)}.$$

78. Case of α_i not all different from zero. The assumption made on page 233, that no α_i is zero, has been in effect throughout all the intervening pages. Suppose now that an equation

$$f(D_1, D_2)z = \phi(x, y)$$

is given, in which some of the α's are zero. It may be written as

$$(\alpha_1 D_1 + \beta_1 D_2)(\alpha_2 D_1 + \beta_2 D_2) \, \cdots \, (\alpha_j D_1 + \beta_j D_2)$$
$$\cdot D_2^{n-i} \cdot z = \phi(x, y),$$

where $\alpha_i \neq 0 \, (i = 1, 2, \cdots, j)$. We may define w by the equation

$$D_2^{n-i}z = w,$$

and obtain

$$(\alpha_1 D_1 + \beta_1 D_2)(\alpha_2 D_1 + \beta_2 D_2) \, \cdots \, (\alpha_j D_1 + \beta_j D_2)w = \phi(x, y).$$

The solution of this may be found by any of the methods already discussed, and then we may obtain

$$z = \int \int \, \cdots \, \int w \, (dy)^{n-i},$$

where each quadrature is performed with x regarded as constant, and an arbitrary function of x is introduced with each quadrature in place of an arbitrary constant.

Exercises

1. Find the general solution of each of the following equations:

(a) $(D_1^2 - 7D_1D_2 + 10D_2^2)z = \dfrac{1}{x^3}$.

(b) $(D_1^2 - 2D_1D_2 + D_2^2)z = xe^{3x+5y}$.

(c) $(D_1^3 + 2D_1^2D_2 - D_1D_2^2 - 2D_2^3)z = \sqrt{3x - 2y}$.

(d) $(D_1^3 + 3D_1^2D_2 + 3D_1D_2^2 + D_2^3)z = \phi(y - x)$.

(e) $(8D_1^3 - 12D_1^2D_2 + 6D_1D_2^2 - D_2^3)z = f(2y + x) + x^3y$.

(f) $(D_1^2 + 6D_1D_2 + D_2^2)(D_1^2 - 6D_1D_2 - 5D_2^2)z =$
$x \cos (y - 3x)$.

(g) $(D_1^2 - D_1D_2 - 6D_2^2)z = (x^2 + y^2)$.

(h) $(D_1^3 - 6D_1^2D_2 + 11D_1D_2^2 - 6D_2^3)z = \sin (x + y) +$
$\cos (2x + y) + e^{3x+y}$.

(i) $(D_1^3 + 2D_1^2D_2 - D_1D_2^2 - 2D_2^3)z = x^2 \sin (2x - 3y) +$
$(x + y)^{2/3}$.

(j) $(D_1^2 + 4D_1D_2 - 6D_2^2)z = (x - 5y)e^{x+y}$.

(k) $(D_1^4 - 5D_1^2D_2^2 + 4D_2^4)z = x(y^2 - 4x^2) + e^x(y^2 - x^2)$.

(l) $(9D_1^2 - 6D_1D_2 + 5D_2^2)z = e^x(4 \cos y + 6 \sin y)$.

2. If a and b are two constants, and f is a homogeneous function of degree n of two arguments such that $f(a, b) \neq 0$, show that a particular integral of

$$f(D_1, D_2)z = \phi(ax + by)$$

is

$$z = \frac{1}{f(a, b)} \int_{c_n}^{ax+by} \int_{c_{n-1}}^{u} \int_{c_{n-2}}^{u} \cdots \int_{c_1}^{u} \phi(u)(du)^n,$$

where c_i are arbitrary constants.

3. Employ the result of Exercise 2 to find particular integrals of:

(a) $(D_1^4 - 6D_1^3D_2 + 5D_1^2D_2^2 - 4D_1D_2^3 + D_2^4)z = (2x + y)^{1/2}$.

(b) $(D_1^6 + 3D_2^6)z = (4x + 3y)^3 + e^{x-y}$.

(c) $(D_1^3 - 2D_1^2D_2 + 4D_1D_2^2)z = \cos (2x) + \sin (x - y)$.

4. Show that the equation $(bD_1 - aD_2)^nz = \phi(ax + by)$ has as particular integral $z = \dfrac{x^n}{n!b!} \phi(ax + by)$ if $b \neq 0$.

5. By use of Exercise 4, find particular solutions of:

(a) $(D_1 - 3D_2)^4z = (3x + y)e^{(3x+y)}$.

(b) $(D_1^3 + 3D_1^2D_2 + 3D_1D_2^2 + D_2^3)z = \cosh (y - x)$.

(c) $(D_1 + 2D_2)^2 z = \sqrt{y - 2x}$.

6. If $D_1^n z \equiv \dfrac{\partial^n z}{\partial x_1^n}$, $D_2^n z \equiv \dfrac{\partial^n z}{\partial x_2^n}$, $D_3^n z \equiv \dfrac{\partial^n z}{\partial x_3^n}$ $(n = 0, 1, 2, \cdots)$, show that $(D_1 + aD_2 + bD_3)z = 0$ has the general solution

$$z = \phi(x_3 - bx_1, x_2 - ax_1).$$

7. Find the general solution of

$$(D_1 + a_1D_2 + b_1D_3)(D_1 + a_2D_2 + b_2D_3)z = 0.$$

8. Find the general solution of

$$(D_1 - 2D_2 + 3D_3)(D_1 + D_2 - 2D_3)z = e^{3x_1 + x_2 - x_3}.$$

9. Find the general solution of

$$(D_1 - D_2 + D_3)(D_1 + 2D_2 + 2D_3)z = \sin x_1 + \cos (x_2 - x_3).$$

79. Non-homogeneous equations. Let us now consider equations of the form

$$f(D_1, D_2)z = \phi(x, y), \tag{18}$$

where the function $f(D_1, D_2)$ is no longer homogeneous in D_1 and D_2. We divide the discussion into two parts, as above, the first being the problem of finding the *complementary function*, viz., the general solution of the *reduced* equation

$$f(D_1, D_2)z = 0, \tag{19}$$

and the second being the problem of finding a particular integral of (18). As before, the general solution of (18) is the sum of a particular integral and the complementary function.

80. Right-hand member zero. If the function $f(D_1, D_2)$ is the product of n linear factors $D_1 + a_iD_2 + b_i$, we have, as a solution of (19),

$$z = z_1 + z_2 + \cdots + z_n,$$

where $z = z_i(x, y)$ is the general solution of

$$(D_1 + a_iD_2 + b_i)z = 0.$$

This equation, which can be written in the form

$$z_x + a_iz_y + b_iz = 0, \tag{20}$$

is of the first order and degree, and the corresponding Lagrange system is

$$\frac{dx}{1} = \frac{dy}{a_i} = \frac{dz}{-b_iz},$$

of which a solution is

$$\begin{cases} y - a_i x = c_1, \\ \log z + b_i x = c_2. \end{cases}$$

Hence the general solution of (20) is

$$\phi(\log z + b_i x, \, y - a_i x) = 0,$$

where ϕ is an arbitrary function. This can be solved for $\log z + b_i x$, and put into the form

$$z = e^{-b_i x} f(y - a_i x),$$

where $f(y - a_i x)$ is an arbitrary function. We have, then, the conclusion that a solution of (19) is

$$z = \sum_{i=1}^{n} e^{-b_i x} f_i(y - a_i x),$$

where $f_1, \cdots, f_n$ are n arbitrary functions.

81. Particular integrals. As we have found on previous occasions, certain forms of the function $\phi(x, y)$ lend themselves to solution by inspection. For example, if $\phi(x, y) \equiv e^{ax+by} v(x, y)$, we have

$$D_1 \phi \equiv a e^{ax+by} v(x, y) + e^{ax+by} D_1 v(x, y) \equiv e^{ax+by}(D_1 + a) v(x, y),$$

and similarly.

$$D_2 \phi \equiv e^{ax+by}(D_2 + b) v(x, y).$$

From these we can readily establish, by induction,

$$f(D_1, D_2) e^{ax+by} v(x, y) \equiv e^{ax+by} f(D_1 + a, D_2 + b) v(x, y). \quad (21)$$

Formula (21) also holds for inverse operators, as we can see if we let

$$f(D_1 + a, D_2 + b) v(x, y) \equiv g(x, y).$$

Then,

$$v(x, y) \equiv \frac{1}{f(D_1 + a, D_2 + b)} g(x, y),$$

and substitution into (21) gives

$$f(D_1, D_2)\left[e^{ax+by} \cdot \frac{1}{f(D_1 + a, D_2 + b)} \cdot g(x, y) \right]$$

$$\equiv e^{ax+by} \cdot [f(D_1 + a, D_2 + b)] \left[\frac{1}{f(D_1 + a, D_2 + b)} \cdot g(x, y) \right]$$

$$\equiv e^{ax+by} g(x, y);$$

hence, upon operating by $\dfrac{1}{f(D_1, D_2)}$, we have

$$\frac{1}{f(D_1, D_2)} \, e^{ax+by}g(x, y) \equiv e^{ax+by} \cdot \frac{1}{f(D_1 + a, D_2 + b)} \cdot g(x, y). \quad (22)$$

The formula holds for any function $g(x, y)$ having continuous partial derivatives of all orders called for by the operator.

If $\phi(x, y) \equiv e^{ax+by}$, then we may apply (22) to obtain

$$\frac{1}{f(D_1, D_2)} \, \phi(x, y) \equiv e^{ax+by} \frac{1}{f(D_1 + a, D_2 + b)} \cdot 1 \equiv e^{ax+by} \cdot \frac{1}{f(a, b)}.$$

This result may be checked by direct use of the operator $f(D_1, D_2)$ and is correct if defined, *i. e.*, if $f(a, b) \neq 0$. In case $f(a, b) = 0$, consider e^{ax+by} as the limit of $e^{ax+hx+by}$ as h approaches zero. We thus obtain the equation

$$\frac{1}{f(D_1, D_2)} \, e^{ax+by+hx} \equiv \frac{1}{f(a + h, b)} \cdot e^{ax+hx+by} \equiv \frac{1}{f(a + h, b)} \, e^{ax+by} \cdot e^{hx}$$

$$\equiv \frac{1}{f(a + h, b)} \, e^{ax+by} \left(1 + hx + \frac{h^2x^2}{2!} + \frac{h^3x^3}{3!} + \cdots \right)$$

$$\equiv \frac{e^{ax+by}}{f(a + h, b)} + \frac{he^{ax+by}}{f(a + h, b)} \cdot \left(x + \frac{hx^2}{2!} + \frac{h^2x^3}{3!} + \cdots \right).$$

Here we must recall that we seek a particular integral of the equation

$$f(D_1, D_2)z = e^{ax+by+hx}, \quad (23)$$

and that the term $\dfrac{e^{ax+by}}{f(a + h, b)}$ is included in the complementary function. Therefore, a particular integral of (23) is

$$\frac{he^{ax+by}}{f(a + h, b)} \left(x + \frac{hx^2}{2!} + \frac{h^2x^3}{3!} + \cdots \right).$$

Now,

$$\lim_{h \to 0} \frac{hxe^{ax+by}}{f(a + h, b) - f(a, b)} \equiv \frac{xe^{ax+by}}{f_a(a, b)},$$

and we may insert the term $-f(a, b)$ in the denominator because its value is zero. By repetition of this process we may show that, if $f_a(a, b) = 0$, we have

$$z = \frac{1}{f(D_1, D_2)} \, e^{ax+by} \equiv \frac{x^2}{2f_{aa}(a, b)} \, e^{ax+by}$$

as a particular integral.

In case $\varphi(x, y) \equiv A \sin (ax + by) + B \cos (ax + by)$, let

$$\frac{1}{f(D_1, D_2)}\, \varphi(x, y) \equiv A_1 \sin (ax + by) + B_1 \cos (ax + by),$$

operate by $f(D_1, D_2)$, and equate coefficients of $\sin (ax + by)$ and $\cos (ax + by)$.   If the equations are inconsistent, then try

$$A_1 x \sin (ax + by) + B_1 x \cos (ax + by),$$

and so on.

It is, of course, permissible to factor the inverse operator and to apply one factor at a time if the evaluation can be carried out.   An important case of this type arises when $\varphi(x, y)$ is a polynomial. We then write

$$\frac{1}{f(D_1, D_2)}\, \varphi(x, y) \equiv \left(\frac{1}{D_1 + a_1 D_2 + b_1}\right) \cdots \left(\frac{1}{D_1 + a_n D_2 + b_n}\right) \varphi(x, y),$$

and evaluate the expression one factor at a time.   If $b_n = 0$,

$$\frac{1}{D_1 + a_n D_2 + b_n} \cdot \varphi(x, y)$$

can be reduced to $\int \varphi(x, c + a_n x)dx$ by the methods of Chapter VIII, with c replaced by $y - a_n x$ after integration.   The result is another polynomial.   If b_n is not zero, we can write

$$\frac{1}{D_1 + a_n D_2 + b_n} \equiv \frac{1}{b_n}\left[1 + \frac{D_1 + a_n D_2}{b_n}\right]^{-1}$$

$$\equiv \frac{1}{b_n}\left[1 - \frac{D_1 + a_n D_2}{b_n} + \left(\frac{D_1 + a_n D_2}{b_n}\right)^2 - \cdots \right],$$

and, since there are only a finite number of the derivatives of a polynomial which are different from zero, $\dfrac{1}{D_1 + a_n D_2 + b_n}\, \varphi(x, y)$ reduces to another polynomial.

Exercises

Find general solutions of the following:

1. $(D_1 + 2D_2 - 3)(D_1 D_2 + D_2^2 - D_2)z = 0.$

2. $(D_1 + 2D_2 - 3)(D_1 D_2 + D_2^2 - D_2)z = x^2 - 2xy.$

3. $(D_1^3 - 4D_1^2 D_2 + 5D_1^2)z = 0.$

4. $(D_1^3 - 4D_1^2D_2 + 5D_1^2)z = e^{2x+y}(x - y)$.

5. $(D_1^3D_2 + 2D_1^2D_2^2 - D_1^2D_2)z = 0$.

6. $(D_1^3D_2 + 2D_1^2D_2^2 - D_1^2D_2)z = \sin(x - 7y)$.

7. $(D_1 + D_2 + 1)(D_1 + D_2 + 2)(D_1 + D_2)z = 0$.

8. $(D_1 + D_2 + 1)(D_1 + D_2 + 2)(D_1 + D_2)z = e^{5x-y}\sinh(x - y)$.

9. $(D_1^2 - 4D_2^2 + D_1 + 2D_2)z = 0$.

10. $(D_1^2 - 4D_2^2 + D_1 + 2D_2)z = x^2 + y^3 + e^{x-4y}$.

11. $(D_1 + 2D_2 - 1)(D_1 - D_2 - 3)(D_1 + D_2 - 5)z = 0$.

12. $(D_1 + 2D_2 - 1)(D_1 - D_2 - 3)(D_1 + D_2 - 5)z = \cosh(x + 5y + 6)$.

13. $(D_1^2 + D_1D_2 + D_2)z = z$.

14. $(D_1^2 + D_1D_2 + D_2)z = z + e^{3x-y+1}$.

82. Other forms of $f(D_1, D_2)$. To solve the equation

$$f(D_1, D_2)z = \varphi(x, y)$$

in case $f(D_1, D_2)$ is not the product of linear factors, let us first assume $z = ce^{ax+by}$ to be a solution of the reduced equation

$$f(D_1, D_2)z = 0.$$

Substituting this value into the equation, we obtain

$$f(a, b)e^{ax+by} = 0,$$

which is true if, and only if, $f(a, b) = 0$. Now the equation

$$f(a, b) = 0$$

is satisfied by an infinity of pairs of numbers (a, b), and hence we may write as our complementary function

$$z = \sum_i c_i e^{a_i x + b_i y}, \qquad f(a_i, b_i) = 0.$$

In finding a particular integral, we employ special methods to evaluate the operation $\dfrac{1}{f(D_1, D_2)} \cdot \varphi(x, y)$. If $\varphi(x, y) \equiv e^{ax+by} \cdot g(x, y)$, we may employ formula (22) to reduce $\dfrac{1}{f(D_1, D_2)} e^{ax+by} g(x, y)$ to $e^{ax+by} \cdot \dfrac{1}{f(D_1 + a, D_2 + b)} g(x, y)$. If $\varphi(x, y) \equiv e^{\alpha x + \beta y}$, we have, as before,

$$\frac{1}{f(D_1, D_2)} e^{\alpha x + \beta y} \equiv \frac{1}{f(\alpha, \beta)} e^{\alpha x + \beta y},$$

unless $f(\alpha, \beta) = 0$. In the latter case we have, again,

$$\frac{1}{f(D_1, D_2)} e^{\alpha x + \beta y} \equiv \frac{x e^{\alpha x + \beta y}}{f_\alpha(\alpha, \beta)},$$

unless $f_\alpha(\alpha, \beta) = 0$, and so on. If $\varphi(x, y) \equiv A \sin (ax + by) + B \cos (ax + by)$, let

$$\frac{1}{f(D_1, D_2)} \varphi(x, y) \equiv A' x^n \sin (ax + by) + B' x^n \cos (ax + by),$$

where n is zero if the resulting equations can be solved for A' and B', and where otherwise it is the smallest positive integer for which the equations can be solved.

If $\varphi(x, y)$ is a polynomial, the expression

$$\frac{1}{f(D_1, D_2)} \varphi(x, y)$$

may be evaluated by expanding $\dfrac{1}{f(D_1, D_2)}$ into an infinite series.

83. Equations reducible to linear equations with constant coefficients. We shall close the treatment of linear partial differential equations of any order with the observation that an equation of the form

$$\sum_{r, s} a_{rs} x^r y^s \frac{\partial^{r+s} z}{\partial x^r \partial y^s} = \psi(x, y)$$

can be reduced to one of the form

$$\sum_{r, s} b_{rs} \frac{\partial^{r+s} z}{\partial \xi^r \partial \eta^s} = \varphi(\xi, \eta)$$

by the transformation $x = e^\xi$, $y = e^\eta$. After reduction, the equation thus becomes one with constant coefficients and may be treated by the methods of the preceding section. In its solution we may replace ξ by $\log x$, and η by $\log y$, to obtain a solution of the given equation.

Exercises

1. Solve the following:

    (a) $(D_1^3 - 2D_1 D_2 + D_2^2 - D_1 + 8)z = e^{2x-y}$.

    (b) $(D_1^2 + D_1 D_2 - D_2^2 + D_1 - D_2)z = \sin (x - y) + \cos (x - 2y)$.

(c) $(D_1^3 + 3D_2^2 + D_1 - 8)z = e^{4x-5y+6} \cos (x + 2y)$.

(d) $(D_1^2 + 2D_1D_2^2 - 3D_2 + 5)z = x^2 + y^3$.

(e) $(D_1^3 + 3D_2^3 + D_1 - 5D_2)z = \sinh (3x - y) +$
$\cosh (3x - y)$.

(f) $(D_1^2 + D_1D_2 + D_1 - D_2 + 1)z = e^{2x}(x^2 - 3xy^2)$.

(g) $(D_1^3 + 3D_2^3 + 3)z = e^{3x-2y}$.

(h) $(D_1^2 + D_1D_2 + D_2^2 + 2D_1 - 3D_2 + 9)z = \sin (3x + 2y)$.

(i) $x^2 z_{xx} - 2xyz_{xy} - y^2 z_{yy} - xz_x + yz_y - 5z = 7x - 5y$.

2. Show that the equation $F(D_1, D_2)z = 0$ is satisfied by

$$z = \frac{\partial}{\partial a} \left(e^{ax+f(a)y}\right) \equiv e^{ax+f(a)y}[x + f'(a)y],$$

where $F(a, f(a)) = 0$. *Hint:* Since $z = \dfrac{e^{ax+f(a)y}}{\Delta a}$ and

$$z = \frac{e^{(a+\Delta a)x+f(a+\Delta a)y}}{\Delta a}$$

are both solutions, their difference, $z = \dfrac{e^{(a+\Delta a)x+f(a+\Delta a)y} - e^{ax+f(a)y}}{\Delta a}$
is a solution, and the limit of this difference as $\Delta a \to 0$ is the solution proposed.

84. Laplace's equation. We conclude this chapter with a few remarks on a celebrated equation, bearing the name of Laplace* and which the student will meet frequently in mathematical physics, *viz.*,

$$v_{xx} + v_{yy} = 0 \qquad (24)$$

or

$$v_{xx} + v_{yy} + v_{zz} = 0, \qquad (25)$$

in the cases, respectively, of two, or three, independent variables. These equations are satisfied, at a point (x, y) in the plane, or (x, y, z) in space, by the function v which represents the potential due to a gravitational, or an electric, or a magnetic, field of force, or again, the temperature due to a steady flow of heat, in a plane lamina or in a solid.

Equation (24), put in the form $(D_1^2 + D_2^2)v = 0$, has been disposed of in the treatment of Equation (6), Section 73, and its solu-

---

* Pierre Simon Laplace (1749–1827), great French mathematician and astronomer.

tion is given by (8) of that article as

$$v = \sum_{j=1}^{\infty} (c_j e^{g_j y} \cos g_j x + d_j e^{h_j y} \sin h_j x). \tag{26}$$

A classical problem in the study of heat flow is that of determining the temperature at any point in a thin rectangular plate of width π and of infinite length, subject to the conditions that the temperature be unity along the short edge, zero along the long edges, and that, further, the temperature decrease continuously as one recedes from the short edge.   The plate is supposed to be insulated so that there is no loss of heat.   The temperature, v, is, then, represented by (26), subject to the conditions (under proper choice of axes)

$$v = 0 \text{ when } x = 0, \tag{I}$$
$$v = 0 \text{ when } x = \pi. \tag{II}$$
$$v = 0 \text{ for } y \ = \ \infty. \tag{III}$$
$$v = 1 \text{ when } y = 0. \tag{IV}$$

Conditions (I) and (II) will, evidently, be met by choosing $c_j = 0$, and (III) by choosing $h_1 = -1$, $h_2 = 0$, $h_3 = -1$, $h_4 = 0$, $\cdots$, so that we get

$$v = d_1 e^{-y} \sin x + d_3 e^{-3y} \sin 3x + d_5 e^{-5y} \sin 5x + \cdots .$$

To fulfill (IV), now, note the expansion, valid for $0 < x < \pi$,

$$1 = \frac{4}{\pi} \left(\sin x + \frac{1}{3} \sin 3x + \frac{1}{5} \sin 5x + \cdots \right).* \tag{27}$$

Hence, if we choose $d_1 = \dfrac{4}{\pi}$, $d_3 = \dfrac{4}{3\pi}$, $d_5 = \dfrac{4}{5\pi}$, $\cdots$ and obtain

$$v = \frac{4}{\pi} \left(e^{-y} \sin x + \frac{1}{3} e^{-3y} \sin 3x + \frac{1}{5} e^{-5y} \sin 5x + \cdots \right), \tag{28}$$

we have the desired function, v.

To solve (25), transform it to cylindrical coördinates, by the substitutions

$$x = r \cos \theta,$$
$$y = r \sin \theta,$$
$$z = z.$$

* *Fourier Series and Spherical Harmonics*, by W. E. Byerly, p. 39.

We leave it to the student, as an exercise (Exercise 2 below) to derive the new form of (25) as

$$v_{rr} + \frac{v_{\theta\theta}}{r^2} + \frac{v_r}{r} + v_{zz} = 0.$$

Assume now a solution in the form

$$v(r,\,\theta,\,z) = f(r) \cdot g(\theta) \cdot h(z).$$

Then the last equation takes the form

$$\frac{f''(r)}{f(r)} + \frac{g''(\theta)}{r^2 g(\theta)} + \frac{f'(r)}{rf(r)} = -\frac{h''(z)}{h(z)},$$

since $v_{rr} = f''(r) \cdot g(\theta) \cdot h(z)$, $v_{\theta\theta} = f(r) \cdot g''(\theta) \cdot h(z)$, and so forth. The left-hand member is, evidently, independent of z. Hence, so is the right-hand member. Consequently, $-\dfrac{h''(z)}{h(z)}$ is a constant, say $-k^2$ (and, of course, the left-hand member equals $-k^2$). The equation $\dfrac{h''(z)}{h(z)} = k^2$, or $(D^2 - k^2)h = 0$, gives at once

$$h(z) = c_1 e^{kz} + c_2 e^{-kz}.$$

Turning to the left-hand member, set equal to $-k^2$, we obtain

$$\frac{r^2 f''(r)}{f(r)} + \frac{rf'(r)}{f(r)} + k^2 r^2 = -\frac{g''(\theta)}{g(\theta)},$$

and, as a while ago, we conclude that $-\dfrac{g''(\theta)}{g(\theta)}$, being independent of θ, as is the left-hand side, must equal a constant, say m^2. Thus

$$\frac{g''(\theta)}{g(\theta)} = -m^2,$$

and

$$r^2 f''(r) + rf'(r) + k^2 r^2 f(r) = m^2 f(r).$$

The first of these gives

$$g(\theta) = c_3 \cos m\theta + c_4 \sin m\theta.$$

The second may be revised, by setting $kr = R$ (hence, $f(r) = F(R)$, $f'(r) = kF'(R)$, $f''(r) = k^2 F''(R)$) to yield

$$R^2 F''(R) + RF'(R) + (R^2 - m^2)F(R) = 0.$$

This is a Bessel Equation [see (24) Section 49], and has for its solution

$$F(R) = c_5 J_m(R) + c_6 J_{-m}(R),$$

or

$$f(r) = c_5 J_m(kr) + c_6 J_{-m}(kr).$$

It thus develops that a solution of (25) is

$$v(r, \theta, z) = (c_1 e^{kz} + c_2 e^{-kz})(c_3 \cos m\theta + c_4 \sin m\theta) \\ (c_5 J_m(kr) + c_6 J_{-m}(kr)), \quad (29)$$

and, by the linearity of the equation, the sum of any finite (or infinite) number of such values of v is a solution.

A sufficient number of initial conditions must, of course, be provided in a given problem, to fix the arbitrary constants as well as the values of k and m.

Exercises

1. Solve (24) by assuming $v = f(x) \cdot g(y)$.   *Hint:* The equation becomes $\dfrac{f''(x)}{f(x)} = -\dfrac{g''(y)}{g(y)}$. Hence, each side is a constant, say $-g^2$. Solve and obtain $f(x) = c_1 \cos gx + c_2 \sin gx$, $g(y) = c_3 e^{gy} + c_4 e^{-gy}$.

Hence, $v = \displaystyle\sum_{j=1}^{\infty} (c_{1j} \cos g_j x + c_{2j} \sin g_j x)(c_{3j} e^{g_j y} + c_{4j} e^{-g_j y})$ is a solution, by the linearity of (24). Assume, without proof, that the summation from $j = 1$ to $j = \infty$ is also a solution. Identify this solution with (26) of the text by setting $c_{1j} c_{3j} = c_j$, $c_{2j} c_{3j} = 0$, $h_j = -g_j$, $c_{1j} c_{4j} = 0$, $c_{2j} c_{4j} = -d_j$.

2. Solve (24) by transforming to polar coördinates.   *Hint:* By $x = r \cos \theta$, $y = r \sin \theta$, and $v_x = v_r r_x + v_\theta \theta_x$, $v_y = v_r r_y + v_\theta \theta_y$, and so forth, obtain

$$v_{xx} = v_r \frac{\sin^2 \theta}{r} + 2v_\theta \frac{\sin \theta \cos \theta}{r^2} + v_{rr} \cos^2 \theta - 2v_{r\theta} \frac{\sin \theta \cos \theta}{r} \\ + v_{\theta\theta} \frac{\sin^2 \theta}{r^2},$$

$$v_{yy} = v_r \frac{\cos^2 \theta}{r} - 2v_\theta \frac{\sin \theta \cos \theta}{r^2} + v_{rr} \sin^2 \theta + 2v_{r\theta} \frac{\sin \theta \cos \theta}{r} \\ + v_{\theta\theta} \frac{\cos^2 \theta}{r^2},$$

thus reducing (24) to

$$\frac{v_r}{r} + v_{rr} + \frac{v_{\theta\theta}}{r^2} = 0.$$

Assume as a solution, $v = f(r) \cdot g(\theta)$, and reduce the last equation to

$$\frac{-g''(\theta)}{g(\theta)} = \frac{rf'(r) + r^2f''(r)}{f(r)}.$$

Conclude that each side of the equation is a constant, say K^2.

Solve $\dfrac{g''(\theta)}{g(\theta)} = -K^2$, also $\dfrac{rf'(r) + r^2f''(r)}{f(r)} = K^2$,

getting

$$f(r) = c_1 r^k + c_2 r^{-k}, \quad g(\theta) = c_3 \cos K\theta + c_4 \sin K\theta,$$

and hence

$$v = (c_1 r^k + c_2 r^{-k})(c_3 \cos K\theta + c_4 \sin K\theta).$$

Therefore, by the linearity of the equation,

$$v = \sum_K (c_{1K} r^K + c_{2K} r^{-K})(c_{3K} \cos K\theta + c_{4K} \sin K\theta).$$

3. For the illustration in the text, compute the temperature, to three decimal places,

(a) at the point $\left(\dfrac{\pi}{2}, 1\right)$ of the plate;

(b) at the point $\left(\dfrac{\pi}{4}, 2\right)$ of the plate.

4. (a) Transform Equation (25) to spherical coördinates, *i. e.*, by $x = \rho \sin \varphi \cos \theta$, $y = \rho \sin \varphi \sin \theta$, $z = \rho \cos \varphi$.

(b) Solve the equation obtained in (a) under the hypothesis that v is independent of θ, *i. e.*, v is a function of ρ and φ only.

Hint: The equation becomes

$$\rho^2 v_{\rho\rho} + v_{\varphi\varphi} + 2pv_\rho + \cot \varphi \cdot v_\varphi = 0.$$

Assume as a solution $v = f(\rho) \cdot g(\varphi)$, and derive

$$\frac{\rho^2 f''(\rho)}{f(\rho)} + \frac{2\rho f'(\rho)}{f(\rho)} = \frac{-g''(\varphi)}{g(\varphi)} - \cot \varphi \frac{g'(\varphi)}{g(\varphi)}.$$

Set each equal to a constant, say k^2. From the left-hand member, set equal to k^2, obtain

$$f(\rho) = c_1 \rho^{\frac{-1+\sqrt{1+4k^2}}{2}} + c_2 \rho^{\frac{-1-\sqrt{1+4k^2}}{2}}.$$

Let $m = \dfrac{-1 + \sqrt{1 + 4k^2}}{2}$; hence $-m - 1 = \dfrac{-1 - \sqrt{1 + 4k^2}}{2}$, $k^2 = m^2 + m$, and obtain,

$$f(\rho) = c_1\rho^m + \frac{c_2}{\rho^{m+1}}.$$

The right-hand member, set equal to k^2, yields

$$g''(\varphi) + \cot \varphi \cdot g'(\varphi) + k^2 g(\varphi) = 0,$$

or

$$g''(\varphi) + \cot \varphi \cdot g'(\varphi) + (m^2 + m)g(\varphi) = 0.$$

Revise this by setting $u = \cos \varphi$, whence $g(\varphi) = h(u)$, $g'(\varphi) = -\sin \varphi \cdot h'(u)$, $g''(\varphi) = h''(u) \cdot \sin^2 \varphi - h'(u) \cdot \cos \varphi$, and reduce the last equation to

$$(1 - u^2)h''(u) - 2uh'(u) + m(m + 1)h(u) = 0,$$

a Legendre equation [see (18), Section 48], which has for a solution, if m is taken as a positive integer,

$$h(u) \equiv P_m(u), \qquad (P_m(u) \text{ a Legendre Polynomial of degree } m),$$

i. e.,

$$g(\varphi) = P_m(\cos \varphi),$$

and the final result is

$$v = \left[c_1\rho^m + \frac{c_2}{\rho^{m+1}} \right] P_m(\cos \varphi), \text{ where } m \text{ is a positive integer.}$$

Again, by the linearity of the equation, we get as a value of v satisfying the equation

$$v = \sum_{m=0}^{\infty} \left[A_m\rho^m + \frac{B_m}{\rho^{m+1}} \right] P_m(\cos \varphi).$$

5. (a) Find the temperature at any point in a thin rectangular plate of width 30 units and of infinite length, subject to the conditions that the temperature be 20° along the short edge, 0° along the long edges, and decrease continually as one recedes from the short edge. The plate is insulated so that there is no loss of heat. *Hint:* Assume the same arrangement of axes as led to conditions I–IV in the text. Then the temperature, $v(x, y)$, is a solution of the equation

$$v_{xx} + v_{yy} = 0,$$

subject to the conditions

$$v(0, y) = 0, \qquad v(30, y) = 0,$$
$$v(x, \infty) = 0, \qquad v(x, 0) = 20.$$

As in Exercise 1 assume $v = f(x) \cdot g(y)$ and obtain

$$v = (c_1 \cos gx + c_2 \sin gx)(c_3 e^{gy} + c_4 e^{-gy}).$$

Show that the first three conditions above will be met by

$$c_1 = 0, \; g = \frac{n\pi}{30}, \; c_3 = 0 \qquad (n = 1, 2, 3, \cdots)$$

so that

$$v = c_2 \sin \frac{n\pi x}{30} \cdot c_4 e^{\frac{-n\pi y}{30}}$$

and by the linearity of the equations, setting $c_2 c_4 = A_n$,

$$v = A_1 \sin \frac{\pi x}{30} e^{\frac{-\pi y}{30}} + A_2 \sin \frac{2\pi x}{30} \cdot e^{\frac{-2\pi y}{30}} + A_3 \sin \frac{3\pi x}{30} \cdot e^{\frac{-3\pi y}{30}} + \cdots .$$

To meet the fourth condition above, we must have

$$20 = A_1 \cdot \sin \frac{\pi x}{30} + A_2 \cdot \sin \frac{2\pi x}{30} + A_3 \sin \frac{3\pi x}{30} + \cdots .$$

Equation (27) of the text gives

$$20 = \frac{80}{\pi} \left(\sin u + \frac{1}{3} \sin 3u + \frac{1}{5} \sin 5u + \cdots \right) \quad 0 < u < \pi,$$

hence,

$$20 = \frac{80}{\pi} \left(\sin \frac{\pi x}{30} + \frac{1}{3} \sin \frac{3\pi x}{30} + \frac{1}{5} \sin \frac{5\pi x}{30} + \cdots \right) \quad 0 < x < 30.$$

Obtain now the solution

$$v = \frac{80}{\pi} \left(\sin \frac{\pi x}{30} \cdot e^{\frac{-\pi y}{30}} + \frac{1}{3} \sin \frac{3\pi x}{30} \cdot e^{\frac{-3\pi y}{30}} + \frac{1}{5} \sin \frac{5\pi x}{30} \cdot e^{\frac{-5\pi y}{30}} + \cdots \right).$$

(b) Find the temperature at any point of the plate in (a) and, instead of 20°, the temperature along the short edge has the value $4x$ at any point $(x, 0)$ of the edge.   *Hint:* For

$$0 < x < a, \; x = \frac{2a}{\pi}\left(\sin\frac{\pi x}{a} - \frac{1}{2}\sin\frac{2\pi x}{a} + \frac{1}{3}\sin\frac{3\pi x}{a} - \cdots\right).$$

6. In a semicircular plate of radius 5 the circumference is kept at a temperature of 10° and the diameter at 0°.   Find the temperature at any point on the plate, the plate being insulated so that there is no loss of heat.   *Hint:* See Exercise 2.

7. (a) By giving x an appropriate value in (27) of the text, find the sum of the convergent series

$$1 - \tfrac{1}{3} + \tfrac{1}{5} - \tfrac{1}{7} + \cdots.$$

(b) Find the sum of the same convergent series, as in (a), by giving appropriate values to x and a in the expansion shown in Exercise 5(b) above.

CHAPTER X

Partial Differential Equations of Order Two

85. Introduction. In this chapter we shall consider z as a function of two independent variables x and y, and employ the notation

$$z_x \equiv p, \; z_y \equiv q,$$
$$z_{xx} \equiv r, \; z_{xy} \equiv s, \; z_{yy} \equiv t.$$

Any partial differential equation of order two, involving two independent variables, may be expressed in the form

$$F(x, y, z, p, q, r, s, t) = 0. \tag{1}$$

A relation as

$$u(x, y, z, p, q) = 0$$

which satisfies (1) identically, is called an *intermediate* integral of (1), and a relation as

$$f(x, y, z) = 0 \tag{2}$$

for which $f_z \not\equiv 0$ and which satisfies (1) identically, is called a *solution* of (1). Since, given an equation of the form (1), our ultimate purpose is to find solutions (2) for which $f_z \not\equiv 0$, we may feel free at any time to divide by x, y, dx, or dy, because $x = c$, a constant, or $y = c$, a constant, cannot yield (2).

We shall treat only certain special cases of (1), and these by special methods:

1. Equations of the form

$$Rr + Ss + Tt = V,$$

where R, S, T, V are functions of x, y, z, p, q, will be treated by Monge's method.

2. Equations of the form

$$Rr + Ss + Tt + U(rt - s^2) = V,$$

where R, S, T, U, V are functions of x, y, z, p, q, will be treated by Monge's method.

3. Equations of the form

$$Rr + Ss + Tt + Pp + Qq + Zz = W,$$

where R, S, T, P, Q, Z, W are functions of x and y, will be dealt with by Laplace's transformations.

None of these methods is adequate to solve every equation of the type to which it applies; nevertheless, they are possessed of considerable generality.

86. Intermediate integrals of a second order differential equation. Let u and v be determined functions of x, y, z, p, q; and let

$$\varphi(u, v) = 0 \tag{3}$$

be an arbitrary relation between u and v. Differentiation of (3) with respect to x and y yields

$$\begin{cases} \varphi_u(u_x + pu_z + ru_p + su_q) + \varphi_v(v_x + pv_z + rv_p + sv_q) = 0, \\ \varphi_u(u_y + qu_z + su_p + tu_q) + \varphi_v(v_y + qv_z + sv_p + tv_q) = 0, \end{cases}$$

and, in order that these equations may be satisfied by values of φ_u and φ_v not both zero, it is necessary and sufficient that

$$\begin{vmatrix} u_x + pu_z + ru_p + su_q & u_y + qu_z + su_p + tu_q \\ v_x + pv_z + rv_p + sv_q & v_y + qv_z + sv_p + tv_q \end{vmatrix} = 0.$$

This condition may be written in the form

$$Rr + Ss + Tt + U(rt - s^2) = V, \tag{4}$$

where

$$U \equiv \begin{vmatrix} u_p & u_q \\ v_p & v_q \end{vmatrix}, \quad R \equiv \begin{vmatrix} u_p & u_y + qu_z \\ v_p & v_y + qv_z \end{vmatrix}, \quad T \equiv \begin{vmatrix} u_x + pu_z & u_q \\ v_x + pv_z & v_q \end{vmatrix},$$

$$S \equiv \begin{vmatrix} u_x + pu_z & u_p \\ v_x + pv_z & v_p \end{vmatrix} + \begin{vmatrix} u_q & u_y + qu_z \\ v_q & v_y + qv_z \end{vmatrix}, \quad V \equiv \begin{vmatrix} u_y + qu_z & u_x + pu_z \\ v_y + qv_z & v_x + pv_z \end{vmatrix},$$

and is a partial differential equation of the second order and second degree which is satisfied identically by (3). The relation (3) is said to be an *intermediate integral* of (4), and in the ensuing sections we shall discuss means of obtaining these intermediate integrals from given partial differential equations of order and degree two. It may be observed, in passing, that if a partial differential equation of the second order and second degree cannot be put into the form (4), it can have no intermediate integral of the form (3). It should also be noticed that these five functions $R, S, T, U,$ and V are all determined in a highly special way by two given functions u and v, and hence it is not to be expected that they should be entirely independent.   In other words, we cannot expect that every equation of the form (4) will have an intermediate integral of the form (3).

87. Monge's method for $Rr + Ss + Tt = V$.   Let us first consider an equation of the form (4), with $U \equiv 0$; that is, an equation

$$Rr + Ss + Tt = V, \tag{5}$$

where R, S, T, and V are given functions of x, y, z, p, and q.   Since we wish to determine z as a function of x and y satisfying (5), we have p and q as functions of x and y, and, hence, the relations

$$\begin{cases} dp = r\,dx + s\,dy, \\ dq = s\,dx + t\,dy. \end{cases} \tag{6}$$

If, now, we multiply (5) by $dx \cdot dy$, (6_1) by $R \cdot dy$, and (6_2) by $T \cdot dx$, and add, we obtain

$$(R\,dp\,dy + T\,dq\,dx - V\,dx\,dy) - (R\,dy^2 - S\,dx\,dy + T\,dx^2)s = 0, \tag{7}$$

an equation free of r and t.   If both of the equations

$$\begin{cases} R\,dy^2 - S\,dx\,dy + T\,dx^2 = 0 \\ R\,dp\,dy + T\,dq\,dx - V\,dx\,dy = 0 \end{cases} \tag{8}$$

called *Monge's equations* after Gaspard Monge (1746–1818), are satisfied by the simultaneous pair

$$\begin{cases} u(x,\,y,\,z,\,p,\,q) = a, \\ v(x,\,y,\,z,\,p,\,q) = b, \end{cases}$$

(a and b arbitrary constants) either identically, or in view of the equation

$$dz = p\,dx + q\,dy, \tag{9}$$

then certainly (7), and therefore (5), is satisfied by that pair.   If such is the case, we can take

$$\varphi(u,\,v) = 0$$

as an intermediate integral of (5).

The equation (8_1) can always be factored into the two equations

$$\begin{aligned} N_1\,dx + M_1\,dy &= 0, \\ N_2\,dx + M_2\,dy &= 0, \end{aligned} \tag{10}$$

and we then have available the system

$$\begin{cases} N_1\,dx + M_1\,dy = 0, \\ R\,dp\,dy + T\,dq\,dx - V\,dx\,dy = 0, \\ p\,dx + q\,dy - dz = 0, \end{cases} \qquad (11)$$

of three ordinary differential equations in the five variables x, y, z, p, and q, and another such system

$$\begin{cases} N_2\,dx + M_2\,dy = 0, \\ R\,dp\,dy + T\,dq\,dx - V\,dx\,dy = 0, \\ p\,dx + q\,dy - dz = 0, \end{cases} \qquad (12)$$

which employs (10_2) in place of (10_1). Since four equations are required to form a determinate system in five variables, either one or both of the above systems may be non-integrable. If $S^2 = 4RT$, the two systems are identical, because, in that case, (10_1) is the same as (10_2). If both systems are integrable and different, they lead to two different intermediate integrals of the form

$$\varphi(u, v) = 0. \qquad (3)$$

Illustration

Consider the equation

$$(x - y)(xz_{xx} - xz_{xy} - yz_{xy} + yz_{yy}) = (x + y)(z_x - z_y). \qquad (13)$$

In the above notation, we have

$$R \equiv x(x - y),\ S \equiv -(x - y)(x + y),\ T \equiv y(x - y),$$
$$V \equiv (x + y)(p - q),$$

and hence the equations (8) become

$$\begin{cases} x(x - y)dy^2 + (x - y)(x + y)dx\,dy + y(x - y)dx^2 = 0, \\ x(x - y)dp\,dy + y(x - y)dq\,dx - (x + y)(p - q)dx\,dy = 0. \end{cases}$$

The first of these yields the two equations

$$dy + dx = 0,\ x\,dy + y\,dx = 0,$$

and the two systems of equations corresponding to (11) and (12) are

$$\begin{cases} dy + dx = 0, \\ x(x - y)dp\,dy + y(x - y)dq\,dx - (x + y)(p - q)dx\,dy = 0, \\ dz = p\,dx + q\,dy, \end{cases} \qquad (14)$$

and

$$\begin{cases} x\,dy + y\,dx = 0, \\ x(x - y)dp\,dy + y(x - y)dq\,dx - (x + y)(p - q)dx\,dy = 0, \\ dz = p\,dx + q\,dy. \end{cases} \qquad (15)$$

Equation (14_1) has the solution

$$y + x = a, \tag{16}$$

and if we substitute $-dx$ for dy and $a - x$ for y in (14_2), the latter becomes, after dx is divided out,

$$-x(2x - a)dp + (a - x)(2x - a)dq + a(p - q)dx = 0,$$

an integrable equation whose solution is

$$\frac{xp - (a - x)q}{2x - a} = b,$$

or, if we change a to $x + y$,

$$\frac{xp - yq}{x - y} = b. \tag{17}$$

Equations (16) and (17) now furnish the intermediate integral

$$\varphi_1\left(\frac{xp - yq}{x - y},\, x + y\right) = 0. \tag{18}$$

Taking up the system (15) in the same way, we find

$$xy = c$$

as the solution of (15_1), and by means of it we reduce (15_2) to

$$-x(x^2 - c)dp + x(x^2 - c)dq + (x^2 + c)(p - q)dx = 0,$$

the solution of which is

$$\frac{(p - q)x}{x^2 - c} = d,$$

or, since $c = xy$,

$$\frac{p - q}{x - y} = d.$$

Thus we have built up another intermediate integral of (13), in the form

$$\varphi_2\left(\frac{p - q}{x - y},\, xy\right) = 0. \tag{19}$$

To solve these intermediate integrals, note that (18) may be solved for $\dfrac{xp - yq}{x - y}$ to obtain

$$\frac{xp - yq}{x - y} = f_1(x + y), \tag{20}$$

and that (19) may be put into the form

$$\frac{p - q}{x - y} = f_2(xy). \tag{21}$$

Equations (20) and (21) may now be solved for p and q to obtain

$$\begin{cases} p = f_1(x + y) - yf_2(xy) \\ q = f_1(x + y) - xf_2(xy). \end{cases}$$

If these values of p and q are substituted into (9), the equation becomes

$$dz = [f_1(x + y) - yf_2(xy)]dx + [f_1(x + y) - xf_2(xy)]dy, \tag{22}$$

which is integrable and has, as solution,

$$z = \int f_1(x + y) \cdot d(x + y) - \int f_2(xy) \cdot d(xy)$$
$$= F_1(x + y) + F_2(xy).$$

88. Integrability of $dz = p\,dx + q\,dy$. It might appear to have been especially fortunate that the equation (22) was found integrable, but we shall prove that (9) is always integrable when systems (11) and (12) are different and both integrable. To show this, let us assume that

$$F(x, y, z, p, q) = 0 \tag{23}$$

is an intermediate integral of (5) coming from (11), and that

$$f(x, y, z, p, q) = 0 \tag{24}$$

is an intermediate integral of (5) coming from (12). By differentiating (23) partially with respect to x and y, we obtain

$$F_x + pF_z + rF_p + sF_q = 0 \tag{25}$$

and

$$F_y + qF_z + sF_p + tF_q = 0. \tag{26}$$

If we eliminate r and t between (5), (25), and (26), we obtain

$$RF_xF_q + pRF_zF_q + TF_yF_p + qTF_zF_p + VF_pF_q$$
$$+ s(RF_q^2 - SF_pF_q + TF_p^2) = 0.$$

If this relation is true identically in s, then the two relations

$$R(F_q)^2 - SF_pF_q + T(F_p)^2 = 0, \tag{27}$$
$$R(F_x + pF_z)F_q + T(F_y + qF_z)F_p + VF_pF_q = 0, \tag{28}$$

must hold. From (27) we see that $\dfrac{F_q}{F_p}$ is one of the roots of the quadratic equation

$$Rm^2 - Sm + T = 0, \tag{29}$$

say,

$$\frac{F_q}{F_p} \equiv m_1. \tag{30}$$

Similarly, since $f(x, y, z, p, q) = 0$ is an intermediate integral, we have

$$\frac{f_q}{f_p} \equiv m_2, \tag{31}$$

where m_2 is the other root of (29). From (30), let us now substitute $m_1 F_p$ for F_q into (28) and divide out F_p, obtaining

$$Rm_1(F_x + pF_z) + T(F_y + qF_z) + m_1 V F_p = 0.$$

If, here, we change m_1 to $\dfrac{T}{Rm_2}$, since $m_1 m_2 \equiv \dfrac{T}{R}$, and multiply through by $\dfrac{m_2}{T}$, we have

$$(F_x + pF_z) + m_2(F_y + qF_z) + \frac{V}{R}F_p = 0. \tag{32}$$

Similarly, by working with the intermediate integral (24) and the relation (31), we obtain

$$(f_x + pf_z) + m_1(f_y + qf_z) + \frac{V}{R}f_p = 0. \tag{33}$$

Between (32) and (33) we may eliminate $\dfrac{V}{R}$, obtaining

$$(F_x + pF_z)f_p - (f_x + pf_z)F_p + m_2(F_y + qF_z)f_p - m_1(f_y + qf_z)F_p = 0,$$

from which, by use of (30) and (31), we draw

$$(F_x + pF_z)f_p - (f_x + pf_z)F_p + (F_y + qF_z)f_q - (f_y + qf_z)F_q = 0.$$

This can be written in the form

$$-F_pf_x - F_qf_y - (pF_p + qF_q)f_z + (F_x + pF_z)f_p + (F_y + qF_z)f_q = 0,$$

which is precisely the condition of Chapter VIII that the equation

$$dz = p\,dx + q\,dy \tag{9}$$

should be integrable, where p and q are determined in terms of x, y, and z, by two equations like (23) and (24).

89. Monge's method for $Rr + Ss + Tt + U(rt - s)^2 = V$. If we follow the plan of Section 87 and eliminate r and t from

$$Rr + Ss + Tt + U(rt - s^2) = V \qquad (4)$$

and

$$\begin{cases} dp = r\,dx + s\,dy, \\ dq = s\,dx + t\,dy, \end{cases} \qquad (6)$$

we obtain

$$s(R\,dy^2 - S\,dx\,dy + T\,dx^2 + U\,dp\,dx + U\,dq\,dy)$$
$$+ R\,dp\,dy + T\,dq\,dx + U\,dp\,dq - V\,dx\,dy = 0. \qquad (34)$$

We see, as before, that this equation will be satisfied if both of the equations

$$\begin{cases} R\,dy^2 - S\,dx\,dy + T\,dx^2 + U\,dp\,dx + U\,dq\,dy = 0, \\ R\,dp\,dy + T\,dq\,dx + U\,dp\,dq - V\,dx\,dy = 0, \end{cases} \qquad (35)$$

are satisfied. These correspond to the Monge equations for the case $U \equiv 0$, the first of which was factorable. In this case neither equation is immediately factorable, so we add an arbitrary multiple of the first to the second and try to select the multiplier in such a way that the resulting equation

$$\lambda(R\,dy^2 - S\,dy\,dx + T\,dx^2 + U\,dp\,dx + U\,dq\,dy)$$
$$+ (R\,dp\,dy + T\,dq\,dx + U\,dp\,dq - V\,dx\,dy) = 0 \qquad (36)$$

can be factored. Since the equation is linear in dp, it is apparent that dp can come into only one factor. The same statement holds for dq, and, since the product $dp \cdot dq$ does appear, dp is in one factor, while dq is in the other. If we assume factors as $(a\,dy + b\,dx + c\,dp)(l\,dy + m\,dx + n\,dq) = 0$, we must have

$$al \equiv R\lambda,\ bm \equiv T\lambda,\ cn \equiv U,$$
$$am + bl \equiv -S\lambda - V,\ an \equiv U\lambda,$$
$$cm \equiv U\lambda,\ bn \equiv T,\ cl \equiv R.$$

If we take $a \equiv \lambda$ and $l \equiv R$, we find

$$b \equiv \frac{T}{U},\ m \equiv U\lambda,$$
$$c \equiv l,\ n \equiv U,$$

and the condition $am + bl \equiv -S\lambda - V$ reduces to

$$U^2\lambda^2 + SU\lambda + TR + UV = 0, \qquad (37)$$

which is a quadratic equation in λ, since $U \not\equiv 0$. Then, in general, (36) factors for two distinct values of λ, say λ_1 and λ_2, the roots of the quadratic (37). In the respective cases, (36) reduces to

$$(\lambda_1 U\,dy + T\,dx + U\,dp)(R\,dy + U\lambda_1\,dx + U\,dq) = 0 \quad (38)$$

and

$$(\lambda_2 U\,dy + T\,dx + U\,dp)(R\,dy + U\lambda_2\,dx + U\,dq) = 0. \quad (39)$$

The student may show that if (36) vanishes for two distinct values of λ, then both of the equations (35) are satisfied, and that, hence, (34) is satisfied. To solve, therefore, we will equate to zero one factor of (38) and one of (39), and solve simultaneously. However, we can obtain no solution by equating the first factors of each or the second factors of each, so we employ simultaneously

$$\begin{cases} \lambda_1 U\,dy + T\,dx + U\,dp = 0, \\ R\,dy + \lambda_2 U\,dx + U\,dq = 0, \end{cases} \quad (40)$$

or

$$\begin{cases} \lambda_2 U\,dy + T\,dx + U\,dp = 0, \\ R\,dy + \lambda_1 U\,dx + U\,dq = 0. \end{cases} \quad (41)$$

If $S^2 = 4(RT + UV)$, (39) has only the one root $\lambda = -\dfrac{S}{2U}$, and both (40) and (41) are supplanted by

$$\begin{cases} -\dfrac{S}{2}\,dy + T\,dx + U\,dp = 0, \\[2mm] R\,dy - \dfrac{S}{2}\,dx + U\,dq = 0, \end{cases} \quad (42)$$

either one of which is sufficient to cause (36) to vanish when λ is replaced by $-\dfrac{S}{2U}$. When we substitute

$$\begin{cases} dp = \dfrac{S}{2U}\,dy - \dfrac{T}{U}\,dx \\[2mm] dq = \dfrac{S}{2U}\,dx - \dfrac{R}{U}\,dy \end{cases}$$

from (42) into (34), we find that it vanishes identically, and hence a solution of (42) yields an integral of (34); that is, an intermediate integral of the given equation (4).

If, where possible, we employ two first integrals, one from (40) and one from (41), we find that they may be solved simultaneously for p and q in such a way that

$$dz = p\,dx + q\,dy \qquad (9)$$

is integrable.   To prove this, let us assume that

$$F(x, y, z, p, q) = 0 \qquad (43)$$

is a solution of (40), and that

$$f(x, y, z, p, q) = 0$$

is a solution of (41).   Then each is an intermediate integral of (4). From (43) we obtain

$$F_x + pF_z + rF_p + sF_q = 0$$

and

$$F_y + qF_z + sF_p + tF_q = 0.$$

If we eliminate r and t between (4) and these two equations, we obtain

$$-R(F_x + pF_z)F_q - T(F_y + qF_z)F_p + U(F_x + pF_z)(F_y + qF_z)$$
$$- VF_pF_q - s\{R(F_q)^2 - SF_qF_p + T(F_p)^2 - U(F_y + qF_z)F_q$$
$$- U(F_x + pF_z)F_p\} = 0.$$

Now, since (43) is an intermediate integral of (4), this equation must hold identically in s, and hence the equations

$$R(F_q)^2 - SF_qF_p + T(F_p)^2 - U(F_y + qF_z)F_q$$
$$- U(F_x + pF_z)F_p = 0 \qquad (44)$$

and

$$-R(F_x + pF_z)F_q - T(F_y + qF_z)F_p$$
$$+ U(F_x + pF_z)(F_y + qF_z) - VF_pF_q = 0 \qquad (45)$$

both hold.   Therefore, the equation obtained by adding λ times (44) to (45) holds for all values of λ, and, in particular, for the two roots of

$$U^2\lambda^2 + SU\lambda + TR + UV = 0. \qquad (37)$$

But if λ is taken as the root λ_1, we find the equation factoring into the form

$$[\lambda_1 UF_q + TF_p - U(F_x + pF_z)][RF_q + U\lambda_1 F_p$$
$$- U(F_y + qF_z)] = 0, \qquad (46)$$

and if $\lambda = \lambda_2$, it factors into

$$[\lambda_2 UF_q + TF_p - U(F_x + pF_z)][RF_q + U\lambda_2 F_p$$
$$- U(F_y + qF_z)] = 0. \qquad (47)$$

Since $F(x, y, z, p, q) = 0$ satisfies both (44) and (45), it causes one factor in (46) to vanish, and one factor of (47) to vanish. The two first factors cannot vanish simultaneously, since $\lambda_1 \neq \lambda_2$, nor can the two second factors vanish simultaneously. Thus we have

$$\lambda_1 U F_q + T F_p - U(F_x + pF_z) = 0 \qquad (48)$$

and

$$R F_q + U\lambda_2 F_p - U(F_y + qF_z) = 0. \qquad (49)$$

Similarly, since $f(x, y, z, p, q) = 0$ is an intermediate integral of (4) and a solution of (41), we obtain

$$\lambda_2 U f_q + T f_p - U(f_x + pf_z) = 0 \qquad (50)$$

and

$$R f_q + U\lambda_1 f_p - U(f_y + qf_z) = 0. \qquad (51)$$

Eliminating T between (48) and (50) and dividing by U, since $U \neq 0$, we have

$$\lambda_1 f_p F_q - \lambda_2 F_p f_q + F_p(f_x + pf_z) - f_p(F_x + pF_z) = 0, \qquad (52)$$

and eliminating R between (49) and (51), we have

$$\lambda_1 f_p F_q - \lambda_2 F_p f_q + f_q(F_y + qF_z) - F_q(f_y + qf_z) = 0. \qquad (53)$$

From (52) and (53) both λ_1 and λ_2 are eliminated by subtraction, giving, upon rearrangement,

$$-F_p f_x - F_q f_y - (pF_p + qF_q)f_z + (F_x + pF_z)f_p + (F_y + qF_z)f_q = 0,$$

which is the condition obtained in Chapter VIII for the integrability of

$$dz = p\, dx + q\, dy, \qquad (9)$$

p and q being determined simultaneously by $F(x, y, z, p, q) = 0$ and $f(x, y, z, p, q) = 0$.

Illustration 1

To solve the equation

$$xq(z - yq)r + 2xypqs + yp(z - xp)t + xyz(rt - s^2)$$
$$= pq(px + qy - z),$$

we have

$$R \equiv xq(z - yq),\ S \equiv 2xypq,\ T \equiv yp(z - xp)$$
$$U \equiv xyz,\ V \equiv pq(px + qy - z),$$

and hence equation (37) for the determination of λ becomes, after division by x^2y^2,

$$z^2\lambda^2 + 2pqz\lambda + p^2q^2 = 0,$$

with the unique solution

$$\lambda = -\frac{pq}{z}.$$

The use of this value of λ in (42) gives the system

$$\begin{cases} -xpq\, dy + p(z - xp)dx + xz\, dp = 0, \\ q(z - yq)dy - pqy\, dx + yz\, dq = 0. \end{cases}$$

If we eliminate dy between the first of these and

$$dz = p\, dx + q\, dy, \tag{9}$$

and eliminate dx between the second and (9), we obtain the system

$$\begin{cases} pz\, dx - xp\, dz + xz\, dp = 0, \\ qz\, dy - yq\, dz + yz\, dq = 0. \end{cases}$$

The first of these has the solution

$$\frac{xp}{z} = a, \tag{54}$$

while the second has the solution

$$\frac{yq}{z} = b. \tag{55}$$

We may, then, take

$$\frac{xp}{z} = f\left(\frac{yq}{z}\right), \tag{56}$$

where the function f is arbitrary, as the general intermediate integral of the given equation. We illustrate two methods of further integration:

First Method. Solve (54) for p and (55) for q, substitute the results in (9), and integrate. This method gives

$$dz = \frac{az}{x} \cdot dx + \frac{bz}{y} \cdot dy,$$

of which the general solution is

$$z = cx^a y^b.$$

Second Method. Let us take a linear function as the arbitrary function f in (56), and write

$$\frac{xp}{z} = m\left(\frac{yq}{z}\right) + n.$$

or

$$xp = myq + nz. \tag{57}$$

(To 57) corresponds the Lagrange system

$$\frac{dx}{x} = \frac{dy}{-my} = \frac{dz}{nz}.$$

From the equation

$$\frac{dx}{x} = \frac{dy}{-my}$$

we obtain the solution

$$x^m y = k,$$

and from the equation

$$\frac{dx}{x} = \frac{dz}{nz}$$

we obtain the solution

$$z = x^n l.$$

If we set l equal to an arbitrary function of k and replace k by $x^m y$, we have

$$z = x^n \phi(x^m y).$$

Illustration 2

To solve the equation

$$2r - 5s + 2t + (rt - s^2) = 2,$$

which is of the form (4) with $R \equiv T \equiv V \equiv 2$, $U \equiv 1$, and $S \equiv -5$, note that (39) reduces to

$$\lambda^2 - 5\lambda + 6 = 0,$$

from which we have $\lambda_1 = 2$, $\lambda_2 = 3$, and the two systems (40) and (41) reduce to

$$\begin{cases} 2dy + 2dx + dp = 0, \\ 2dy + 3dx + dq = 0, \end{cases} \tag{58}$$

and

$$\begin{cases} 3dy + 2dx + dp = 0, \\ 2dy + 2dx + dq = 0, \end{cases} \tag{59}$$

As the solution of (58) we have

$$\begin{cases} p + 2y + 2x = a, \\ q + 2y + 3x = b, \end{cases}$$

or the intermediate integral

$$p + 2y + 2x = f(q + 2y + 3x). \tag{60}$$

Similarly, the system (59) has the solution

$$\begin{cases} p + 3y + 2x = c, \\ q + 2y + 2x = d, \end{cases}$$

and yields the intermediate integral

$$p + 3y + 2x = g(q + 2y + 2x). \tag{61}$$

As means of further integrating these intermediate integrals, we shall employ three methods.

First Method. Let us replace the arbitrary function f of (60) by a linear function, and obtain

$$p + 2y + 2x = m(q + 2y + 3x) + n.$$

This may be solved by employing Lagrange's system

$$\frac{dx}{1} = \frac{dy}{-m} = \frac{dz}{n + 3mx + 2my - 2x - 3y},$$

and its solution is thus found to be

$$z = nx - x^2 - 2xy - y^2 + \frac{m}{2} x^2 + \phi(y + mx), \tag{62}$$

where m and n are arbitrary constants and ϕ is an arbitrary function. If we treat the intermediate integral (61) by the same method we obtain

$$z = nx - x^2 - 3xy - y^2 - \frac{m}{2} x^2 + \phi(y + mx). \tag{63}$$

Second Method. If we regard α and β as parameters, the intermediate integral (60) can be expressed by the equations

$$\begin{cases} p + 2y + 2x = \alpha, \\ q + 2y + 3x = f(\alpha), \end{cases} \tag{64}$$

and (61) can be expressed as

$$\begin{cases} p + 3y + 2x = \beta, \\ q + 2y + 2x = g(\beta). \end{cases} \tag{65}$$

Subtracting (64_1) from (65_1), we obtain

$$y = \beta - \alpha,$$

and subtracting (65_2) from (64_2) we obtain

$$x = -g(\beta) + f(\alpha).$$

If we substitute the value of p from (64_1) and that of q from (65_2) into

$$dz = p\,dx + q\,dy, \tag{9}$$

we obtain

$$\begin{aligned}
dz &\equiv \{\alpha - 2(x+y)\}dx + \{g(\beta) - 2(x+y)\}dy \\
&\equiv -2(x+y)(dx+dy) + \alpha\,dx + g(\beta)dy \\
&\equiv -d(x+y)^2 + \alpha\{f'(\alpha)d\alpha - g'(\beta)d\beta\} + g(\beta)\{d\beta - d\alpha\} \\
&\equiv -d(x+y)^2 + \alpha f'(\alpha)d\alpha - \alpha g'(\beta)d\beta - g(\beta)d\alpha + g(\beta)d\beta \\
&\equiv -d(x+y)^2 + d[\alpha \cdot f(\alpha)] - f(\alpha)d\alpha - d[\alpha g(\beta)] + g(\beta)d\beta
\end{aligned}$$

$\therefore$

$$z = -(x+y)^2 + \alpha f(\alpha) - \int f(\alpha)d\alpha - \alpha g(\beta) + \int g(\beta)d\beta.$$

If, now, we write $\int f(\alpha)d\alpha \equiv F(\alpha)$ and $\int g(\beta)d\beta \equiv G(\beta)$, we have the solution expressed parametrically in the form

$$\begin{aligned}
z &= -(x+y)^2 + \alpha F'(\alpha) - \alpha G'(\beta) - F(\alpha) + G(\beta), \\
x &= F'(\alpha) - G'(\beta), \\
y &= \beta - \alpha.
\end{aligned}$$

We may express this by a single equation as

$$z = -(x+y)^2 + \alpha x - F(\alpha) + G(\alpha + y),$$

or

$$z = -x^2 - 2xy + \alpha x + \phi(y),$$

where we have dropped the terms $F(\alpha)$ and $-y^2$ by assuming them to be absorbed into the arbitrary function ϕ, which may involve α as an arbitrary constant. This solution, we note, is an instance of (62), obtained by the first method, with $m = 0$.

If, in the above, we had chosen to employ $p = \beta - 2x - 3y$ from (65_1) and $q = f(\alpha) - 2y - 3x$ from (64_2), we would have obtained

$$dz = (\beta - 2x - 3y)dx + [f(\alpha) - 2y - 3x]dy,$$

whose general solution can be reduced to $z = -x^2 - 3xy + \beta x + F(y)$, an instance of (63) with $m = 0$.

Third Method. This method affords results comparable in generality to those of the second method. We begin with the equation

$$p + 2y + 2x = \alpha, \tag{66}$$

an instance of (60), and obtain

$$p + 3y + 2x = \alpha + y.$$

If, now, we solve (61) for $q + 2y + 2x$, we obtain

$$q + 2y + 2x = \phi(p + 3y + 2x) = \phi(\alpha + y), \tag{67}$$

where ϕ is quite arbitrary. If we substitute for p from (66) and for q from (67) into

$$dz = p \, dx + q \, dy, \tag{9}$$

we have

$$dz = (\alpha - 2x - 2y)dx + [\phi(\alpha + y) - 2x - 2y]dy,$$

which has, as solution,

$$z = \alpha x - x^2 - 2xy - y^2 + \psi(\alpha + y),$$

or

$$z = \alpha x - x^2 - 2xy - y^2 + G(y) = \alpha x - x^2 - 2xy + H(y).$$

This same method may be applied again, by setting

$$p + 3y + 2x = \alpha$$

and

$$q + 2y + 3x = f(\alpha - y),$$

and drawing therefrom the solution

$$z = -x^2 - 3xy + \alpha x + F(y).$$

Exercises

Solve the following equations:

1. $r - a^2 t = 0.$

2. $qs - pt = 0.$

3. $r + 2s + t = 0.$

4. $y^2(s - t) = x.$

5. $r \sin^3 y - t \sin y = -q \cos y.$

6. $r \operatorname{sech}^2 x - t \operatorname{sech}^2 y + q \operatorname{sech}^2 y \tanh y - p \operatorname{sech}^2 x \tanh x = 0.$

7. $x^2 r + 2xys + y^2 t = 0.$

8. $(x + y)(r - t) + 4p = 0.$

9. $(2 + 3q)^2 r - 2(2 + 3q)(1 + 3p)s + (1 + 3p)^2 t = 0.$

10. $2x(x - 2y)r + (4y^2 - x^2)s + y(x - 2y)t = (x + 2y)$ $(2p - q)$.

11. $3r - 6s + 4t - (rt - s^2) = 3$.

12. $5r + 2s + 5t - 4(rt - s^2) = 6$.

13. $4r - 3s - 3t + 2(rt - s^2) = 4$.

14. $2r + 5s + 3t + 6(rt - s^2) = 0$.

15. $xqr - (x + y)s + ypt + xy(rt - s^2) = 1 - pq$.

16. $2x^2y\, qr + 2(px + qy)s + 2xy^2\, pt + (x^2y^2 - 1)(rt - s^2) +$ $4xy\, pq = 0$.

17. $xq(2xy - 1)r + (px^2 + qy^2)s + yp(2xy - 1)t$ $+ xy(xy - 1)(rt - s^2) = pq(1 - 4xy)$.

90. Laplace's transformation. We shall first follow through an illustration afforded by the second order partial differential equation

$$r + 3s + 2t = x + y. \tag{68}$$

Monge's auxiliary equation

$$R(dy)^2 - S\, dy\, dx + T(dx)^2 = 0 \tag{8_1}$$

becomes

$$(dy)^2 - 3\, dy\, dx + 2(dx)^2 = 0,$$

and has as solutions

$$y - 2x = c_1,\, y - x = c_2.$$

If we now employ new independent variables defined by

$$\xi = y - 2x,\, \eta = y - x,$$

we find

$$p \equiv z_x = -2z_\xi - z_\eta,$$
$$q \equiv z_y = z_\xi + z_\eta,$$
$$r \equiv p_x = 4z_{\xi\xi} + 4z_{\xi\eta} + z_{\eta\eta},$$
$$s \equiv p_y \equiv q_x = -2z_{\xi\xi} - 3z_{\xi\eta} - z_{\eta\eta},$$
$$t \equiv q_y = z_{\xi\xi} + 2z_{\xi\eta} + z_{\eta\eta},$$

and, if we substitute these values into (68), the latter becomes

$$z_{\xi\eta} = 2\xi - 3\eta.$$

Integration with respect to η gives

$$z_\xi = 2\xi\eta - \frac{3}{2}\eta^2 + \phi'(\xi),$$

where $\phi'(\xi)$ is an arbitrary function of ξ, and this in turn may be integrated with respect to ξ, which gives the solution

$$z = \xi^2 \eta - \frac{3}{2} \xi \eta^2 + \phi(\xi) + f(\eta).$$

Returning now to the original variables, we have

$$z = (y - 2x)^2(y - x) - \frac{3}{2}(y - 2x)(y - x)^2 + \phi(y - 2x) + f(y - x),$$

or

$$z = -\frac{1}{2} y^3 + y^2 x + \frac{1}{2} y x^2 - x^3 + \phi(y - 2x) + f(y - x),$$

which reduces to

$$z = \frac{1}{2} y x^2 - \frac{1}{3} x^3 + \phi(y - 2x) + f(y - x),$$

where $\frac{1}{6}(y - 2x)^3$ is absorbed by ϕ, and $-\frac{2}{3}(y - x)^3$ is absorbed by f. Let us now consider the equation

$$Rr + Ss + Tt + Pp + Qq + Zz = W, \qquad (69)$$

in which R, S, T, P, Q, Z, and W are functions of x and y. This equation is of the form (5), with $R \equiv R$, $S \equiv S$, $T \equiv T$, $V \equiv W - Pp - Qq - Zz$, and the auxiliary equation

$$R(dy)^2 - S\,dy\,dx + T(dx)^2 = 0 \qquad (8_1)$$

gives two equations

$$\begin{cases} N_1\,dx + M_1\,dy = 0, \\ N_2\,dx + M_2\,dy = 0. \end{cases} \qquad (10)$$

If $S^2 \not\equiv 4RT$, the two equations are distinct and have distinct solutions

$$\xi(x, y) = a,$$
$$\eta(x, y) = b.$$

In this case we employ the transformation to new independent variables, defined by

$$\begin{cases} \xi = \xi(x, y), \\ \eta = \eta(x, y), \end{cases}$$

given by Laplace in 1773. By differentiation we find

$$p \equiv z_x = z_\xi \cdot \xi_x + z_\eta \cdot \eta_x,$$
$$q \equiv z_y = z_\xi \cdot \xi_y + z_\eta \cdot \eta_y,$$
$$r = z_{\xi\xi}(\xi_x)^2 + 2z_{\xi\eta} \cdot \xi_x\eta_x + z_{\eta\eta}(\eta_x)^2 + z_\xi \cdot \xi_{xx} + z_\eta \cdot \eta_{xx},$$
$$s = z_{\xi\xi}\xi_x\xi_y + z_{\xi\eta}(\xi_x\eta_y + \xi_y\,\eta_x) + z_{\eta\eta} \cdot \eta_x\eta_y + z_\xi \cdot \xi_{xy} + z_\eta \cdot \eta_{xy},$$
$$t = z_{\xi\xi}(\xi_y)^2 + 2z_{\xi\eta} \cdot \xi_y\eta_y + z_{\eta\eta}(\eta_y)^2 + z_\xi \cdot \xi_{yy} + z_\eta \cdot \eta_{yy},$$

and if these be substituted into (69), we note that the coefficient of $z_{\xi\xi}$ is

$$R(\xi_x)^2 + S\xi_x\xi_y + T(\xi_y)^2,$$

which is zero identically because $\xi(x,\ y) = a$ is a solution of (8). Similarly, the coefficient of $z_{\eta\eta}$ is given by

$$R(\eta_x)^2 + S\eta_x\eta_y + T(\eta_y)^2,$$

which also vanishes identically. The equation will therefore be of the form

$$z_{\xi\eta} + Lz_\xi + Mz_\eta + Nz = V, \tag{70}$$

where L, M, N, and V are functions of ξ and η.

In the above illustration the functions L, M, and N were all zero, and the equation was solved by quadratures. Such will not always be the case, but the equation can always be written in the form

$$\left(\frac{\partial}{\partial\xi} + M\right)\left(\frac{\partial}{\partial\eta} + L\right)z + \left(N - LM - \frac{\partial L}{\partial\xi}\right)z = V. \tag{71}$$

In case $N - LM - \dfrac{\partial L}{\partial\xi}$ happens to be zero identically, we can solve as follows. Let

$$\left(\frac{\partial}{\partial\eta} + L\right)z = \zeta, \tag{72}$$

and thus obtain from (71)

$$\left(\frac{\partial}{\partial\xi} + M\right)\zeta = V. \tag{73}$$

Solve (73) for $\zeta = \varphi(\xi, \eta)$, substitute the solution in (72), and solve for z. Equation (70) can also be written as

$$\left(\frac{\partial}{\partial\eta} + L\right)\left(\frac{\partial}{\partial\xi} + M\right)z + \left(N - LM - \frac{\partial M}{\partial\eta}\right)z = V,$$

and hence if the quantity $N - LM - \dfrac{\partial M}{\partial \eta}$ vanishes, we may come immediately to a solution. If neither of the quantities $N - LM - \dfrac{\partial L}{\partial \xi}$, $N - LM - \dfrac{\partial M}{\partial \eta}$ is found to be zero, we may change the dependent variable as follows. Let

$$\left(\frac{\partial}{\partial \eta} + L \right) z = \zeta, \tag{72}$$

and substitute in (71) to obtain

$$\left(\frac{\partial}{\partial \xi} + M \right) \zeta + \left(N - LM - \frac{\partial L}{\partial \xi} \right) z = V,$$

from which we have

$$z = \frac{1}{N - LM - \dfrac{\partial L}{\partial \xi}} \left[V - M\zeta - \frac{\partial \zeta}{\partial \xi} \right].$$

If we substitute this into (72), we obtain a new equation which reduces to the form

$$\zeta_{\xi\eta} + \mathcal{L}\, \zeta_\xi + \mathcal{M}\zeta_\eta + \mathcal{N}\, \zeta = \mathcal{U}, \tag{74}$$

where $\mathcal{L}$, $\mathcal{M}$, $\mathcal{N}$, and $\mathcal{U}$ are new functions of ξ and η. In the same way it is possible to begin with the substitution

$$\left(\frac{\partial}{\partial \xi} + M \right) z = \zeta$$

and derive an equation like (74). If, in either of the new equations, one of the relations

$$\mathcal{N} - \mathcal{L}\mathcal{M} - \frac{\partial \mathcal{L}}{\partial \xi} \equiv 0, \quad \mathcal{N} - \mathcal{L}\mathcal{M} - \frac{\partial \mathcal{M}}{\partial \eta} \equiv 0,$$

holds, the equation may be solved, as before. If such is not the case, one may again pass to new equations of similar form. Unfortunately the process will sometimes prove unfruitful, as will certainly be the case for the equation

$$z_{\xi\eta} + z_\xi + z_\eta + 2z = 0,$$

since it is left unaltered in form by the above transformations.

If $S^2 \equiv 4RT$, the auxiliary equation (8_1) reduces to

$$(N_1 dx + M_1 dy)^2 = 0,$$

which has the solution

$$\xi(x, y) = a. \tag{75}$$

Since (75) is a solution of (8_1), we have

$$R(\xi_x)^2 + S\xi_x\xi_y + T(\xi_y)^2 = 0,$$

or, taking the square root,

$$2R\xi_x + S\xi_y = 0,$$

or

$$S\xi_x + 2T\xi_y = 0.$$

If we now transform the dependent variables by the transformation

$$\begin{cases} \xi = \xi(x, y), \\ \eta = y, \end{cases}$$

we obtain the equation

$$z_{\eta\eta} + Lz_\xi + Mz_\eta + Nz = V.$$

In case L should vanish, we may look upon this as an ordinary linear differential equation determining z as a function of η, and in its solution employ arbitrary functions of ξ rather than arbitrary constants.

Exercises

Solve the following:

1. $2r - 3s + t - 4p + q - 6z + 2x + 2y = 0.$

2. $(2y - x)(2x - 3y)(6r + 7s + 2t) + (5x - 6y)p + (2x - 2y)q = 4(2x - 3y)^3(2y - x) + 2(2y - x)^3(2x - 3y) - 2z.$

3. $z_{xx} - y^2 z_{xy} + 2y^2 z_y - 4z = x - \dfrac{1}{y}.$

4. $r - t \cosh^2 x - p \tanh x = 0.$

5. $x(x + y)r + (x^2 - y^2)s - y(x + y)t - (x - y)(p + q) = 0.$

6. $xy(t - r) + (x^2 - y^2)(s - 2) = py - qx.$

7. $z_{xx} + 2z_{xy} + z_{yy} + 5z_x + 5z_y + 6z = 6.$

8. $xz_{xx} - 2xz_{xy} + xz_{yy} - (1 + 12x^2)(z_x - z_y) + 20x^3[z - 2(x + y)^2] = 0.$

9. $25y^2 z_{xx} + 10y^2 z_{xy} + y^2 z_{yy} + 35yz_x + 7yz_y = 10x - 50y - 5z.$

10. $r - 2s + t = y + \varphi(x + y).$

11. $x^2 r + 2xys + y^2 t + xp + yq - 9z = \log x - \log y.$

12. $x(4 + y)^2(x^2 z_{xx} + 2xyz_{xy} + y^2 z_{yy}) - 2xy(4 + y)(xz_x + yz_y) + 2xy^2 z = 2y^2(x + y)(4 + y)^3.$

Table of Integrals

1. $\displaystyle \int (ax+b)^n dx = \frac{1}{a}\frac{(ax+b)^{n+1}}{n+1},\ n \ne -1.$

2. $\displaystyle \int \frac{dx}{(ax+b)} = \frac{1}{a}\log(ax+b).$

3. $\displaystyle \int x^m(ax+b)^n\,dx$

$\displaystyle = \frac{1}{a(m+n+1)}\left[x^m(ax+b)^{n+1} - mb\int x^{m-1}(ax+b)^n dx \right],$

$\displaystyle = \frac{1}{m+n+1}\left[x^{m+1}(ax+b)^n + nb\int x^m(ax+b)^{n-1}dx \right],$

$$m > 0,\ m+n+1 \ne 0.$$

4. $\displaystyle \int \frac{dx}{x(ax+b)} = \frac{1}{b}\log\frac{x}{ax+b}.$

5. $\displaystyle \int \frac{dx}{x(ax+b)^2} = \frac{1}{b(ax+b)} + \frac{1}{b^2}\log\frac{x}{ax+b}.$

6. $\displaystyle \int \frac{dx}{x^2(ax+b)} = -\frac{1}{bx} + \frac{a}{b^2}\log\frac{ax+b}{x}.$

7. $\displaystyle \int \frac{dx}{x^2(ax+b)^2} = -\frac{b+2ax}{b^2x(ax+b)} + \frac{2a}{b^3}\log\frac{ax+b}{x}.$

8. $\displaystyle \int \frac{xdx}{(ax+b)^2} = \frac{b}{a^2(ax+b)} + \frac{1}{a^2}\log(ax+b).$

9. $\displaystyle \int \frac{x^2\,dx}{(ax+b)^3} = \frac{1}{a^3}\left[\log(ax+b) + \frac{2b}{ax+b} - \frac{b^2}{2(ax+b)^2} \right].$

10. $\displaystyle \int \frac{\sqrt{ax+b}}{x}\,dx = 2\sqrt{ax+b} + b\int \frac{dx}{x\sqrt{ax+b}}.$

11(a). $\displaystyle \int \frac{dx}{x\sqrt{ax+b}} = \frac{1}{\sqrt{b}}\log\frac{\sqrt{ax+b}-\sqrt{b}}{\sqrt{ax+b}+\sqrt{b}},\ \text{for } b>0.$

   (b). $\displaystyle \int \frac{dx}{x\sqrt{ax+b}} = \frac{2}{\sqrt{-b}}\tan^{-1}\sqrt{\frac{ax+b}{-b}},\ \text{for } b<0.$

12. $\displaystyle\int \frac{dx}{x^2 \sqrt{ax+b}} = -\frac{\sqrt{ax+b}}{bx} - \frac{a}{2b}\int \frac{dx}{x\sqrt{ax+b}}.$

13. $\displaystyle\int \frac{x^m dx}{\sqrt{ax+b}} = \frac{2x^m \sqrt{ax+b}}{(2m+1)a} - \frac{2mb}{(2m+1)a}\int \frac{x^{m-1}dx}{\sqrt{ax+b}}.$

14. $\displaystyle\int \frac{dx}{x^n \sqrt{ax+b}} = \frac{-\sqrt{ax+b}}{(n-1)bx^{n-1}}$
$$- \frac{(2n-3)a}{(2n-2)b}\int \frac{dx}{x^{n-1}\sqrt{ax+b}}.$$

15. $\displaystyle\int \frac{dx}{a^2-x^2} = \frac{1}{2a}\log\frac{a+x}{a-x}.$

16. $\displaystyle\int \sqrt{a^2-x^2}\,dx = \frac{x}{2}\sqrt{a^2-x^2} + \frac{a^2}{2}\sin^{-1}\frac{x}{a}.$

17. $\displaystyle\int \frac{\sqrt{a^2-x^2}}{x}\,dx = \sqrt{a^2-x^2} - a\log\frac{a+\sqrt{a^2-x^2}}{x}.$

18. $\displaystyle\int \frac{\sqrt{a^2-x^2}}{x^2}\,dx = -\frac{\sqrt{a^2-x^2}}{x} - \sin^{-1}\frac{x}{a}.$

19. $\displaystyle\int x\sqrt{a^2-x^2}\,dx = -\tfrac{1}{3}(\sqrt{a^2-x^2})^3.$

20. $\displaystyle\int \frac{dx}{\sqrt{a^2-x^2}} = \sin^{-1}\frac{x}{a}.$

21. $\displaystyle\int \frac{x\,dx}{\sqrt{a^2-x^2}} = -\sqrt{a^2-x^2}.$

22. $\displaystyle\int \frac{x^2\,dx}{\sqrt{a^2-x^2}} = -\frac{x}{2}\sqrt{a^2-x^2} + \frac{a^2}{2}\sin^{-1}\frac{x}{a}.$

23. $\displaystyle\int \frac{x^3\,dx}{\sqrt{a^2-x^2}} = \frac{(a^2-x^2)^{3/2}}{3} - a^2\sqrt{a^2-x^2}.$

24. $\displaystyle\int (a^2-x^2)^{3/2}\,dx = \tfrac{1}{4}x(a^2-x^2)^{3/2} + \tfrac{3}{8}a^2x\sqrt{a^2-x^2}$
$$+ \tfrac{3}{8}a^4\sin^{-1}\frac{x}{a}.$$

25. $\displaystyle\int \frac{dx}{x\sqrt{x^2-a^2}} = -\frac{1}{a}\sin^{-1}\frac{a}{x}.$

26. $\displaystyle\int \frac{dx}{x^2\sqrt{a^2-x^2}} = -\frac{1}{a^2x}\sqrt{a^2-x^2}.$

27. $\int \sqrt{x^2 \pm a^2}\, dx = \frac{1}{2}x\sqrt{x^2 \pm a^2} \pm \frac{1}{2}a^2 \log(x + \sqrt{x^2 \pm a^2}).$

28. $\int \dfrac{dx}{\sqrt{x^2 \pm a^2}} = \log(x + \sqrt{x^2 \pm a^2}).$

29. $\int \dfrac{dx}{x\sqrt{a^2 \pm x^2}} = \dfrac{1}{a}\log\dfrac{x}{a + \sqrt{a^2 \pm x^2}}.$

30. $\int \dfrac{\sqrt{a^2 \pm x^2}}{x}\, dx = \sqrt{a^2 \pm x^2} + a\log\dfrac{x}{a + \sqrt{a^2 \pm x^2}}.$

31. $\int \dfrac{\sqrt{x^2 - a^2}}{x}\, dx = \sqrt{x^2 - a^2} + a\sin^{-1}\dfrac{a}{x}.$

32. $\int \dfrac{x\, dx}{\sqrt{x^2 \pm a^2}} = \sqrt{x^2 \pm a^2}.$

33. $\int \dfrac{x^2\, dx}{\sqrt{x^2 \pm a^2}} = \dfrac{x}{2}\sqrt{x^2 \pm a^2} \mp \dfrac{a^2}{2}\log(x + \sqrt{x^2 \pm a^2}).$

34. $\int \dfrac{dx}{x^2\sqrt{x^2 \pm a^2}} = \mp\dfrac{\sqrt{x^2 \pm a^2}}{a^2 x}.$

35. $\int \dfrac{dx}{(\sqrt{a^2 - x^2})^3} = \dfrac{x}{a^2\sqrt{a^2 - x^2}}.$

36. $\int \dfrac{dx}{(\sqrt{x^2 \pm a^2})^3} = \dfrac{\pm x}{a^2\sqrt{x^2 \pm a^2}}.$

37(a). $\int \dfrac{dx}{ax^2 + bx + c} =$

$\dfrac{1}{\sqrt{b^2 - 4ac}}\log\dfrac{2ax + b - \sqrt{b^2 - 4ac}}{2ax + b + \sqrt{b^2 - 4ac}},\ b^2 > 4ac.$

(b). $\int \dfrac{dx}{ax^2 + bx + c} = \dfrac{2}{\sqrt{4ac - b^2}}\tan^{-1}\dfrac{2ax + b}{\sqrt{4ac - b^2}},$
$b^2 < 4ac.$

(c). $\int \dfrac{dx}{ax^2 + bx + c} = -\dfrac{2}{2ax + b},\ b^2 = 4ac.$

38. $\int \dfrac{x\,dx}{ax^2 + bx + c} = \dfrac{1}{2a}\log(ax^2 + bx + c) -$
$\dfrac{b}{2a}\int\dfrac{dx}{ax^2 + bx + c}.$

39. $\displaystyle\int \frac{x^2 dx}{ax^2 + bx + c} = \frac{x}{a} - \frac{b}{2a^2} \log (ax^2 + bx + c)$

$$+ \frac{b^2 - 2ac}{2a^2} \int \frac{dx}{ax^2 + bx + c}.$$

40. $\displaystyle\int \frac{dx}{x(ax^2 + bx + c)} = \frac{1}{2c} \log \frac{x^2}{ax^2 + bx + c}$

$$- \frac{b}{2c} \int \frac{dx}{(ax^2 + bx + c)}.$$

41. $\displaystyle\int \frac{dx}{x^2(ax^2 + bx + c)} = \frac{b}{2c^2} \log \left(\frac{ax^2 + bx + c}{x^2} \right) - \frac{1}{cx}$

$$+ \left(\frac{b^2}{2c^2} - \frac{a}{c} \right) \int \frac{dx}{(ax^2 + bx + c)}.$$

42(a). $\displaystyle\int \frac{dx}{\sqrt{ax^2 + bx + c}} = \frac{1}{\sqrt{a}} \log (2ax + b$

$$+ 2\sqrt{a}\sqrt{ax^2 + bx + c}), \ a > 0.$$

(b). $\displaystyle\int \frac{dx}{\sqrt{ax^2 + bx + c}} = \frac{1}{\sqrt{-a}} \sin^{-1} \frac{-2ax - b}{\sqrt{b^2 - 4ac}}, \ a < 0.$

43. $\displaystyle\int \frac{x\,dx}{\sqrt{ax^2 + bx + c}} = \frac{\sqrt{ax^2 + bx + c}}{a}$

$$- \frac{b}{2a} \int \frac{dx}{\sqrt{ax^2 + bx + c}}.$$

44. $\displaystyle\int \sqrt{ax^2 + bx + c}\,dx = \frac{2ax + b}{4a} \sqrt{ax^2 + bx + c}$

$$+ \frac{4ac - b^2}{8a} \int \frac{dx}{\sqrt{ax^2 + bx + c}}.$$

45. $\displaystyle\int x\sqrt{ax^2 + bx + c}\,dx = \frac{(ax^2 + bx + c)^{3/2}}{3a}$

$$- \frac{b}{2a} \int \sqrt{ax^2 + bx + c}\,dx.$$

46. $\displaystyle\int \frac{dx}{x\sqrt{ax^2 + bx + c}} = -\frac{1}{\sqrt{c}} \log \left(\frac{\sqrt{ax^2 + bx + c} + \sqrt{c}}{x} \right.$

$$\left. + \frac{b}{2\sqrt{c}} \right), \ c > 0.$$

47. $\displaystyle\int \frac{dx}{x\sqrt{ax^2 + bx + c}} = \frac{1}{\sqrt{-c}} \sin^{-1} \frac{bx + 2c}{x\sqrt{b^2 - 4ac}}, \ c < 0.$

48. $\int \sin x \, dx = -\cos x, \quad \int \cos x \, dx = \sin x.$

49. $\int \sin^2 x \, dx = \frac{1}{2}x - \frac{1}{2}\sin x \cos x = \frac{1}{2}x - \frac{1}{4}\sin 2x.$

50. $\int \cos^2 x \, dx = \frac{1}{2}x + \frac{1}{2}\sin x \cos x = \frac{1}{2}x + \frac{1}{4}\sin 2x.$

51. $\int \sin^3 x \, dx = -\frac{1}{3}(\sin^2 x + 2) \cos x.$

52. $\int \cos^3 x \, dx = \frac{1}{3}(\cos^2 x + 2) \sin x.$

53. $\int \sin^n x \, dx = -\frac{\sin^{n-1} x \cos x}{n} + \frac{n-1}{n} \int \sin^{n-2} x \, dx.$

54. $\int \cos^n x \, dx = \frac{\cos^{n-1} x \sin x}{n} + \frac{n-1}{n} \int \cos^{n-2} x \, dx.$

55. $\int \sin^2 x \cos^2 x \, dx = -\frac{1}{8}(\frac{1}{4}\sin 4x - x).$

56(a). $\int \cos^m x \sin^n x \, dx = \frac{\cos^{m-1} x \sin^{n+1} x}{m+n}$
$$+ \frac{m-1}{m+n} \int \cos^{m-2} x \sin^n x \, dx.$$

(b). $\int \cos^m x \sin^n x \, dx = -\frac{\sin^{n-1} x \cos^{m+1} x}{m+n}$
$$+ \frac{n-1}{m+n} \int \cos^m x \sin^{n-2} x \, dx.$$

57. $\int \tan x \, dx = -\log \cos x, \quad \int \operatorname{ctn} x \, dx = \log \sin x.$

58. $\int \tan^2 x \, dx = \tan x - x, \quad \int \operatorname{ctn}^2 x \, dx = -\operatorname{ctn} x - x.$

59. $\int \tan^n x \, dx = \frac{\tan^{n-1} x}{n-1} - \int \tan^{n-2} x \, dx.$

60. $\int \operatorname{ctn}^n x \, dx = -\frac{\operatorname{ctn}^{n-1} x}{n-1} - \int \operatorname{ctn}^{n-2} x \, dx.$

61. $\int \sec x \, dx = \log (\sec x + \tan x).$

62. $\int \csc x \, dx = \log(\csc x - \operatorname{ctn} x).$

63. $\int \sec^2 x \, dx = \tan x, \quad \int \csc^2 x \, dx = -\cot x.$

64. $\int \sec^3 x \, dx = \dfrac{\sin x}{2 \cos^2 x} + \dfrac{1}{4} \log \dfrac{1 + \sin x}{1 - \sin x}.$

65. $\int \csc^3 x \, dx = -\dfrac{\cos x}{2 \sin^2 x} + \dfrac{1}{4} \log \dfrac{1 - \cos x}{1 + \cos x}.$

66. $\int \sec^n x \, dx = \dfrac{\tan x \sec^{n-2} x}{n-1} + \dfrac{n-2}{n-1} \int \sec^{n-2} x \, dx.$

67. $\int \csc^n x \, dx = -\dfrac{\cot x \csc^{n-2} x}{n-1} + \dfrac{n-2}{n-1} \int \csc^{n-2} x \, dx.$

68. $\int x \sin x \, dx = \sin x - x \cos x.$

69. $\int x \cos x \, dx = \cos x + x \sin x.$

70. $\int x^2 \sin x \, dx = 2x \sin x - (x^2 - 2) \cos x.$

71. $\int x^2 \cos x \, dx = 2x \cos x + (x^2 - 2) \sin x.$

72. $\int x^n \sin x \, dx = -x^n \cos x + n \int x^{n-1} \cos x \, dx.$

73. $\int x^n \cos x \, dx = x^n \sin x - n \int x^{n-1} \sin x \, dx.$

74. $\int x \sin^n x \, dx = \dfrac{\sin^{n-1} x (\sin x - nx \cos x)}{n^2}$
$$+ \dfrac{n-1}{n} \int x \sin^{n-2} x \, dx.$$

75. $\int x \cos^n x \, dx = \dfrac{\cos^{n-1} x (\cos x + nx \sin x)}{n^2}$
$$+ \dfrac{n-1}{n} \int x \cos^{n-2} x \, dx.$$

76. $\int \dfrac{\sin x \, dx}{x^m} = -\dfrac{1}{m-1} \dfrac{\sin x}{x^{m-1}} + \dfrac{1}{m-1} \int \dfrac{\cos x \, dx}{x^{m-1}}.$

77. $\displaystyle\int \frac{\cos x\, dx}{x^m} = -\frac{1}{m-1}\frac{\cos x}{x^{m-1}} - \frac{1}{m-1}\int \frac{\sin x\, dx}{x^{m-1}}.$

78. $\displaystyle\int \sin mx \sin nx\, dx = \frac{\sin (m-n)x}{2(m-n)} - \frac{\sin (m+n)x}{2(m+n)}.$

79. $\displaystyle\int \sin mx \cos nx\, dx = -\frac{\cos (m-n)x}{2(m-n)} - \frac{\cos (m+n)x}{2(m+n)}.$

80. $\displaystyle\int \cos mx \cos nx\, dx = \frac{\sin (m-n)x}{2(m-n)} + \frac{\sin (m+n)x}{2(m+n)}.$

81. $\displaystyle\int \sin^{-1} x\, dx = x \sin^{-1} x + \sqrt{1-x^2}.$

82. $\displaystyle\int \cos^{-1} x\, dx = x \cos^{-1} x - \sqrt{1-x^2}.$

83. $\displaystyle\int \tan^{-1} x\, dx = x \tan^{-1} x - \tfrac{1}{2} \log (1 + x^2).$

84. $\displaystyle\int x^n \sin^{-1} x\, dx = \frac{x^{n+1} \sin^{-1} x}{n+1} - \frac{1}{n+1}\int \frac{x^{n+1}dx}{\sqrt{1-x^2}}.$

85. $\displaystyle\int x^n \cos^{-1} x\, dx = \frac{x^{n+1} \cos^{-1} x}{n+1} + \frac{1}{n+1}\int \frac{x^{n+1}dx}{\sqrt{1-x^2}}.$

86. $\displaystyle\int x^n \tan^{-1} x\, dx = \frac{x^{n+1} \tan^{-1} x}{n+1} - \frac{1}{n+1}\int \frac{x^{n+1}dx}{1+x^2}.$

87. $\displaystyle\int e^{ax}\, dx = \frac{e^{ax}}{a},\ \int a^x\, dx = \frac{a^x}{\log a}.$

88. $\displaystyle\int xe^{ax}\, dx = \frac{e^{ax}}{a^2} (ax - 1).$

89. $\displaystyle\int x^n e^{ax}\, dx = \frac{x^n e^{ax}}{a} - \frac{n}{a}\int x^{n-1} e^{ax}\, dx.$

90. $\displaystyle\int \frac{e^{ax}}{x^n}\, dx = \frac{1}{n-1}\left[-\frac{e^{ax}}{x^{n-1}} + a \int \frac{e^{ax}}{x^{n-1}}\, dx\right],\ n \neq 1.$

91. $\displaystyle\int e^{ax} \sin bx\, dx = \frac{e^{ax}(a \sin bx - b \cos bx)}{a^2 + b^2}.$

92. $\displaystyle\int e^{ax} \cos bx\, dx = \frac{e^{ax}(b \sin bx + a \cos bx)}{a^2 + b^2}.$

93. $\displaystyle\int e^{ax}\cos^{n} x\, dx = \frac{e^{ax}\cos^{n-1} x(a\cos x + n\sin x)}{a^{2}+n^{2}}$
$$+ \frac{n(n-1)}{a^{2}+n^{2}}\int e^{ax}\cos^{n-2} x\, dx.$$

94. $\displaystyle\int e^{ax}\sin^{n} x\, dx = \frac{e^{ax}\sin^{n-1} x(a\sin x - n\cos x)}{a^{2}+n^{2}}$
$$+ \frac{n(n-1)}{a^{2}+n^{2}}\int e^{ax}\sin^{n-2} x\, dx.$$

95. $\displaystyle\int \log x\, dx = x\log x - x.$

96. $\displaystyle\int x^{n}\log x\, dx = x^{n+1}\left[\frac{\log x}{n+1} - \frac{1}{(n+1)^{2}}\right].$

97. $\displaystyle\int x^{n}(\log x)^{m}\, dx = \frac{x^{n+1}}{n+1}(\log x)^{m} - \frac{m}{n+1}\int x^{n}(\log x)^{m-1}\, dx.$

98. $\displaystyle\int \frac{x^{n}dx}{(\log x)^{m}} = -\frac{x^{n+1}}{(m-1)(\log x)^{m-1}} + \frac{n+1}{m-1}\int \frac{x^{n}dx}{(\log x)^{m-1}}.$

99. $\displaystyle\int e^{ax}\log x\, dx = \frac{e^{ax}\log x}{a} - \frac{1}{a}\int \frac{e^{ax}}{x}\, dx.$

NATURAL LOGARITHMS—0.00 TO 10.09

	0	1	2	3	4	5	6	7	8	9
0.0		5.395	6.088	6.493	6.781	7.004	7.187	7.341	7.474	7.592
0.1	7.697	7.793	7.880	7.960	8.034	8.103	8.167	8.228	8.285	8.339
0.2	8.391	8.439	8.486	8.530	8.573	8.614	8.653	8.691	8.727	8.762
0.3	8.796	8.829	8.861	8.891	8.921	8.950	8.978	9.006	9.032	9.058
0.4	9.084	9.108	9.132	9.156	9.179	9.201	9.223	9.245	9.266	9.287
0.5	9.307	9.327	9.346	9.365	9.384	9.402	9.420	9.438	9.455	9.472
0.6	9.489	9.506	9.522	9.538	9.554	9.569	9.584	9.600	9.614	9.629
0.7	9.643	9.658	9.671	9.685	9.699	9.712	9.726	9.739	9.752	9.764
0.8	9.777	9.789	9.802	9.814	9.826	9.837	9.849	9.861	9.872	9.883
0.9	9.895	9.906	9.917	9.927	9.938	9.949	9.959	9.970	9.980	9.990
1.0	0.0 0000	0995	1980	2956	3922	4879	5827	6766	7696	8618
1.1	9531	*0436	*1333	*2222	*3103	*3976	*4842	*5700	*6551	*7395
1.2	0.1 8232	9062	9885	*0701	*1511	*2314	*3111	*3902	*4686	*5464
1.3	0.2 6236	7003	7763	8518	9267	*0010	*0748	*1481	*2208	*2930
1.4	0.3 3647	4359	5066	5767	6464	7156	7844	8526	9204	9878
1.5	0.4 0547	1211	1871	2527	3178	3825	4469	5108	5742	6373
1.6	7000	7623	8243	8858	9470	*0078	*0682	*1282	*1879	*2473
1.7	0.5 3063	3649	4232	4812	5389	5962	6531	7098	7661	8222
1.8	8779	9333	9884	*0432	*0977	*1519	*2058	*2594	*3127	*3658
1.9	0.6 4185	4710	5233	5752	6269	6783	7294	7803	8310	8813
2.0	9315	9813	*0310	*0804	*1295	*1784	*2271	*2755	*3237	*3716
2.1	0.7 4194	4669	5142	5612	6081	6547	7011	7473	7932	8390
2.2	8846	9299	9751	*0200	*0648	*1093	*1536	*1978	*2418	*2855
2.3	0.8 3291	3725	4157	4587	5015	5442	5866	6289	6710	7129
2.4	7547	7963	8377	8789	9200	9609	*0016	*0422	*0826	*1228
2.5	0.9 1629	2028	2426	2822	3216	3609	4001	4391	4779	5166
2.6	5551	5935	6317	6698	7078	7456	7833	8208	8582	8954
2.7	9325	9695	*0063	*0430	*0796	*1160	*1523	*1885	*2245	*2604
2.8	1.0 2962	3318	3674	4028	4380	4732	5082	5431	5779	6126
2.9	6471	6815	7158	7500	7841	8181	8519	8856	9192	9527
3.0	9861	*0194	*0526	*0856	*1186	*1514	*1841	*2168	*2493	*2817
3.1	1.1 3140	3462	3783	4103	4422	4740	5057	5373	5688	6002
3.2	6315	6627	6938	7248	7557	7865	8173	8479	8784	9089
3.3	9392	9695	9996	*0297	*0597	*0896	*1194	*1491	*1788	*2083
3.4	1.2 2378	2671	2964	3256	3547	3837	4127	4415	4703	4990
3.5	5276	5562	5846	6130	6413	6695	6976	7257	7536	7815
3.6	8093	8371	8647	8923	9198	9473	9746	*0019	*0291	*0563
3.7	1.3 0833	1103	1372	1641	1909	2176	2442	2708	2972	3237
3.8	3500	3763	4025	4286	4547	4807	5067	5325	5584	5841
3.9	6098	6354	6609	6864	7118	7372	7624	7877	8128	8379
4.0	8629	8879	9128	9377	9624	9872	*0118	*0364	*0610	*0854
4.1	1.4 1099	1342	1585	1828	2070	2311	2552	2792	3031	3270
4.2	3508	3746	3984	4220	4456	4692	4927	5161	5395	5629
4.3	5862	6094	6326	6557	6787	7018	7247	7476	7705	7933
4.4	8160	8387	8614	8840	9065	9290	9515	9739	9962	*0185
4.5	1.5 0408	0630	0851	1072	1293	1513	1732	1951	2170	2388
4.6	2606	2823	3039	3256	3471	3687	3902	4116	4330	4543
4.7	4756	4969	5181	5393	5604	5814	6025	6235	6444	6653
4.8	6862	7070	7277	7485	7691	7898	8104	8309	8515	8719
4.9	8924	9127	9331	9534	9737	9939	*0141	*0342	*0543	*0744
5.0	1.6 0944	1144	1343	1542	1741	1939	2137	2334	2531	2728
5.1	2924	3120	3315	3511	3705	3900	4094	4287	4481	4673
5.2	4866	5058	5250	5441	5632	5823	6013	6203	6393	6582
5.3	6771	6959	7147	7335	7523	7710	7896	8083	8269	8455
5.4	8640	8825	9010	9194	9378	9562	9745	9928	*0111	*0293
5.5	1.7 0475	0656	0838	1019	1199	1380	1560	1740	1919	2098
5.6	2277	2455	2633	2811	2988	3166	3342	3519	3695	3871
5.7	4047	4222	4397	4572	4746	4920	5094	5267	5440	5613
5.8	5786	5958	6130	6302	6473	6644	6815	6985	7156	7326
5.9	7495	7665	7834	8002	8171	8339	8507	8675	8842	9009
	0	1	2	3	4	5	6	7	8	9

Tabular value—10 (applies to rows 0.0 through 0.9)

TABLE OF

NATURAL LOGARITHMS—0.00 TO 10.09

	0	1	2	3	4	5	6	7	8	9
6.0	1.7 9176	9342	9509	9675	9840	*0006	*0171	*0336	*0500	*0665
6.1	1.8 0829	0993	1156	1319	1482	1645	1808	1970	2132	2294
6.2	2455	2616	2777	2938	3098	3258	3418	3578	3737	3896
6.3	4055	4214	4372	4530	4688	4845	5003	5160	5317	5473
6.4	5630	5786	5942	6097	6253	6408	6563	6718	6872	7026
6.5	7180	7334	7487	7641	7794	7947	8099	8251	8403	8555
6.6	8707	8858	9010	9160	9311	9462	9612	9762	9912	*0061
6.7	1.9 0211	0360	0509	0658	0806	0954	1102	1250	1398	1545
6.8	1692	1839	1986	2132	2279	2425	2571	2716	2862	3007
6.9	3152	3297	3442	3586	3730	3874	4018	4162	4305	4448
7.0	4591	4734	4876	5019	5161	5303	5445	5586	5727	5869
7.1	6009	6150	6291	6431	6571	6711	6851	6991	7130	7269
7.2	7408	7547	7685	7824	7962	8100	8238	8376	8513	8650
7.3	8787	8924	9061	9198	9334	9470	9606	9742	9877	*0013
7.4	2.0 0148	0283	0418	0553	0687	0821	0956	1089	1223	1357
7.5	1490	1624	1757	1890	2022	2155	2287	2419	2551	2683
7.6	2815	2946	3078	3209	3340	3471	3601	3732	3862	3992
7.7	4122	4252	4381	4511	4640	4769	4898	5027	5156	5284
7.8	5412	5540	5668	5796	5924	6051	6179	6306	6433	6560
7.9	6686	6813	6939	7065	7191	7317	7443	7568	7694	7819
8.0	7944	8069	8194	8318	8443	8567	8691	8815	8939	9063
8.1	9186	9310	9433	9556	9679	9802	9924	*0047	*0169	*0291
8.2	2.1 0413	0535	0657	0779	0900	1021	1142	1263	1384	1505
8.3	1626	1746	1866	1986	2106	2226	2346	2465	2585	2704
8.4	2823	2942	3061	3180	3298	3417	3535	3653	3771	3889
8.5	4007	4124	4242	4359	4476	4593	4710	4827	4943	5060
8.6	5176	5292	5409	5524	5640	5756	5871	5987	6102	6217
8.7	6332	6447	6562	6677	6791	6905	7020	7134	7248	7361
8.8	7475	7589	7702	7816	7929	8042	8155	8267	8380	8493
8.9	8605	8717	8830	8942	9054	9165	9277	9389	9500	9611
9.0	9722	9834	9944	*0055	*0166	0276	*0387	*0497	*0607	*0717
9.1	2.2 0827	0937	1047	1157	1266	1375	1485	1594	1703	1812
9.2	1920	2029	2138	2246	2354	2462	2570	2678	2786	2894
9.3	3001	3109	3216	3324	3431	3538	3645	3751	3858	3965
9.4	4071	4177	4284	4390	4496	4601	4707	4813	4918	5024
9.5	5129	5234	5339	5444	5549	5654	5759	5863	5968	6072
9.6	6176	6280	6384	6488	6592	6696	6799	6903	7006	7109
9.7	7213	7316	7419	7521	7624	7727	7829	7932	8034	8136
9.8	8238	8340	8442	8544	8646	8747	8849	8950	9051	9152
9.9	9253	9354	9455	9556	9657	9757	9858	9958	*0058	*0158
10.0	2.3 0259	0358	0458	0558	0658	0757	0857	0956	1055	1154
	0	1	2	3	4	5	6	7	8	9

NATURAL LOGARITHMS—10 TO 99

	0	1	2	3	4	5	6	7	8	9
1	2.30259	39790	48491	56495	63906	70805	77259	83321	89037	94444
2	99573	*04452	*09104	*13549	*17805	*21888	*25810	*29584	*33220	*36730
3	3.40120	43399	46574	49651	52636	55535	58352	61092	63759	66356
4	68888	71357	73767	76120	78419	80666	82864	85015	87120	89182
5	91202	93183	95124	97029	98898	*00733	*02535	*04305	*06044	*07754
6	4.09434	11087	12713	14313	15888	17439	18965	20469	21951	23411
7	24850	26268	27667	29046	30407	31749	33073	34381	35671	36945
8	38203	39445	40672	41884	43082	44265	45435	46591	47734	48864
9	49981	51086	52179	53260	54329	55388	56435	57471	58497	59512

NATURAL LOGARITHMS—100 TO 499

	0	1	2	3	4	5	6	7	8	9
10	4.6 0517	1512	2497	3473	4439	5396	6344	7283	8213	9135
11	4.7 0048	0953	1850	2739	3620	4493	5359	6217	7068	7912
12	8749	9579	*0402	*1218	*2028	*2831	*3628	*4419	*5203	*5981
13	4.8 6753	7520	8280	9035	9784	*0527	*1265	*1998	*2725	*3447
14	4.9 4164	4876	5583	6284	6981	7673	8361	9043	9721	*0395
15	5.0 1064	1728	2388	3044	3695	4343	4986	5625	6260	6890
16	7517	8140	8760	9375	9987	*0595	*1199	*1799	*2396	*2990
17	5.1 3580	4166	4749	5329	5906	6479	7048	7615	8178	8739
18	9296	9850	*0401	*0949	*1494	*2036	*2575	*3111	*3644	*4175
19	5.2 4702	5227	5750	6269	6786	7300	7811	8320	8827	9330
20	9832	*0330	*0827	*1321	*1812	*2301	*2788	*3272	*3754	*4233
21	5.3 4711	5186	5659	6129	6598	7064	7528	7990	8450	8907
22	9363	9816	*0268	*0717	*1165	*1610	*2053	*2495	*2935	*3372
23	5.4 3808	4242	4674	5104	5532	5959	6383	6806	7227	7646
24	8064	8480	8894	9306	9717	*0126	*0533	*0939	*1343	*1745
25	5.5 2146	2545	2943	3339	3733	4126	4518	4908	5296	5683
26	6068	6452	6834	7215	7595	7973	8350	8725	9099	9471
27	9842	*0212	*0580	*0947	*1313	*1677	*2040	*2402	*2762	*3121
28	5.6 3479	3835	4191	4545	4897	5249	5599	5948	6296	6643
29	6988	7332	7675	8017	8358	8698	9036	9373	9709	*0044
30	5.7 0378	0711	1043	1373	1703	2031	2359	2685	3010	3334
31	3657	3979	4300	4620	4939	5257	5574	5890	6205	6519
32	6832	7144	7455	7765	8074	8383	8690	8996	9301	9606
33	9909	*0212	*0513	*0814	*1114	*1413	*1711	*2008	*2305	*2600
34	5.8 2895	3188	3481	3773	4064	4354	4644	4932	5220	5507
35	5793	6079	6363	6647	6930	7212	7493	7774	8053	8332
36	8610	8888	9164	9440	9715	9990	*0263	*0536	*0808	*1080
37	5.9 1350	1620	1889	2158	2426	2693	2959	3225	3489	3754
38	4017	4280	4542	4803	5064	5324	5584	5842	6101	6358
39	6615	6871	7126	7381	7635	7889	8141	8394	8645	8896
40	9146	9396	9645	9894	*0141	*0389	*0635	*0881	*1127	*1372
41	6.0 1616	1859	2102	2345	2587	2828	3069	3309	3548	3787
42	4025	4263	4501	4737	4973	5209	5444	5678	5912	6146
43	6379	6611	6843	7074	7304	7535	7764	7993	8222	8450
44	8677	8904	9131	9357	9582	9807	*0032	*0256	*0479	*0702
45	6.1 0925	1147	1368	1589	1810	2030	2249	2468	2687	2905
46	3123	3340	3556	3773	3988	4204	4419	4633	4847	5060
47	5273	5486	5698	5910	6121	6331	6542	6752	6961	7170
48	7379	7587	7794	8002	8208	8415	8621	8826	9032	9236
49	9441	9644	9848	*0051	*0254	*0456	*0658	*0859	*1060	*1261
	0	1	2	3	4	5	6	7	8	9

Answers to Exercises

Section 4, page 9

1. (a) $xy' - 2y + x = 0.$

(b) $xy' - y = 0.$

(c) $y'^2 + xy' = y.$

(d) $y'' = 0.$

(e) $x^2y'' - 2xy' + 2y = 0.$

(f) $xyy'' - 2xy'^2 + 2yy' = 0.$

(g) $y'' - 2y' + y = 0.$

(h) $y'' + a^2y = 0.$

(i) $y''' - 2y'' + 2y' = \frac{1}{2}.$

(j) $y''' - 2y'' + y' = 2x$
$\quad\quad - 4.$

2. $x + yy' = 0.$

3. $2xy' - y = 0.$

4. $y'' = 0.$

5. $xy'^2 - yy' + 1 = 0.$

6. $12y = 12xy' - 9y'^2 - 4.$

Section 5, page 13

1. (a) $y = 2x + 2 - e^x.$

(b) $y = x - 1; 4y = x + 2.$

(c) $y = 0; y = x + 1; y = -x - 1.$

3. $8y = 2x - x^2 - 1.$

4. $x^2 + y^2 = c^2.$

5. $(x + 2)^2 + (y - 3)^2 = c^2.$

Section 6, page 14

1. (a) $y = e^x.$

(b) $y = e^{2x}(e^{-\pi} \sin x - \cos x).$

(c) $y = xe^{2x}.$

Section 7, page 15

2. (a) $2xz_x + yz_y = 2z.$

(b) $xz_x + yz_y = 2z.$

(c) $2xz_x + yz_y = z.$

(d) $xz_x - xz_y = 2z.$

(e) $(2y - 1)z_x - z_y = 0.$

3. (a) $y'^2 - 2xy' + 2y = 0.$

(b) $xy'' = y' + y'^3.$

(c) $(xy' - y)(x + yy') = y'a^2.$

(e) $[y''(y - 2) + (1 + y'^2)]^2 = (1 + y'^2)^3.$

(f) $y' = -2.$

4. (a) $y + 7x = 20.$

(b) $2x + 2y = \pi.$

(c) $R = \frac{1}{4}(10)^{3/2}.$

(d) $2x + y = 0, R = -(5)^{3/2}/2,$
$\quad\quad 3x + y = 1, R = -(10)^{3/2}/4.$

5. (a) $\pi/2.$

293

7. (a) $y = 1 + 2x + \dfrac{7x^2}{2!} + \dfrac{14x^3}{3!} + \cdots$.

(b) $y = -1 + 2x - \dfrac{3x^2}{2!} + \dfrac{4x^3}{3!} + \cdots$.

(c) $y = 3 - \dfrac{x^2}{2} - \dfrac{x^4}{8} + \cdots$.

9. (a) $y = 2 + \dfrac{2(x-1)^3}{3!} + \cdots$.

(b) $y = 3 + (x-1) - \dfrac{5(x-1)^2}{2!} - \dfrac{6(x-1)^3}{3!} + \cdots$.

12. (a) Minimum points: $x = 0$, $y < \frac{2}{3}$.
Maximum points: $x = 0$, $y > \frac{2}{3}$.
Points of inflection: $3x^2 = 1$.

(b) Minimum points: $y = -e^x$.
Points of inflection: $y = -2e^x$.

Section 8, page 22

1. (a) $x - 2y = c$. (b) $y = cxe^{y + \frac{1}{x}}$.

(c) $e^{-y}(1 + x^2)^{5/2} = cx^5(y - 1)$.

(d) $(x^2 + 2)^8(y + 2)^3 = cy^2(y - 2)$.

(e) $e^{\frac{x^3}{3} - x^2} = c(1 + y)^{-1}$.

(f) $x\sqrt{y^2 - 1} + \sqrt{1 - x^2} = cy$.

(g) $2s + \sin 2t = c$. (h) $2e^{x^3} + 3e^{y^2} = c$.

2. $x^2 + y^2 = c^2$. **3.** $s = 1 - e^{-2}$.

4. $v = 5 - 4e^{-\frac{g}{5}t}$. **5.** $v = R\sqrt{g/2640s}$.

$s = 25 + \dfrac{20}{g}(e^{-g} - 1)$.

Section 9, page 25

1. (a) Not exact. (h) $5x^2y^4 + x^2 - 2y^3 - 4y = c$.

(b) $2xy + 3x^2 = c$. (i) $e^{-\frac{1}{xy}} + \dfrac{1}{xy} = c$.

(c) Not exact. (j) $\tan x \tan y = c$.

(d) $ax^3 + 3bx^2y + 3cxy^2 + gy^3 = k$. (k) $x^2y - \sin x - y = c$.

(l) $x \tan y - x^3 = c$.

(e) $x^4 + 10x^2y^2 + 2y^4 = c$. (m) $ye^x = c$.

(f) Not exact. (n) Not exact.

(g) $7x^2 - 6xy + 4y^2 + 4x - 10y = c$.

(o) $\sinh x \cosh y - \sinh x + \cosh y = c$.

(p) $x^2 \tan y + x \sin 2y - e^y = c$.

2. $b = -5$.

4. $2y^2 - 2xy + 6y - x^2 + 2x = 8$.

Section 10, page 29

1. (a) y^{-2}; $2x + 3y \log y = cy$.

(b) $\dfrac{1}{x^2 + y^2}$; $\log (x^2 + y^2) = c + 4 \tan^{-1} \dfrac{y}{x}$.

(c) $\dfrac{1}{xy^2}$; $\log x - \dfrac{x}{y} = c$.   (d) x; $x^2 - xy^3 = c$.

(e) $\dfrac{1}{x(x^2 + y^2)}$; $\log x + \tan^{-1} \dfrac{x}{y} = c$.

(f) $\dfrac{1}{x^2 y^2}$; $xy^2 - 1 = cxy$.

(g) $\dfrac{1}{x^3 y^3}$; $2(x + y) + \dfrac{1}{2x^2 y^2} = c$.

(h) $\dfrac{1}{y^2}$; $\dfrac{2x}{y} + \dfrac{\log y}{y} = c$.

(i) $\dfrac{1}{x^2 y^2}$; $\dfrac{x}{y} + \dfrac{y}{x} + \log x + \log y = c$.

(j) $1/xy$; $2ax + 3 \log x + 3a \log y = c$.

(k) $\dfrac{1}{x^4}$; $\sin x - \dfrac{py^2}{x^2} = c$.

(l) $1/y^2$; $e^{x/y} + \log y = c$.
(m) $\cosh x$; $y \sinh x + x \sinh y = c$.
(n) $3x^2 y^2 - 6xy^2 + 2y^3 = c$.
(o) $x + y - \sqrt{x^2 + y^2} = c$.

2. $N\mu_x - M\mu_y = \mu(M_y - N_x)$.   **4.** $\log xy^3 = c + xy$.

5. $x^{-2} y^{-2} + 4x^{-1} y^{-1} + 2 \log x = c$.

6. $\dfrac{6}{(xy)^{1/2}} - \dfrac{2}{(xy)^{3/2}} + \log \dfrac{x^3}{y^6} = c$.

7. $\log (xy^4) + \cos (xy) = c$.   **20.** $2x^{-3} y^3 - x^{-6} y^3 = c$.

8. $1/Mx$.

9. $xy = c$.   **21.** $bx + a \log \dfrac{x^3}{y} = c$.

12. $x^{-3} y^{-2} - x^{-1} y^{-1} + \log x = c$.   **22.** $x^{-1} y^{-1} (mx^r y^s + \mu x^\rho y^\sigma)^{-1}$.

15. $x^3 = cy^2$.   **23.** $x^4 y^3 = c$.

16. $x^5 y^{-1} = c$ **24.** $y^2 = cx^3$.

18. $3x^{21/8} y^{7/4} + 7x^{-3/8} y^{3/4} = c$.   **26.** $e^{\int g(y)\,dy}$.

19. $3x^{-1} y^2 + \log xy = c$.

27. $10xy(y^3 - 5)^2 + 2y^5 - 25y^2 = c.$

28. $3x^4 + 8x^3y + 6x^2y^2 = c.$

29. $12x^3y - 84x^2y + 3x^4 + 192xy - 8x^3 - 144y = c.$

30. $x^2(2y^2 + 1) = c.$ **31.** $4x^3y - x^4 = c.$

Section 11, page 31

4. (a) $y^2 + 4xy - x^2 = c.$

(b) $cx^{4\sqrt{3}} = \dfrac{x\sqrt{3} - 2y}{x\sqrt{3} + 2y}.$

(c) $\log x + \dfrac{y}{2x} + \dfrac{1}{4}\sin\dfrac{2y}{x} + c = 0.$

(d) $(x^2 - 2y^2)(x^2 + y^2)^2 = c.$ (e) $e^{\frac{y}{x}} = cx/(1 - cx).$

(f) $cx^2 = y + \sqrt{x^2 + y^2}.$

9. (a) $x^3 + y^3 = cxy.$ (c) $\csc\dfrac{y}{x} - \operatorname{ctn}\dfrac{y}{x} + \log x = c.$

(b) $x^2\sinh\dfrac{y}{x} = c.$

10. $1/Mx.$

12. (a) $x^2 + xy - y^2 = c.$

(b) $3x^3 - 3x^2y + 3xy^2 - y^3 = c.$

13. The constant equals 1.

14. (c) $cx^2 = \dfrac{y - x}{y + x}.$

17. (a) $e^{\frac{2y}{x}} - x^2 = c.$

(b) $4y^3 + (6xy^2 - 3x^3)\sin\left(\dfrac{2y}{x}\right) + 6x^2y\cos\left(\dfrac{2y}{x}\right) + 12x = cx^3.$

(c) $\dfrac{x}{y}\sqrt{\dfrac{3y - x}{x}} + 3\tan^{-1}\sqrt{\dfrac{3y - x}{x}} = x + c.$

18. $x^2 + y^2 = cy.$

Section 12, page 35

1. $(x - 3y + 1)(x - 2y + 2) = c.$

2. $(4x - y + 2)^3(x + 2y - 5)^{-1} = c.$

3. $\log(3x^2 + 3y^2 + 3xy - 6x - 9y + 7)$

$$= c - \dfrac{6}{\sqrt{3}}\tan^{-1}\dfrac{3x + 3y - 5}{(x - y + 1)\sqrt{3}}.$$

4. $2(x+3)^2 + 2(x+3)(y+1) - 3(y+1)^2 = e.$

6. $(3x + 3y - 2)(3x - y)^3(2y - 1)^{-3} = c.$

7. $4x - 8y + 5 = ce^{4x+8y}.$

8. $(2 - 15x + 5y)^4 = ce^{10y-5x}.$

9. $3x - 3y = 2\log(3x + 6y - 1) + c.$

11. $7x - 28y + 2\log(28x^2 - 28xy + 7y^2 - 16x + 8y + 2)$
$$+ \frac{9}{2\sqrt{2}}\log\frac{14x - 7y - 4 - \sqrt{2}}{14x - 7y - 4 + \sqrt{2}} = c.$$

12. $x^2 + 4xy^3 = c.$

13. $(x + y + 1)^2(7x - 2y + 4)(3x + 2)^{-1} = c.$

14. $14y + 7x + 6\log(21y - 14x - 9) = c.$

Section 13, page 37

1. (a) $ye^{\sin x} = x + c.$ (b) $y = \frac{2x^3}{7} + \frac{c}{\sqrt{x}}.$

(c) $y = e^{\frac{-3x^2}{2}}\left[\int e^{\frac{3x^2}{2}}\sin 2x\, dx + c\right].$

(d) $y^2 e^{\frac{1}{x}} = e^x + c.$

(e) $\tan y = \frac{x^2 + 1}{3} + \frac{c}{\sqrt{x^2 + 1}}.$

(f) $(2y + 1)e^{x^2} = 2x + c.$ (g) $xy = 2x\log x + c_1 + c_2 x.$

2. (a) $x = e^y\int e^{-y}\log y\, dy + ce^y.$

(b) $\sin x + \frac{y^2}{4} + \frac{y}{8} + \frac{1}{32} = ce^{4y}.$

(c) $x = e^{(x+c)\cos y}.$

(d) $x = (y + c)e^{\cos^{-1}y}.$

3. (a) $4x\sin y + 2x\cos 2x = c + \sin 2x.$

(b) $256y^3\tan x = 32y^4 + (32y^3 - 12y)\sin 4y + (24y^2 - 3)$
$$\cos 4y + c.$$

7. $v = \int\frac{Q(x)}{f(x)}\, dx \therefore y = f(x)\left[\int\frac{Q(x)}{f(x)}\, dx + c\right].$

Section 14, page 39

1. (a) $cy + (y + 3)e^{\frac{3x^2}{2}} = 0.$

(b) $2x = -2t^2x^2\log x + t^2x^2 + ct^2.$

(c) $2y^2 - 2y + \log (2y + 1) + \dfrac{8}{x(2y + 1)} = c.$

(d) $y^2 = \dfrac{2x + c}{\sin^2 x}.$

(e) $\dfrac{1}{y} = \dfrac{2 + x}{2 - x} [c - \log (2 + x)].$

(f) $xy \log x + 1 = cxy.$

2. $2 \csc y + \sin x + \cos x = ce^{-x}.$

3. $\cot^2 u + 2e^{x^2} \displaystyle\int e^{-x^2} \, dx = ce^{x^2}.$

Section 15, page 43

1. $\cos \theta \, ds = \sqrt{a^2 \tan^2 \theta + b^2 \sec^2 \theta} \, d\theta.$

2. $y = \tan x + \dfrac{c}{\cos^2 xe^{\cos^2 x} \left(1 - c \displaystyle\int \sec^2 xe^{-\cos^2 x} \, dx\right)}$

4. $y(1 - x) = c(y - x^2).$

5. $\left(\dfrac{\log^2 x}{x} - \dfrac{\log x}{x^2} + \dfrac{2}{x} - 2x \log^2 x + 4x^2 \log x - 4x\right)\dfrac{dy}{dx}$

$+ \left(2 - \dfrac{\log x}{x^2} + \dfrac{4}{x} - \dfrac{1}{x^2} - 2 \log x\right) y^2$

$+ \left(\dfrac{\log^2 x}{x^2} - \dfrac{2}{x^2} + 2 \log^2 x - 4x - 4 + \dfrac{1}{x^3}\right) y$

$+ \left(- \dfrac{4 \log^2 x}{x} + 4 \log x + 4 + \dfrac{2 \log x}{x^2} - \dfrac{2}{x^2}\right) = 0.$

6. 1, 1, 1.

7. 3, b.

8. $y = \tan x + \dfrac{e^{-\int \left(\frac{2 \tan x}{\cos x - 1} + \csc x\right) dx}}{\displaystyle\int \dfrac{e^{-\int \left(\frac{2 \tan x}{\cos x - 1} + \csc x\right) dx}}{\cos x - 1} \, dx + c}.$

Section 16, page 46

1. $y = c(x - 2) - 4.$

4. $x^2 + y^2 = 10x.$

2. $y^2 = c(2x + 1).$

5. $\dfrac{x}{y - x} - \log (y - x) = c.$

3. $(3 + \pi - 3\theta)\rho^2 = 3.$

6. $y^2 - x^2 = c.$

7. $N \, dx - M \, dy = 0.$

8. $x^2 + 2x - 2y + 2 \log (x - 1) - 2 \log (y - 1) = c.$

9. $(3x - 2y + 5)^2(4x + y + 1) = c.$

10. (a) $x^2 + 2y^2 = c^2.$

(b) $2x^2 + y^2 + 4x = c.$

13. $y^{1-e^2} = cx.$

14. $x^2 + y^2 = 2a^2 \log cx.$

11. $y = ce^{\frac{x}{2}} + c^{-1}e^{-\frac{x}{2}}.$

15. $2cy = c^2x^2 - 1.$

12. $x^2 - y^2 = c.$

16. $s = 2e^t - 1.$

17. $s = 10(t + 1) \log (t + 1) - 8t + 3.$

18. $s = 2k\sqrt{t} - \cos t + c.$

19. $\dfrac{1 + bv + b^2v^2}{(1 - bv)^2 e^{-2\sqrt{3}\tan^{-1}\frac{1+2bv}{\sqrt{3}}}} = ce^{6gbt}.$

20. $(mg - kv)e^{\frac{k}{m}(t-t_0)} = mg + kv_0.$

21. $q = q_0 e^{\frac{1}{RC}(t_0-t)}.$

22. $i = i_0 e^{\frac{R}{L}(t_0-t)}.$

23. $i = \dfrac{et}{L} + k.$

28. $q = CE + (q_0 - CE)e^{\frac{1}{RC}(t_0-t)}.$

29. $i = \dfrac{1}{RC}(CE - q_0)e^{\frac{1}{RC}(t_0-t)}.$

30. $i = \dfrac{CE\omega}{1 + R^2C^2\omega^2}(\cos \omega t + RC\omega \sin \omega t - e^{\frac{-t}{RC}}).$

31. Impedance $= \dfrac{1}{C\omega}\sqrt{1 + R^2C^2\omega^2}$

33. $Ri = v + (Ri_0 - v)e^{\frac{R}{L}(t_0-t)}.$

35. 158 minutes.

36. $\dfrac{ds}{dt} = ks; s = ce^{kt}; s = 6^{1-\frac{t}{2}}.$

38. $t = 15(7 + 2\sqrt{10})$ minutes.

39. $h_0 = \dfrac{49}{81}$ feet; $\dfrac{625}{1296}$ feet.

40. $t = c - 960\sqrt{h} - 1920 \log |\sqrt{h} - 2|$; $h = 4$ feet.

41. (a) 11 minutes; (b) 8 minutes.

42. $t = \dfrac{4 \log 25}{\log 2}$ hours.

43. $s = 5(3^{3/5})$ pounds; $t = 8 + \dfrac{8 \log 5}{\log 3}$.

44. 16 hours.

45. 5 lbs. of 1st substance remain; 1.47 lbs. of 1st substance and 18.82 lbs. of 2nd.

46. $x = \dfrac{ak_1}{k_1 + k_2} [1 - ce^{(k_1+k_2)t}]$.

48. $s = 9125 \ (e^{2/5} - 1)$ dollars $= \$4487.90$.

49. $n = n_0 e^{\frac{t \log 2}{50}}$.

50. $n = 20,000 + \dfrac{50,000}{\log 2} = 92,134$.

51. $\theta = \dfrac{kr^3}{8} + c_1 r$.

52. 40.2 pounds.

53. 30.7 pounds.

54. $(.044)\%$.

Section 17, page 53

1. $xy = ce^{\frac{x}{y} - y^2}$.

2. $r \sin \theta = c$.

3. $x = ce^{\text{arc tan}\frac{y}{x}}$.

4. $13x^{-25}y^{-15} - 5x^{-26}y^{-13} = c$.

5. $(x^2 - 3y^2)^2 = cx$.

6. $\log y - \sinh^{-1}\left(\dfrac{x}{y}\right) = c$.

7. $30y + 12x + 5 = cx^6$.

8. $(u^2 - 1)e^{v^2} = c$.

9. $x^{-1}z^{-1} = 2x^{-1}(\log x + 1) + c$.

10. $3v^4 - 36uv + 4u^3 = c$.

11. $y^2 = x \log x + cx$.

12. $\cos x \cos y = c$.

13. $y = \dfrac{x^2}{2} + c_1 \log \tan \dfrac{x}{2} + c_2$.

14. $x^{1/6}y^{7/18}(x - 7) = c$.

15. $y = -x + c_1 e^x + c_2$.

16. $x - \sin y = c \cos y$.

17. $\dfrac{1}{r^3} + \sin \theta + 2 \sin \theta \cos^2 \theta = c \cos^3 \theta$.

18. $y = c_1 x^2 + c_2$.

19. $u + ve^{\frac{u}{v}} = c$.

20. $\log (x^2 + y^2 + 6x + 4y + 13) + \text{arc tan}\dfrac{x + 2y + 7}{2x - y + 4} = c$.

21. $5y + 15x + 11 \log (10y + 5x - 12) = c$.

22. $x = cye^{\frac{1}{2xy}}$.

23. $s = cte^{\frac{2}{\sqrt{st}}}$.

24. $\log x + 3e^{xy} - 2e^{-xy} = c$.

25. $4x^3y + xy^2 = c$.

26. $\pi x + x^2y - 6xy^2 + 12y^3 = c$.

27. $y^2e^{2x} + 4x^2e^{2x} = c$.

28. $\csc \theta = ce^{3/10 \sec^2 \phi}$.

29. $x^{-3/2}y^{-3} + 3x^{1/2}y^{-5} = c$.

30. $r\sqrt{\dfrac{1 + \sin \theta}{1 - \sin \theta}} + \log \dfrac{1 + \sin \theta}{1 - \sin \theta} - 2 \log \cos \theta - \sin \theta = c$.

31. $2ue^v + e^v - 4u = c$.

32. $e^{\frac{y^2}{2}}(1 - 4x + 2xy^2) = c$.

33. $\log y = \dfrac{x^2}{8y^2} + c$.

34. $x \sin \dfrac{y}{x} = c$.

35. $(4x - y - 6)^5(-x + 4y - 9)^5 = c(5x - 5y + 3)$.

36. $3 \log x - 4 \log (1 + x^2y^2) - 2 \log y = c + \arctan xy$.

37. $3x^2ye^{2x} - y^3e^{2x} + e^{3x} = c$.

38. $y\sqrt{1 + x^2} + 2 \log \dfrac{1 + \sqrt{1 + x^2}}{x} = c$.

39. $y^2 = 4 + ce^{-x^2}$.

40. $ax^3 + 3bx^2y + 3cxy^2 + gy^3 = k$.

41. $M = ax^3 + 3bx^2y + 3cxy^2 + gy^3; N = bx^3 + 3cx^2y + 3gxy^2 + hy^3$.

42. $x^4 + 3x^3y + 3x^2y^2 - xy^3 + 5y^4 = c$.

43. $xy = c$.

44. $t = 10(\sqrt{7} - 1)(\sqrt{10} + 3)$ minutes.

45. $(m + n - 1)x^{1-m} = k(m - 1)y^n + cy^{1-m}$.

46. $i = i_0 + \dfrac{V}{L\omega}(\cos \omega t_0 - \cos \omega t)$.

47. $q = \dfrac{V}{1 + R^2c^2\omega^2}\{c \sin \omega t - Rc^2\omega \cos \omega t\} + Ke^{-\frac{t}{Rc}}$.

48. $i = \dfrac{V\omega}{1 + R^2c^2\omega^2}\{c \cos \omega t + Rc^2\omega \sin \omega t\} - \dfrac{K}{Rc}e^{-\frac{t}{Rc}}$.

49. $i = \dfrac{V}{R} + \left(i_0 - \dfrac{V}{R}\right)e^{\frac{R}{L}(t_0-t)}$.

50. $i = \dfrac{V}{R^2 + L^2\omega^2}(R \sin \omega t - L\omega \cos \omega t) + ke^{-\frac{Rt}{L}}$.

51. Paraboloid of revolution.

53. $M_x + N_y \equiv 0$.

55. (a) $4x^2 - 4y^2$.

(b) 0.

63. $y(1 + c \cos x) = c \sin x + \sin x \cos x.$

64. 202.7 cu. ft.

Section 19, page 60

1. $8y = -x^2 + 2x - 1.$

5. $y^2 = 3x^2.$

2. $4y = 3x^2.$

6. $27x^2 = 4y^3.$

3. $12y = -x^4.$

7. $27x^4 = -4(1 + y^3)^3.$

4. $16y^2 = (4x - 5)^2.$

Section 20, page 62

1. $y = ce^{3x}; \ y = x^2 + c.$

2. $\begin{cases} x = 2 \log p + 6p + c, \\ y = 2p + 3p^2. \end{cases}$

3. $cy^2 + 6xy^2 + 1 = 0; \ x(y + c) = 2.$

4. $x = 2 \sec (2y + c).$

5. $(5x - y)^2 = c(x^2 - 1).$

6. $x(n^2 + p^2 + p \sqrt{n^2 + p^2}) = c;$
$y \sqrt{n^2 + p^2} = c.$

7. $r \sec \theta = c.$

8. $3y - x^3 = c; \ 2 + x^2 y = cy; \ 1 + 3xy^3 = cy^3.$

9. $y^2 - x^2 = c; \ y = c; \ x^4 = c(x^2 - y^2).$

10. $(y - ce^{2x})(2y - x^2 - c) = 0.$

11. $(2y + \cos 2x - c)(\sin 2y - ce^{-2x}) = 0.$

12. $4(9 + cx^2) = c^2 y^2.$

13. $\begin{cases} x = \dfrac{p}{2 \sqrt{1 + p^2}} \log (p + \sqrt{1 + p^2}) + \dfrac{cp}{\sqrt{1 + p^2}}, \\ y = \dfrac{p}{2} - \dfrac{1}{2 \sqrt{1 + p^2}} \log (p + \sqrt{1 + p^2}) - \dfrac{c}{\sqrt{1 + p^2}}. \end{cases}$

14. $\begin{cases} x = c + \displaystyle\int \dfrac{3 \, dp}{(5 - p) \sqrt{1 - p^2}} \\ y = 3 \cos^{-1} p + 5x. \end{cases}$

15. $\begin{cases} x = \dfrac{c - 2p}{p^2} \\ y = \dfrac{2c - 4p}{p} + 2 \log p - \log 4. \end{cases}$

16. $y^2 = c(2x + 1)$.

17. $xy = \left(\dfrac{x^2}{3} + c\sqrt{x}\right)^2$; $y = 0$.

Section 22, page 65

1. $y^2 + cx - c^2 = 0$.

2. $x = 2p - p^2$, $y = p^2 - \dfrac{2p^3}{3} + c$.

3. $256c^3y = 64c^2x^2 - 16cx + 1$; $y = \dfrac{8x^3}{27}$.

4. $y = c^{3/2}p^{3/2}$, $x = 3c^{3/2}p^{1/2} + \dfrac{1}{3c}$; $64y = x^6$.

5. $y = \dfrac{p^2}{2} + p\cos p - \sin p + c$, $x = p + \cos p$.

6. $\log y - \dfrac{p}{y} - \dfrac{p^2}{2y^2} = c$, $x = \dfrac{p}{y} + \log p - \log y$.

7. $\tan^2 y = c^2 + 2cx$.

8. $\begin{cases} x = -2p - 2\log(p-1) + c, \\ y = -p^2 - 2p - 2\log(p-1) + c. \end{cases}$

9. $\begin{cases} x = \dfrac{p(c + \sin^{-1}p)}{\sqrt{1-p^2}}, \\ y = -p + \dfrac{c + \sin^{-1}p}{\sqrt{1-p^2}}. \end{cases}$

10. (a) $y = cx + \dfrac{a^2}{c}$; $y^2 = 4a^2x$.

(b) $y = cx + 2c^2 - c$; $(x-1)^2 + 8y = 0$.

(c) $y = cx + \sqrt{c^3 - c^2 + c - 1}$; $\begin{cases} x = \dfrac{-1 + 2p - 3p^2}{2(p^3 - p^2 + p - 1)^{1/2}}, \\ y = \dfrac{-p^3 + p - 2}{2(p^3 - p^2 + p - 1)^{1/2}}. \end{cases}$

(d) $y = (x-5)c + c^2$; $(x-5)^2 + 4y = 0$.

(e) $y = cx + \log c$; $xe^{y+1} + 1 = 0$.

(f) $(y - cx)(3c - 1) = 5c^2$; $\begin{cases} y = \dfrac{5p^2}{(3p-1)^2}, \\ x = \dfrac{-5p(3p-2)}{(3p-1)^2}. \end{cases}$

(g) $e^{y-cx} = c^2$; $4 - x^2e^{y+2} = 0$.

(h) $\log y = cx + c^2$; $y = e^{\frac{-x^2}{4}}$.

11. $y^2 = 4 + 4x^2$.

12. $4y^3 - 27x^2 = 0$.

13. $27y - 2x^3 = 0$.

14. $4y = x^2$.

15. $x^2 + y^2 = 25$.

16. $(x - 5\ \cos\ c)^2 + (y - 5\ \sin\ c)^2 = 1$; $(p^2 + 1)(x^4 + 2x^2y^2 + y^4 + 576) + 8xyp - 4(13x^2p^2 + 12y^2p^2 + 12x^2 + 13y^2) = 0$; $x^2 + y^2 = 26 \pm 10$.

18. $3y = e^{\frac{x^2}{4}}$.

20. $y = 0$; $y = \dfrac{2x^3}{27}$.

21. Particular.

22. Singular.

23. $3y^2 = x^2$.

24. $y^2 = cx$.

25. $y = c(1 + p^2)^{-\frac{1}{2}}(p + \sqrt{1 + p^2})^{-1/a}(p + a\sqrt{1 + p^2})$; $x = c(1 + p^2)^{-\frac{1}{2}}(p + \sqrt{1 + p^2})^{-1/a}$.

26. $x^5y^2 + cy + cyx^6 + c^2x = 0$.

27. $x^2 + y^2 - 2xy + 2c(x + y) + c^2 = 0$.

28. $y^{1 - \frac{n}{t}} - x^{1 - \frac{n}{t}} = c$.

32. (a) $(c - 4y)^2 - 48x = 0$.

(b) $y^2 - 2cy - cx^2y + c^2(x^2 + 1) = 0$.

(c) $x = \dfrac{2y - 4p}{p^2}$; $y = px + \dfrac{4p\log p - cp}{p - 2}$.

(d) $4y = 2p(5p + \sqrt{1 + 4p^2}) - \log(2p + \sqrt{1 + 4p^2}) + c$; $x = 5p + \sqrt{1 + 4p^2}$.

(e) $\sqrt{x - x^2} - \tan^{-1}\sqrt{\dfrac{1 - x}{x}} = \pm y + c$.

(f) $y = cxe^{1/x}$.

34. (a) $x^2y^2 - y^2 + 2cxy + c^2 = 0$.

(b) $(x^2 - 9)c^2 - 2xyc + y^2 - 9 = 0$; $x^2 + y^2 = 9$.

(c) $e^{2y-2c} - 2xe^{y-c} + 1 = 0$.

(d) $y + \displaystyle\int \sqrt[3]{\dfrac{x \pm a}{x}}\ dx = c$.

(e) $x = c + \log\dfrac{p + \sqrt{p^2 + 9}}{p^2}$; $y = -2p + \sqrt{p^2 + 9}$.

(f) $4y = 2cx^2 + 3c^2$; $12y + x^4 = 0$.

(g) $y = cx + (c - r)(c - s)$; $4y + (r + s - x)^2 = 4rs$.

(h) $y = cx + \sqrt{a^2 + c^2}$; $y = |a|\sqrt{1 - x^2}$.

(i) $x^2c^2 - 2cxy + c + y^2 = 0$; $4xy = 1$.

(j) $(y - cx)(3c - 5) - 15c = 0$; $x = \dfrac{75}{(3p - 5)^2}$, $y = \dfrac{45p^2}{(3p - 5)^2}$.

(k) $4y^3 + 4cy^{3/2} + c^2 = 9e^{2x}$.

(l) $x = c + p + \dfrac{3p^2}{4}$; $y = \dfrac{p^2 + p^3}{2}$.

(m) $x = \dfrac{c}{a^2 + p^2 + p\sqrt{a^2 + p^2}}$; $y = \dfrac{c}{\sqrt{a^2 + p^2}}$.

(n) $\cos(x + c) = \log y$; $\log^2 y = 1$.

(o) $x = \dfrac{1}{a} \pm \dfrac{\sqrt{1 + p^2}}{ap}$; $y = c \pm \dfrac{1}{a}\log\dfrac{1 + \sqrt{1 + p^2}}{p}$.

(p) $y = cx - c^2$; $4y - x^2 = 0$.

(q) $y = \dfrac{9}{4c} + cx^2$; $y^2 = 9x^2$.

(r) $s = 5p^5 + p^2$; $t = \dfrac{25p^4}{4} + 2p + c$.

(s) $\sin(y - cx) = \pm\dfrac{1}{\sqrt{1 + c^2}}$; $x = \dfrac{1}{1 + p^2}$, $y = \dfrac{p}{1 + p^2} + \text{arc cot } p$.

(t) $(r - ce^\theta)(r + \cos\theta + c)\left(e^r - c\cot\dfrac{\theta}{2}\right) = 0$.

(u) $\log y = ce^x + c^2$; $4\log y = -e^{2x}$.

35. Particular.

38. $y^2 + 2cy + c^2 - \dfrac{x^4}{4} = 0$.

39. $y^2 - 2cxy + c^2x^2 + ck = 0$; $xy = \dfrac{k}{4}$.

40. $(x - a)^2 + (y - b)^2 = c^2$.

41. $(y - cx)^2 = \dfrac{c^2k^2}{1 + c^2}$; $x^{2/3} + y^{2/3} = k^{2/3}$.

42. $x = \dfrac{a\cos 7\theta + 7a\cos\theta}{2}$, $y = \dfrac{-a\sin 7\theta + 7a\sin\theta}{2}$.

43. $y = px + \dfrac{4}{27p^2}$.

44. $y = cx - 2c^2$; $8y = x^2$.

45. $y = cx + \dfrac{3c}{c - 1}$; $x = \dfrac{3}{(p - 1)^2}$, $y = \dfrac{3p^2}{(p - 1)^2}$.

Section 25, page 74

1. (a) $y = c_1e^{3x} + c_2e^{-x}$.

    (b) $y = c_1 + c_2e^x + c_3e^{-2x/3}$.

    (c) $y = c_1 + c_2e^{x/2} + c_3e^{2x}$.

    (d) $y = c_1e^{2x} + c_2e^{-4x}$.

    (e) $y = c_1e^x + c_2e^{-x} + c_3e^{x\sqrt{3}} + c_4e^{-x\sqrt{3}}$.

    (f) $y = c_1e^{ax} + c_2e^{-ax} + c_3e^{bx}$.

    (g) $y = c_1 + c_2e^x + c_3e^{2x} + c_4e^{-x}$.

7. $y = 1 - 2e^{-2x}$.

9. 9 sinh 2 ft.; 3 cosh 2 ft./sec.

8. $2e^3 - 1$ ft.; $8e^3$ ft./sec.

10. $y = (c_1 + c_2 x)e^{2x}$.

Section 26, page 76

2. (a) $y = e^{2x}[c_1 \cos (3x) + c_2 \sin (3x)]$.

(b) $y = c_1 + e^{-3x}(c_2 \cos x + c_3 \sin x)$.

(c) $y = e^{-3x}[c_1 \cos (4x) + c_2 \sin (4x)]$.

6. 4 ft., -4 ft./sec.

9. 0.17 sec.

7. Period $= \dfrac{2\pi}{7}$

10. $20 \dfrac{d^2s}{dt^2} + 4 \dfrac{ds}{dt} + s = 0$.

8. $b > a^2,\ \dfrac{2\pi}{\sqrt{b - a^2}}$.

Section 27, page 79

2. (a) $y = c_1 + c_2 x + c_3 e^{-2x}$.

(b) $y = c_1 + c_2 x + c_3 e^x + c_4 x e^x$.

(c) $y = c_1 + c_2 x + c_3 x^2 + c_4 e^x + c_5 e^{2x}$.

(d) $y = c_1 e^x + c_2 x e^x + c_3 e^{-2x} + c_4 x e^{-2x}$.

(e) $y = c_1 e^{-x} + c_2 x e^{-x} + c_3 x^2 e^{-x} + c_4 e^{2x}$.

(f) $y = c_1 + c_2 x + e^x(c_3 \cos 2x + c_4 \sin 2x)$.

(g) $y = c_1 + c_2 e^x + c_3 x e^x$.

(h) $y = c_1 + c_2 x + (c_3 + c_4 x) \cos 2x + (c_5 + c_6 x) \sin 2x$.

4. $y = c_1 + (c_2 + c_3 x) \cos 2x + (c_4 + c_5 x) \sin 2x$.

Section 28, page 83

1. $y = c_1 + c_2 e^{-2x} - \frac{36}{5} \cos x + \frac{72}{5} \sin x$.

2. $y = c_1 e^x + c_2 e^{-2x} - x^2 + \dfrac{x}{2} - \dfrac{3}{4}$.

3. $y = c_1 e^x + c_2 e^{2x} + c_3 e^{-2x} + \dfrac{x^4}{4} + x^3 + \dfrac{15x^2}{4} + \dfrac{27x}{4} + \dfrac{67}{8}$.

4. $y = c_1 e^x + c_2 e^{3x} + c_3 e^{-3x} + \dfrac{2x}{9} + \dfrac{5}{9}$.

5. $y = (c_1 + c_2 x)e^x + c_3 e^{-3x} + \dfrac{x^3}{3} + \dfrac{5x^2}{3} + \dfrac{41x}{9} + \dfrac{166}{27}$.

6. $y = c_1 + c_2 e^x + c_3 e^{2x} + \frac{1}{3}x^3 + \frac{3}{4}x^2 + \frac{7}{4}x$.

7. $y = c_1 + c_2 x + c_3 e^x - \dfrac{x^3}{3} - \dfrac{5x^2}{2}$.

8. $y = c_1 + c_2 e^{-x} + c_3 e^{3x} - \dfrac{x^3}{9} + \dfrac{2x^2}{9} + \dfrac{31x}{27}$.

9. $y = c_1e^x + c_2e^{-x} + c_3 \sin 2x + c_4 \cos 2x + \frac{3}{52}e^{3x} + \frac{1}{20}x \cos 2x.$

10. $y = c_1 + c_2e^{3x} + c_3e^{-x} + \dfrac{3 \sin x}{10} + \dfrac{3 \cos x}{5}.$

11. $y = c_1e^x + c_2e^{-x} + c_3 \cos x + c_4 \sin x + \dfrac{\cos 2x - 2 \sin 2x}{15}.$

12. $y = c_1 + c_2x + c_3 \cos 2x + c_4 \sin 2x - \frac{1}{3} \sin x - \frac{2}{45} \cos 3x.$

13. $9y = -x \cos 3x.$ **17.** $y = e^{2x}.$

14. $y = x^2 \sin x/8.$ **18.** $y = 2e^{-x}.$

15. $y = (x \sin 2x)/16.$ **19.** $y = \dfrac{x^2}{6} + \dfrac{4x}{9} - xe^x.$

16. $y = \dfrac{x \sin x}{6} + \dfrac{\sin 3x}{40}.$ **20.** $y = x^2e^{3x}/3.$

21. (a) $y = -x^2e^x/2.$ (b) $y = -\frac{1}{4}e^x + \frac{1}{10}xe^{2x} - \frac{2}{15}xe^{-3x}.$

22. $y = -\frac{1}{4}e^x + \frac{1}{10}xe^{2x} - \frac{2}{15}xe^{-2x}.$

23. $y = (\frac{1}{10}x^2 - \frac{7}{50}x + \frac{39}{500})e^{2x}.$

25. $y = -e^x \sin x/3.$

26. $y = -\dfrac{e^{3x}}{27}(3x + 7).$

27. $y = \frac{1}{5}(2e^{3x} - \sin x).$

28. $y = -\dfrac{x^3}{6} - \dfrac{x^2}{4} + \dfrac{\sin x - 2 \cos x}{5}.$

29. $y = e^x \left(\dfrac{x^3}{6} - \dfrac{3x^2}{4} + \dfrac{7x}{4} + \dfrac{3 \sin x + \cos x}{10} \right).$

30. $y = \dfrac{xe^{ax}}{a - b} + \dfrac{2xe^{bx}}{b - a} + \dfrac{(ab - 1) \cos x - (a + b) \sin x}{a^2b^2 + a^2 + b^2 + 1}.$

31. $-1.$ **33.** $\pi/12 \sqrt{3}$ seconds.

32. $s = \frac{300}{17}.$ **34.** $6 \sqrt{\pi}/5$ seconds.

Section 29, page 89

1. (a) $y = c_1 + c_2e^{2x} - \dfrac{2 \sin x + \cos x}{5}.$

(b) $y = c_1 + c_2e^x + c_3e^{-3x} - \dfrac{x^2}{6} - \dfrac{8x}{9}.$

(c) $y = c_1e^{ax} + c_2e^{-bx} + \dfrac{2e^{3x}}{(3 - a)(3 + b)}.$

(d) $y = c_1e^x + c_2e^{-x} + c_3e^{2x} + \dfrac{xe^x}{4}(1 + x).$

(e) $y = c_1 + (c_2 + c_3x)e^{2x} + e^x - \dfrac{\sin 2x}{16}.$

Section 30, page 93

1. (a) $y = c_1 \cos ax + c_2 \sin ax + \dfrac{\sin ax}{a^2} \log (\csc ax - \cot ax)$.

(b) $y = c_1 + c_2 e^{ax} + c_3 e^{-ax}$

$$+ e^{2ax} \left[\frac{1}{12a^3} + \frac{(4 - 11a^2) \sin 2x + 3a(4 - a^2) \cos 2x}{4(a^2 + 1)(a^2 + 4)(9a^2 + 4)} \right].$$

(c) $y = c_1 e^{3x} + c_2 e^{-4x} - \dfrac{x}{12} + \dfrac{13 \sin x}{170} + \dfrac{\cos x}{170} - \dfrac{1}{144}$.

(d) $y = c_1 + c_2 \sin x + c_3 \cos x + \dfrac{e^x}{2} + x^2 - x$.

2. $y = \dfrac{x^5 \log x}{12} - \dfrac{7x^5}{144}$.

3. $y = \dfrac{\log^3 x}{4x} + \dfrac{3 \log^2 x}{4x} + \dfrac{9 \log x}{8x} + \dfrac{3}{4x}$.

Section 32, page 95

1. (a) $y = c_1 x^2 + c_2 x^3$.

(b) $y = c_1 x^2 + c_2 x^4 - \dfrac{x^2 \cosh x}{2} + x^4 \displaystyle\int \frac{\sinh x}{2x^2}\, dx$.

(c) $y = c_1 + c_2 x^3 + \dfrac{c_3}{x^2}$.

(d) $y = c_1 + c_2 x^a + \dfrac{c_3}{x^a}$.

(e) $y = c_1 + c_2 x + c_3 x^4 - \dfrac{x^3}{3} + \dfrac{x \log x}{3}$.

3. (a) $y = c_1(2 - x)^5 + c_2(2 - x)^{-3}$.

(b) $y = c_1(1 + 2x)^3 + c_2(1 + 2x)^{-1} - \dfrac{3x}{16} - \dfrac{5}{96}$.

4. $y = c_1 x^5 + \dfrac{c_2}{x}$.

5. (a) $y = \dfrac{c_1}{x} + \dfrac{c_2 \log x}{x}$.

(b) $y = c_1 + c_2 \log x + c_3 (\log x)^2$.

(c) $y = c_1 + c_2 \log x + c_3 x^3$.

6. (a) $y = x(c_1 \cos 3 \log x + c_2 \sin 3 \log x)$.

(b) $y = c_1 \cos 2 \log x + c_2 \sin 2 \log x$.

(c) $y = c_1(1 - 3x) + \dfrac{c_2}{1 - 3x} - \dfrac{\log^2 (1 - 3x)}{9} - \dfrac{2}{9}$.

(d) $y = c_1 + c_2 \sin \log (x + 3) + c_3 \cos \log (x + 3)$.

Section 33, page 98

2. (a) $(x + \sin x)y = c_1x^2 + c_2x + c_3 - \cos x.$

(b) $(e^x + 2x)y = \dfrac{1}{24x} + c_1x^3 + c_2x^2 + c_3x + c_4.$

(c) $y \tan \dfrac{x}{2} = \displaystyle\int \tan \dfrac{x}{2} (c_1x \csc x + c_2 \csc x - \cot x)\, dx + c_3.$

(d) $y(x^2 + 1)^2 = x^5 \left[\dfrac{\log x}{5} - \dfrac{1}{25} \right] + 2x^3 \left[\dfrac{\log x}{3} - \dfrac{1}{9} \right] + x \log x$
$$- x + c_1(x^4 + 2x^2) + c_2(x^3 + 3x) + c_3.$$

(e) $y = c_1 + c_2(x + 2)^{\frac{3+\sqrt{5}}{2}} + c_3(x + 2)^{\frac{3-\sqrt{5}}{2}} + x - \log x.$

4. (f) $x\mu'' + \mu' - x^2\mu = 0.$

Section 34, page 101

1. (a) $y = c_1x^3 + c_2.$

(b) $y = x^3 + c_1x^2 + c_2.$

(c) $y = -x + 2 \log (x + 1) + 2.$

(d) $y = c;\ y = c_1 \tan (c_1x + c_2).$

(e) $\pm c_1x = c_2 + 2(c_1y - 1)^{\frac{1}{2}}.$

(f) $2x - 2 = \log (\log y).$

(g) $y = - \log \cos (x + c_1) + c_2.$

(h) $y = c_1x^2 + c_2x^3 + c_3.$

Section 35, page 105

1. (a) $\begin{cases} x = e^t + \dfrac{5 \sin t}{17} - \dfrac{3 \cos t}{17} - 3c_1e^{4t} + c_2, \\ y = -\dfrac{2}{3} e^t - \dfrac{\sin t}{17} + \dfrac{4 \cos t}{17} + 4c_1e^{4t}. \end{cases}$

(b) $\begin{cases} x = 2c_1e^{\frac{(-5+\sqrt{5})t}{2}} + 2c_2e^{\frac{(-5-\sqrt{5})t}{2}}, \\ y = (-1 + \sqrt{5})c_1e^{\frac{(-5+\sqrt{5})t}{2}} - (1 + \sqrt{5})c_2e^{\frac{(-5-\sqrt{5})t}{2}}. \end{cases}$

(c) $\begin{cases} x = c_1 \cos 2t - c_2 \sin 2t - \dfrac{5}{4}, \\ y = c_1 \sin 2t + c_2 \cos 2t + \dfrac{3t}{2}. \end{cases}$

(d) $\begin{cases} x = 3c_1t - c_2e^{4t} + c_3, \\ y = c_1 + 4c_2e^{4t}. \end{cases}$

(e) $\begin{cases} x = c_1 + c_2t - c_3e^{-2t} + \dfrac{t^3}{6} + \dfrac{t^2}{4} - \dfrac{1}{16} e^{2t} - \dfrac{1}{8} e^{-2t}(1 + 2t), \\ y = c_4 + 2c_3e^{-2t} + \dfrac{t}{2} - \dfrac{t^2}{2} + \dfrac{1}{8} e^{2t} + \dfrac{1}{4} e^{-2t} + \dfrac{1}{2} te^{-2t}. \end{cases}$

(f) $\begin{cases} x = 4c_1e^t + c_2e^{t/2} + c_3e^{-t/2} + \frac{4}{15}e^{2t}, \\ y = 3c_1e^t - t + 1. \end{cases}$

(g) $\begin{cases} x = c_1e^t + c_2(1 + \sqrt{5})e^{\frac{(1+\sqrt{5})t}{2}} + c_3(1 - \sqrt{5})e^{\frac{(1-\sqrt{5})t}{2}}, \\ y = c_4 - 2c_2e^{\frac{(1+\sqrt{5})t}{2}} - 2c_3e^{\frac{(1-\sqrt{5})t}{2}}. \end{cases}$

(h) $\begin{cases} x = c_1 + c_2 \sin(t\sqrt{2}) + c_3 \cos(t\sqrt{2}) + e^{2t} + \cos t, \\ y = c_4 + c_2\sqrt{2} \cos(t\sqrt{2}) - c_3\sqrt{2} \sin(t\sqrt{2}) \\ \qquad\qquad\qquad\qquad\qquad\qquad + 3e^{2t} - \sin t. \end{cases}$

4. (a) $\begin{cases} x = A_1e^{2t} - 2A_2e^{3t}, \\ y = -A_1e^{2t} + A_2e^{3t}. \end{cases}$ (b) $\begin{cases} x = A_1e^{3t} + 3A_2e^{-t}, \\ y = -A_1e^{3t} + A_2e^{-t}. \end{cases}$

6. (a) $\begin{cases} x = A_1e^{3t} + A_2te^{3t}, \\ y = (A_1 - A_2)e^{3t} + A_2te^{3t}. \end{cases}$

(b) $\begin{cases} x = A_1e^{2t} + A_2te^{2t}, \\ y = (A_1 + A_2)e^{2t} + A_2te^{2t}. \end{cases}$

8. (a) $\begin{cases} x = e^{2t}(A_1 \sin t + A_2 \cos t), \\ y = e^{2t}(A_2 \sin t - A_1 \cos t). \end{cases}$

(b) $\begin{cases} x = e^{3t}[5A_1 \sin 2t + 5A_2 \cos 2t], \\ y = e^{3t}[(A_1 + 2A_2) \sin 2t + (A_2 - 2A_1) \cos 2t]. \end{cases}$

10. (a) $\begin{cases} x = 3A_1e^t + 4A_2e^{2t} + 2A_3e^{3t}, \\ y = 2A_1e^t + A_2e^{2t} + 2A_3e^{3t}, \\ z = 3A_1e^t + A_2e^{2t} + 3A_3e^{3t}. \end{cases}$

(b) $\begin{cases} x = 2A_1 + 3A_2e^{2t} + 4A_3e^{-t}, \\ y = 2A_1 + 2A_2e^{2t} + A_3e^{-t}, \\ z = 3A_1 + 3A_2e^{2t} + A_3e^{-t}. \end{cases}$

11. $\begin{cases} 3x = 2e^{2t} + e^{-t}, \\ 3y = 2e^{2t} - 2e^{-t}. \end{cases}$

Section 36, page 110

1. (a) $y = c_1 + c_2e^x + c_3e^{-x}.$

(b) $y = c_1e^x + e^{-\frac{x}{2}}\left(c_2 \cos \frac{x\sqrt{15}}{2} + c_3 \sin \frac{x\sqrt{15}}{2}\right).$

(c) $y = c_1 + c_2x + (c_3 + c_4x)e^{ax} + \frac{x^4}{12a^2} + \frac{2x^3}{3a^3} + \frac{(6 - a^2)x^2}{2a^4}.$

(d) $y = c_1e^{2x} + c_2e^{-2x} + c_3xe^{-2x} + \frac{e^{3x}}{25} - \frac{1}{4}.$

(e) $y = c_1 + c_2e^{x/2} + c_3e^x + c_4e^{3x/2} + \frac{18}{65} \sin x - \frac{14}{65} \cos x.$

(f) $y = c_1 e^{-2x} + e^{2x}(c_2 \cos x + c_3 \sin x)$.

(g) $y = c_1 + c_2 x + e^{4x}(c_3 \cos 2x + c_4 \sin 2x) + \dfrac{x^4}{240} + \dfrac{x^3}{150}$

$\qquad + \dfrac{11x^2}{2000} + \dfrac{1}{45} e^{3x}$.

(h) $y = c_1 e^x + c_2 x e^x + c_3 e^{-2x} + c_4 x e^{-2x} + \sin 2x$.

(i) $y = c_1 e^{2x} + c_2 e^{ax} + c_3 e^{-ax} + \dfrac{1}{3(a^2 - 1)} [2 \sinh x + \cosh x]$.

(j) $y = c_1 e^{3x} + c_2 e^{-x/2} + c_3 x e^{-x/2} + e^x$.

(k) $y = e^{ax} \left(c_1 + c_2 x + c_3 x^2 + \dfrac{x^3}{6} \right)$.

(l) $y = (c_1 + c_2 x) \sin ax + (c_3 + c_4 x) \cos ax + \dfrac{1}{4a^4} \cosh ax$.

(m) $y = c_1 x^2 + c_2 x^3 + x^2 \log x + \dfrac{x^4}{2}$.

(n) $y = c_1 x + c_2 x \log x + \dfrac{c_3}{x^2} + \dfrac{x^4 \log x}{9} - \dfrac{x^4}{9} - \dfrac{3x^3 \log x}{10} - \dfrac{x^3}{25}$.

(o) $y = \dfrac{c_1}{2 - x} + c_2(2 - x)^3$.

(p) $y = c_1 x^2 + c_2 x^2 \log x + 5x$.

(q) $y = c_1 + (3 + 2x)[c_2 \cos \log (3 + 2x) + c_3 \sin \log (3 + 2x)]$.

(r) $y = c_1 + c_2 e^{-x} + e^{2x} \left(c_3 + \dfrac{x^4}{24} - \dfrac{5x^3}{36} + \dfrac{19x^2}{72} - \dfrac{65x}{216} \right)$.

(s) $y = e^x(c_1 + c_2 x - 2 \log (x - 1))$.

(t) $e^{-y} = 2 \sin \left(x + \dfrac{\pi}{6} \right)$.

(u) $y = \dfrac{2}{c_1} + c_2 e^{c_1 x}$.

(v) $y = \dfrac{x^2}{2} + c_1(x \sqrt{1 - x^2} + \sin^{-1} x) + c_2$.

2. (a) $y = 2e^{3x} \sin 2x$.

(b) $y = e^x - e^{-4x} + 2x$.

(c) $y = x^3(2 \cos \log x^2 - \sin \log x^2)$.

3. (a) $(x^2 + 3x)y' + (x - 4)y = 3(x^2 + 3x)^{19/3} + c_1$,

$\qquad\qquad$ or

$$y \frac{(x^2 + 3x)^{7/3}}{x^{11/3}} = \frac{9x}{17} (x + 3)^{17/3} - \frac{27}{340} (x + 3)^{29/3}$$

$$+ c_1 \int \frac{(x + 3)^{4/3} \, dx}{x^{7/3}} + c_2.$$

(b) $y' - y \sin x = \dfrac{x^2 \log x}{2} - \dfrac{3x^2}{4} + c_1 x + c_2,$

or

$$e^{\cos x} y = c_3 + \int e^{\cos x} \left[\frac{x^2 \log x}{2} - \frac{3x^2}{4} + c_1 x + c_2 \right] dx.$$

(c) $xy' + (\log x - 2)y = \dfrac{x^3}{3} + c_1 x + c_2,$

or

$$y \frac{\sqrt{e^{\log^2 x}}}{x^2} = c_3 + \int \sqrt{e^{\log^2 x}} \left(\frac{x}{3} + \frac{c_1}{x^2} + \frac{c_2}{x^3} \right) dx.$$

(d) $y = c_1 x^{-2} + c_2 x^2 + c_3 x + c_4 + \dfrac{4}{5} x^3.$

(e) $y \sin x = \dfrac{\cot x}{4} + \int \log \sin x \, dx + c_1 x^3 + c_2 x^2 + c_3 x + c_4.$

4. (a) $y = \dfrac{e^x}{2} + \dfrac{c_1}{xe^x} + \dfrac{c_2 e^x}{x}.$

(b) $\mu = c_1 x + c_2 x^2$ (c_1, c_2 arbitrary constants).

5. (a) $y = u \cos 2x$, where u is defined by

$$u' = \frac{\sqrt{\sin 2x} \log \tan x}{2 \cos^2 2x} + \frac{\sqrt{\sin 2x}}{2 \cos 2x} + \frac{c_1 \sqrt{\sin 2x}}{\cos^2 2x}.$$

(b) $y = ux \sin x$, where

$$u = - \int \cot x \csc x \log \cos x \, dx + c_1 \csc x + c_2.$$

(c) $y = u \log x$, where $u' = \dfrac{1 - \log x}{\log^2 x} \left[c + \int \dfrac{dx}{1 - \log x} \right].$

(d) $y = \dfrac{3x^3}{4} + c_1 x \log x + c_2 x.$

(e) $y = ue^x$, where

$$u' = \frac{2x - x^2}{e^x} \left[c_1 + c_2 \left(\frac{1}{2 - x} - \frac{1}{x} + \log \frac{x}{2 - x} \right) \right].$$

8. (a) $y = \dfrac{1}{\sqrt{\sin x}} (c_1 e^{2x} + c_2 e^{-2x}).$

(b) $y = \dfrac{1}{\sqrt{x}} \left(c_1 e^x + c_2 e^{-x} + \dfrac{xe^x}{2} \right).$

(c) $y = e^{-x^2} [c_1 \cos \log x^{\frac{\sqrt{3}}{2}} + c_2 \sin \log x^{\frac{\sqrt{3}}{2}}] \sqrt{x}.$

(d) $y = \sqrt{\dfrac{e^x}{x^x}} \left(c_1 x^2 + \dfrac{c_2}{x} + \dfrac{x^2 \log x}{3} \right).$

10. (a) $y = e^{e^x}(c_1 + c_2 e^x) + e^x + 2.$

(b) $y = e^{\frac{\cos x}{2}} \left[c_1 \cos \frac{\sqrt{3} \cos x}{2} + c_2 \sin \frac{\sqrt{3} \cos x}{2} \right].$

(c) $y = c_1(\sec x)^{\frac{3+\sqrt{13}}{2}} + c_2(\sec x)^{\frac{3-\sqrt{13}}{2}}$.

11. (a) $y = e^{x^2}(c_1 \cos x + c_2 \sin x + 1)$.

(b) $y = c_1 x^{\frac{-1+\sqrt{17}}{8}} + c_2 x^{\frac{-1-\sqrt{17}}{8}} - \log x - 1$.

(c) $y = c_1 \dfrac{x^x}{e^x} + c_2 \dfrac{e^x}{x^x}$.

(d) $y = \sqrt{\cos x}\left(c_1 x^3 + \dfrac{c_2}{x^2} - \dfrac{x^2}{4}\right)$.

(e) $y = e_i^{-\frac{1}{3}x^{3/2}}\left(c_1 e^{3x} + c_2 e^{-3x} - \dfrac{x}{9}\right)$.

12. (c) $y = \dfrac{-5x^9 + 4c}{x^{11} + cx^2}$.

(d) $y = -\dfrac{\log x + c \log^3 x + 2c \log x}{1 + c \log^2 x}$.

(e) $y = \dfrac{\csc x(e^{-x} - 4ce^{4x})}{e^{-x} + ce^{4x}}$.

(g) $x(1-x)(x - \log x)(1 - \log x)y' = x - x^2 - x \log x + x \log^2 x$
$\quad - y(1 - x^2 - x + x \log^2 x) + y^2(1 - 2x + x \log x)$.

13. (a) $x = 3c_1 e^{8t} + c_2 e^{-2t}$; $y = 4c_1 e^{8t} - 2c_2 e^{-2t}$.

(b) $u = e^{-3x}(13c_1 \cos 4x + 13c_2 \sin 4x)$;
$v = e^{-3x}[(6c_1 - 4c_2) \cos 4x + (4c_1 + 6c_2) \sin 4x]$.

(c) $x = e^{4t}(2c_1 + 2c_2 t)$; $y = e^{4t}(2c_1 - c_2 + 2c_2 t)$.

(d) $u = 2c_1 e^{4x} + 4c_2 e^{-2x} + c_3 e^x$; $y = 3c_1 e^{4x} + 3c_2 e^{-2x}$; $z = 18c_1 e^{4x}$.

(e) $x = c_1 \cos t + c_2 \sin t + 3t^2 - t - 1$;
$y = c_1 \sin t - c_2 \cos t + t^2 + 2$.

(f) $x = \dfrac{5e^{2t}}{17} + \dfrac{3t}{7} - \dfrac{1}{49} + 2ce^{-7t/5}$;

$y = -\dfrac{e^{2t}}{17} + \dfrac{t}{7} - \dfrac{26}{49} + 3ce^{-7t/5} + \dfrac{1}{2}e^{-t}$.

(g) $x = 2c_1 + 4c_2 e^{t/2} - t^2 - 4t + \dfrac{\sin 2t + 4 \cos 2t}{34}$;

$y = c_1 + c_2 e^{t/2} - \dfrac{t^2}{2} - t + 2 + \dfrac{9 \sin 2t + 2 \cos 2t}{68}$.

(h) $x = c_1 + c_3 e^{t\sqrt{2}} + c_4 e^{-t\sqrt{2}}$;
$y = c_2 + c_3(1 - \sqrt{2})e^{t\sqrt{2}} + c_4(1 + \sqrt{2})e^{-t\sqrt{2}}$.

(i) $x = c_1 e^t + c_2 e^{-t} + 7c_3 \cos 3t + 7c_4 \sin 3t + \dfrac{14t}{9}$;

$y = -c_1 e^t - c_2 e^{-t} + 3c_3 \cos 3t + 3c_4 \sin 3t - \dfrac{4t}{3}$.

15. $v = -\sqrt{2gR}$.

17. Period $= \pi/2$ seconds.

18. (b) Period = $2\pi \sqrt{l/g}$.

19. $x^2 - y^2 = c$.

21. $y = \dfrac{3\omega l^2 x^2 - 2\omega x^4}{48EI}$; maximum $y = \dfrac{5\omega l^4}{384EI}$.

22. (a) $y = \dfrac{\omega}{6EI} (3lx^2 - x^3)$; maximum $y = \dfrac{\omega l^3}{3EI}$.

(b) $y = \dfrac{1}{24EI} (5400x^2 - 120x^3 + x^4)$; maximum $y = \dfrac{101250}{EI}$.

(c) $y = \dfrac{1}{48EI} (30720x^2 - 496x^3 + 3x^4)$; maximum $y = \dfrac{1568000}{3EI}$.

25. $q = \sin 20t(1 - e^{-10t}) - 4 \cos 20t$;
$i = 10 \sin 20t(8 + e^{-10t}) + 20 \cos 20t(1 - e^{-10t})$.

26. $q = 10 - e^{-10t}(10 \cos 20t + 5 \sin 20t)$;
$i = 250e^{-10t} \sin 20t$; $q \to 10$; $i \to 0$.

27. .9140 amps.; $40 \sqrt{73}/219$ amps.

28. $b = 8$; constants 6 and -4.

29. $\omega = 500$ pounds.

30. $k = \sqrt{128 - 9\pi^2}$.

31. $x = \dfrac{3e^t}{4} - \dfrac{3e^{-t}}{4} - \dfrac{\sin t}{2}$;

$y = \dfrac{3e^t}{8} - \dfrac{3e^{-t}}{8} + \dfrac{\sin t}{4}$.

32. $6s = 1 + \cos (8 \sqrt{3}\, t)$.

33. $s = e^{\frac{-16t}{675}} \left[\dfrac{1}{6} \cos \dfrac{8 \sqrt{1366871}}{675} t \right.$

$\left. + \dfrac{1}{3 \sqrt{1366871}} \sin \dfrac{8 \sqrt{1366871}}{675} t \right] + \dfrac{1}{6}$.

36. $i_1 = c_1 + e^{-700t}(5c_2 \cos 100t + 5c_2 \sin 100t)$

$+ \dfrac{580 \sin 300t - 90 \cos 300t}{689}$;

$i_2 = c_1 + e^{-700t}[(-6c_2 - 3c_3) \cos 100t + (2c_2 - 6c_3) \sin 100t]$

$+ \dfrac{328 \sin 300t - 336 \cos 300t}{689}$.

41. $L_1 + L_2$.

42. $R_1 R_2/(R_1 + R_2)$.

Section 38, page 126

1. (a) $y = 1.02660$. (b) $y_2 = 1.02660$. (c) $y = 1.0266$.

2. $y = 1.005$.

3. $y_4 = 2 - 2x + \dfrac{3x^2}{2} - \dfrac{x^3}{2} + \dfrac{x^4}{8} - \dfrac{x^5}{120}$;

$y = 2 - 2x + \dfrac{3x^2}{2} - \dfrac{x^3}{2} + \dfrac{x^4}{8} - \dfrac{x^5}{40} + \cdots$

6. (a) $y_3 = \dfrac{x^2}{2} + \dfrac{x^5}{20} + \dfrac{x^8}{160} + \dfrac{x^{11}}{4400}$.

$y = \dfrac{x^2}{2} + \dfrac{x^5}{20} + \dfrac{x^8}{160} + \cdots$

(b) $y_3 = .0049995$; $y = .0049995$.

8. $y_2 = 1 + 2x - \dfrac{x^2}{2} + \dfrac{x^3}{6}$; $z_2 = 2 - x - \dfrac{3x^2}{2} - \dfrac{4x^3}{3}$.

9. $y_3 = x + \dfrac{x^2}{2} + \dfrac{x^4}{12} + \dfrac{x^7}{252}$; $z_3 = 1 + \dfrac{x^3}{6} - \dfrac{x^4}{12} + \dfrac{x^6}{120}$.

10. $y_3 = 1 + \dfrac{4x^3}{3} + \dfrac{x^4}{2} + \dfrac{x^5}{20}$; $z_3 = 2x + \dfrac{x^2}{2} - \dfrac{x^3}{6} + \dfrac{x^4}{3}$;

$u_3 = 1 + x - \dfrac{x^2}{2} - \dfrac{x^3}{3}$.

11. (a) $y = 1 + 2x - \dfrac{x^2}{2} - \dfrac{x^3}{2} + \cdots$; $z = 2 - x - \dfrac{3x^2}{2}$
$$- x^3 + \cdots$$

(b) $y = x + \dfrac{x^2}{2} + \cdots$; $z = 1 + \dfrac{x^3}{6} + \cdots$

(c) $y = 1 + \dfrac{4x^3}{3} + \cdots$; $z = 2x + \dfrac{x^2}{2} - \dfrac{x^3}{6} + \cdots$;

$u = 1 + x - \dfrac{x^2}{2} - \dfrac{x^3}{3} + \cdots$.

13. (a) $y = 1 + x - \dfrac{x^2}{2} + \dfrac{5x^3}{6} - \dfrac{5x^4}{12} + \cdots$.

(b) $y_3 = 1 + x - \dfrac{x^2}{2} + \dfrac{5x^3}{6}$.

14. (a) $y = -1 + x - x^2 + \dfrac{2x^3}{3} - \dfrac{x^4}{3} + \cdots$.

(b) $y_3 = -1 + x - x^2 + \dfrac{2x^3}{3} - \dfrac{x^4}{12}$.

Section 39, page 133

1. (a)

x	0.4	0.5
y	1.5836	1.7974

(b)

x	0.4	0.5
y	1.290	1.339

(c)

x	1.8	2.0	2.2
y	0.7261	0.6065	0.4867

2. (a) 1.175.   (b) 0.60.

Section 42, page 141

1.

x	y
.2	.0999
.4	.1984
.6	.2922

2.

x	y
.05	.4890
.10	.4811
.15	.4758
.20	.4734
.25	.4734

3. $x = 17,421$ ft.; $t = 31.19$ sec.

Section 43, page 145

3. (a) $y = Ax + x^2$.

(b) $y = -\dfrac{1}{2} + \dfrac{1 + 2A}{2} \left(1 + x^2 + \dfrac{x^4}{2} + \dfrac{x^6}{6} + \dfrac{x^8}{24} + \cdots \right)$

$= -\dfrac{1}{2} + ce^{x^2}$.

(c) $y = c + (1 - c)x + cx^2 + \left(\dfrac{1}{2} - c \right) x^3 + \left(c - \dfrac{1}{3} \right) x^4$

$+ \left(\dfrac{3}{8} - c \right) x^5 + \cdots$.

4. (a) $y = A(1 + x) + \dfrac{A - A^2}{2} x^2 + \dfrac{A - 5A^2 + 2A^3}{6} x^3$

$+ \dfrac{A - 17A^2 + 26A^3 - 6A^4}{24} x^4 + \cdots$

(b) $y = A - A^2x + \dfrac{1 + 2A^3}{2} x^2 - \dfrac{A + 3A^4}{3} x^3$

$+ \dfrac{5A^2 + 12A^5}{12} x^4 + \cdots$.

(c) $y = A + \dfrac{A}{1 + A} x + \dfrac{1 + 3A + A^2}{2(1 + A)^3} x^3$

$+ \dfrac{1 + A - 5A^2 - 2A^3}{6(1 + A)^5} x^4 + \cdots$.

(d) $y = A - \dfrac{1}{2A} x^2 - \dfrac{1+2A}{8A^3} x^4 - \dfrac{8A^2 + 10A + 3}{48A^5} x^6 - \cdots$.

5. $y = A - x - \dfrac{x^2}{2A} - \dfrac{2x^3}{3A^2} - \dfrac{9x^4}{8A^3} - \cdots$.

7. (a) $y' = A + x + \dfrac{x^2}{2} - \dfrac{x^3}{3} + \dfrac{x^4}{4} - \dfrac{x^5}{5} + \cdots$

$\qquad\qquad\qquad\qquad\qquad = A + 2x - \log(x+1);$

$\quad y = A(x+1) + x^2 + x - (x+1)\log(x+1).$

(b) $y = x(A-1) + x^2 - x \log x.$

Section 44, page 152

1. (a) $y = A(1 - x^2) + B\left(x - \dfrac{x^3}{3!} - \dfrac{x^5}{5!} - \dfrac{3x^7}{7!} - \cdots\right.$

$\left. \qquad\qquad - \dfrac{3\cdot 5\cdot 7\,\cdots\,(2n-3)}{(2n+1)!} x^{2n+1} - \cdots\right).$

(b) $y = A\left(\dfrac{1}{x} + \dfrac{x^2}{3} - \dfrac{x^5}{36} + \dfrac{5x^8}{2268} - \cdots\right)$

$\qquad\qquad + B\left(x - \dfrac{x^4}{15} + \dfrac{x^7}{180} - \dfrac{7x^{10}}{17820} + \cdots\right).$

(c) $y = A\left(x - \dfrac{x^3}{5} + \dfrac{x^5}{5\cdot 7} - \cdots\right.$

$\qquad\qquad + (-1)^n \dfrac{x^{2n+1}}{5\cdot 7\cdot 9\,\cdots\,(2n+3)} + \cdots\Big)$

$\qquad + B\left(\dfrac{1}{x^2} - \dfrac{1}{2} + \dfrac{x^2}{2\cdot 4} - \dfrac{x^4}{2\cdot 4\cdot 6}\right.$

$\qquad\qquad + \cdots + (-1)^{n-1}\dfrac{x^{2n}}{2\cdot 4\cdot 6\,\cdots\,(2n+2)} + \cdots\Big).$

(d) $y = A\left(1 + \sum_{n=1} \dfrac{x^{-2n}}{2\cdot 4\cdot 6\,\cdots\,(2n)}\right)$

$\qquad\qquad + B\left(\dfrac{1}{x} + \sum_{n=1} \dfrac{x^{-2n-1}}{3\cdot 5\cdot 7\,\cdots\,(2n+1)}\right).$

(e) $y = A\left(1 - \dfrac{1}{5x^2}\right) + B\left(x^3 + \dfrac{5x}{2} - \dfrac{15}{8x} + \dfrac{5}{48x^3} + \cdots\right).$

(f) $y = Ax + \dfrac{B}{x^3}.$

2. (a) $y = A\left(1 + \sum_{n=1} \dfrac{(-1)^n \cdot x^{3n}}{(3n+1)!}\right) + B\left(\dfrac{1}{x} + \sum_{n=1} \dfrac{(-1)^n x^{3n-1}}{(3n)!}\right)$

$\qquad\qquad + C\left(\sum_{n=1} \dfrac{(-1)^{n-1} x^{3n-2}}{(3n-1)!}\right).$

(b) $y = Cx^2 + A\left(1 - \dfrac{2 \cdot 1}{3 \cdot 4 \cdot 5} \cdot \dfrac{1}{x^3}\right.$

$$-\sum_{n=3} \frac{2(2 \cdot 5 \cdot 8 \cdots (3n-4))(2 \cdot 5 \cdot 8 \cdots (3n-7))}{(3n-1)! \cdot x^{3n-3}}\Bigg)$$

$$+ B\left(x - \frac{1 \cdot 2}{4!} \cdot \frac{1}{x^2}\right.$$

$$+\sum_{n=2} \frac{(1 \cdot 4 \cdot 7 \cdots (3n-2))(-2 \cdot 1 \cdot 4 \cdot 7 \cdots (3n-5))}{(3n+1)! \cdot x^{3n-1}}\Bigg).$$

(c) $y = c_1 x^2 + c_2 x^{\frac{-7+\sqrt{17}}{2}} + c_3 x^{\frac{-7-\sqrt{17}}{2}}.$

3. $y = A + B \tan^{-1} x;\ y = A + B \tan^{-1} \dfrac{1}{x}.$

4. (a) $y = A\left(1 + \dfrac{1}{3}x^3 + \sum_{n=1} \dfrac{(-1)^n 2 \cdot 5 \cdots (3n-1)}{3 \cdot 6 \cdots (3n+3)} x^{3n+3}\right)$

$$+ B\left(x^2 + \sum_{n=1} (-1)^n \frac{4 \cdot 7 \cdots (3n-2)}{5 \cdot 8 \cdots (3n+2)} x^{3n+2}\right);$$

also

$$y = A\left(x + \frac{1}{3x^2} + \sum_{n=1} (-1)^n \frac{2 \cdot 5 \cdots (3n-1)}{3 \cdot 6 \cdots (3n+3)x^{3n+2}}\right)$$

$$+ \frac{B}{x}\left(1 + \sum_{n=1} (-1)^n \frac{1 \cdot 4 \cdots (3n-2)}{5 \cdot 8 \cdots (3n+2)x^{3n}}\right).$$

(b) $y = \dfrac{A + Bx^3}{x^2 + 1}.$

Section 45, page 154

1. (a) $y_1 = x^{-2} + \sum_{n=1} \dfrac{2^n x^{3n-2}}{[3 \cdot 6 \cdots (3n)]^2},$

$$y = y_1\left[A + B\int \frac{dx}{x^5 y_1^2}\right].$$

(b) $y_1 = \sum_{n=0} \dfrac{x^n}{(n!)^2},\ y = y_1\left[A + B\int \dfrac{dx}{xy_1^2}\right].$

(c) $y_1 = 1 + \sum_{n=1} \dfrac{(-1)^n}{[2 \cdot 4 \cdots (2n)]^2 x^{2n}},\ y = y_1\left[A + B\int \dfrac{dx}{xy_1^2}\right].$

(d) $y = (A + B \log x)(1 - x) + 4Bx;$

also

$$y = (A + B \log x)(x - 1) - 4B.$$

(e) $y_1 = \sum_{n=0} \dfrac{n+1}{n!x^n},\ y = y_1\left[A + B\int \dfrac{e^{1/x}\,dx}{xy_1^2}\right].$

(f) $y_1 = x - \dfrac{1}{4x} - \displaystyle\sum_{n=2} \dfrac{1 \cdot 3 \cdot 5 \cdots (2n-3)}{[2 \cdot 4 \cdot 6 \cdots (2n)]^2 x^{2n-1}}$,

$y = y_1 \left[A + B \displaystyle\int \dfrac{x e^{1/2x^2} dx}{y_1^2} \right]$.

Section 46, page 156

1. (a) $y_1 = -\dfrac{x}{2} + \dfrac{x^3}{2^2 \cdot 4} - \dfrac{x^5}{2^2 \cdot 4^2 \cdot 6} + \cdots$,

$y = y_1 \left[A + B \displaystyle\int \dfrac{dx}{x y_1^2} \right]$.

(b) $y_1 = \displaystyle\sum_{n=3} \dfrac{(-1)^n x^n}{n!(n-3)!}$, $y = y_1 \left[A + B \displaystyle\int \dfrac{x^2 \, dx}{y_1^2} \right]$.

(c) $y_1 = -\dfrac{x}{2} + \dfrac{x^2}{1^2 \cdot 2 \cdot 3} - \dfrac{x^3}{1^2 \cdot 2^2 \cdot 3 \cdot 4} + \cdots$,

$y = y_1 \left[A + B \displaystyle\int \dfrac{dx}{x y_1^2} \right]$.

(d) $y_1 = -\dfrac{x}{6} + \dfrac{x^2}{1^2 \cdot 2 \cdot 3 \cdot 4} - \dfrac{x^3}{1^2 \cdot 2^2 \cdot 3 \cdot 4 \cdot 5} + \cdots$,

$y = y_1 \left[A + B \displaystyle\int \dfrac{dx}{x^2 y_1^2} \right]$.

(e) $y_1 = \dfrac{1}{2x} + \dfrac{1}{2^2 \cdot 4x^3} + \dfrac{1 \cdot 3}{2^2 \cdot 4^2 \cdot 6x^5} + \dfrac{1 \cdot 3 \cdot 5}{2^2 \cdot 4^2 \cdot 6^2 \cdot 8x^7} + \cdots$,

$y = y_1 \left[A + B \displaystyle\int \dfrac{e^{1/2x^2} dx}{x y_1^2} \right]$.

Section 47, page 159

1. (a) $y = \dfrac{x^4}{9} \left[1 - \dfrac{2x^2}{4 \cdot 5} + \dfrac{2 \cdot 3x^4}{(4 \cdot 5)(5 \cdot 7)} - \dfrac{2 \cdot 3 \cdot 4x^6}{(4 \cdot 5 \cdot 6)(5 \cdot 7 \cdot 9)} + \cdots \right]$.

(b) $y = \dfrac{1}{2x} + \dfrac{x}{4} \left[1 - \dfrac{2x^3}{4 \cdot 7} + \dfrac{2 \cdot 5x^6}{(4 \cdot 7)(7 \cdot 10)} \right.$

$\left. - \dfrac{2 \cdot 5 \cdot 8x^9}{(4 \cdot 7 \cdot 10)(7 \cdot 10 \cdot 13)} + \cdots \right]$.

(c) $y = \dfrac{2}{x} - \dfrac{1}{9x^3} \left[1 + \dfrac{2}{5^2 \cdot x^2} + \dfrac{2 \cdot 4}{(5 \cdot 7)^2 x^4} + \dfrac{2 \cdot 4 \cdot 6}{(5 \cdot 7 \cdot 9)^2 x^6} + \cdots \right]$.

3. (a) $y = 2y_1 \displaystyle\int \dfrac{dx}{x^4 y_1 + x^5 y_1'} - \dfrac{2}{x} \displaystyle\int \dfrac{y_1 \, dx}{x^3 y_1 + x^4 y_1'}$, where

$y_1 = x^2 - \dfrac{3}{2 \cdot 5} x^4 + \dfrac{3x^6}{(2 \cdot 4) \cdot 7} - \dfrac{3x^8}{(2 \cdot 4 \cdot 6) \cdot 9} + \cdots$.

(b) $y = y_1 \int \dfrac{dx}{x^4 y_1' + x^3 y_1} - \dfrac{1}{x} \int \dfrac{y_1\, dx}{x^3 y_1' + x^2 y_1}$, where

$$y_1 = \sum_{n=1}^{\infty} (-1)^{n-1} \frac{2nx^n}{(n+1)!}.$$

Section 50, page 176

1. (a) $2F\left(-\dfrac{n}{2}, \dfrac{-n+1}{2}, \dfrac{1}{2}, x^2\right).$

(b) $2nxF\left(\dfrac{-n+1}{2}, \dfrac{-n+2}{2}, \dfrac{3}{2}, x^2\right).$

(c) $2xF\left(\dfrac{1}{2}, 1, \dfrac{3}{2}, x^2\right).$

(d) $F(1, 1, 1, -x)$; divergent for $x = \pm 1$.

(e) $F(1, 1, 1, x)$; divergent for $x = \pm 1$.

(f) $\lim\limits_{\substack{\alpha \to \infty \\ \beta \to \infty}} x \cdot F\left(\alpha, \beta, \dfrac{3}{2}, -\dfrac{x^2}{4\alpha\beta}\right).$

(g) $\lim\limits_{\beta \to \infty} F\left(1, \beta, 1, \dfrac{x}{\beta}\right).$

2. (a) $y = A \cdot F(1, 2, 3, x) + \dfrac{B}{x^2} \cdot F(-1, 0, -1, x) =$

$A \cdot F(1, 2, 3, x) + \dfrac{B}{x^2}$; converges for $|x| < 1$ and $x = -1$.

(b) $y = \dfrac{A}{x^2} \cdot F\left(2, 2, 4, \dfrac{1}{x}\right) + Bx \cdot F\left(-1, -1, -2, \dfrac{1}{x}\right)$

$= \dfrac{A}{x^2} \cdot F\left(2, 2, 4, \dfrac{1}{x}\right) + B\left(x - \dfrac{1}{2}\right)$; converges for $|x| > 1$ and $x = -1$.

3. (a) Converges for $8 > x > 2$.   (b) Converges for all values of x.

5. $(x^2 + x)y'' + [(\alpha + \beta + 1)x + \gamma]y' + \alpha\beta \cdot y = 0.$

6. $(x^2 + x)y'' + (3x + 2)y' + y = 0.$

7. $\dfrac{\alpha(\alpha + 1) \cdots (\alpha + m - 1) \cdot \beta(\beta + 1) \cdots (\beta + m - 1)}{\gamma(\gamma + 1) \cdots (\gamma + m - 1)}.$

$$F(\alpha + m, \beta + m, \gamma + m, x).$$

8. $(z^2 - z)\dfrac{d^2y}{dz^2} + [(\alpha + \beta + 1)z - \gamma]\dfrac{dy}{dz} + \alpha\beta y = 0$, where

$$\alpha + \beta + 1 = \frac{D}{A}, \; \alpha\beta = \frac{F}{A}, \gamma = \frac{Dm + E}{2Am + B}.$$

9. $y = AF\left(2, -\dfrac{5}{2}, \dfrac{3}{8}, \dfrac{2-x}{4}\right)$

$$+ B\left(\frac{2-x}{4}\right)^{5/8} F\left(\frac{21}{8}, -\frac{15}{8}, \frac{13}{8}, \frac{2-x}{4}\right).$$

ANSWERS TO EXERCISES

21

Section 51, page 177

1. (a) $y = \dfrac{A}{x}\left(1 - \dfrac{x}{2}\right) + Bx^2\left(\dfrac{1}{6} - \dfrac{2x}{4!} + \dfrac{3x^2}{5!} - \dfrac{4x^3}{6!} + \cdots\right).$

(b) $y = A\left(1 - \dfrac{x^2}{2} + \dfrac{x^4}{8} + \dfrac{x^6}{80} + \cdots\right)$

$$+ Bx\left(1 - \dfrac{x^2}{2} + \dfrac{x^4}{40} + \dfrac{3x^6}{560} + \cdots\right).$$

(c) $y = y_1\left[A + B\displaystyle\int \dfrac{x\,dx}{y_1^2}\right]$, where $y_1 = \displaystyle\sum_{n=0} \dfrac{(-1)^n x^{2n+1}}{4^n \cdot (n!)^2}.$

(d) $y = A\left(x^3 + \dfrac{3x}{4}\right) + B\left(1 + \dfrac{9x^2}{2} + \dfrac{15x^4}{8} - \dfrac{7x^6}{16} + \cdots\right);$

also

$$y = A\left(x^3 + \dfrac{3x}{4}\right) + B\left(\dfrac{1}{x^3} - \dfrac{3}{4x^5} + \dfrac{9}{16x^7} - \dfrac{7}{16x^9} + \cdots\right).$$

(e) $y = A\left(1 + \dfrac{x^3}{3}\displaystyle\sum_{n=2} \dfrac{(-1)^{n-1}x^{3n}}{(3\cdot6\,\cdots\,3n)(2\cdot5\,\cdots\,(3n-4))}\right)$

$$+ Bx^4\left(1 + \displaystyle\sum_{n=1}(-1)^n \cdot \dfrac{x^{3n}}{(3\cdot6\,\cdots\,3n)(7\cdot10\,\cdots\,(3n+4))}\right).$$

(f) $y = Ax^3\left(1 + \dfrac{2}{x^2} - \dfrac{1}{x^4}\right) + B\left[1 - \dfrac{1}{2\cdot5}\cdot\dfrac{1}{x^2} - \right.$

$$\dfrac{1\cdot1}{(2\cdot4)(5\cdot7)}\cdot\dfrac{1}{x^4} - \dfrac{1\cdot3}{(2\cdot4\cdot6)(5\cdot7\cdot9)}\cdot\dfrac{1}{x^6} - \cdots \left.\right] + \dfrac{1}{x} +$$

$$\dfrac{1}{2x^2}\left[1 + \displaystyle\sum_{n=1} \dfrac{1\cdot3\,\cdots\,(2n-1)}{(4\cdot6\,\cdots\,(2n+2))(7\cdot9\,\cdots\,(2n+5))}\cdot\dfrac{1}{x^{2n}}\right].$$

(g) $y = c_1 y_1 + c_2 y_2 + y_1\displaystyle\int \dfrac{y_2\,dx}{x^3(y_1' y_2 - y_1 y_2')} - y_2\displaystyle\int \dfrac{y_1\,dx}{x^3(y_1' y_2 - y_1 y_2')},$

where $y_1 = 3\displaystyle\sum_{n=1} \dfrac{(-1)^{n+1}(2n-1)!\,x^{2n+1}}{2^{3n-4}(n+2)![(n-1)!]^2},$

$$y_2 = y_1\displaystyle\int \dfrac{e^{-x^2/2}\,dx}{xy_1^2}.$$

10. (a) $xF\left(\dfrac{1}{2}, \dfrac{1}{2}, \dfrac{3}{2}, x^2\right).$

(b) $xF\left(\dfrac{1}{2}, 1, \dfrac{3}{2}, -x^2\right).$

(c) $\displaystyle\lim_{\substack{\alpha\to\infty\\\beta\to\infty}} F\left(\alpha, \beta, \dfrac{1}{2}, \dfrac{x^2}{4\alpha\beta}\right).$

12. $(x^2 + x)y'' + [(\beta - n + 1)x + \beta]y' - n\beta y = 0$ (β arbitrary).

14. One form of solution:

$$y = AF\left(2, -2, \frac{-1}{2}, \frac{1-x}{2}\right) + B\left(\frac{1-x}{2}\right)^{3/2} F\left(\frac{7}{2}, -\frac{1}{2}, \frac{5}{2}, \frac{1-x}{2}\right).$$

Section 55, page 184

1. (a) $x^2y - x + y \cos z - z^2 = c.$

(b) $x^2 + y^2 - 2 \tan^{-1} \dfrac{x}{y} + 2z = c.$

(c) $x^2 + y^2 + \log z + \dfrac{x}{z} = c.$

(d) $x - \dfrac{z}{y + a} = c.$

(e) $y + \sqrt{4 - z^2 - (x - 1)^2} = c.$

(f) $e^{xy} + e^{yz} + e^{zx} = c.$

(g) $x \sinh y + y \sinh z + z \sinh x = c.$

2. (a) $\log x - \dfrac{z}{x} + zy = c.$

(b) $e^x(x + y + z) = c.$

(d) $y(z - \sin^{-1} x) - z \sqrt{1 - x^2} = c.$

(f) $x \sec y + z \tan y - \sec y = c.$

4. (a) $x^2(yz + xy + x^2) = c.$ (c) $y^2\left(\dfrac{y}{z} - \log \dfrac{x}{z}\right) = c.$

(b) $xy^2(xz + y^2) = c.$ (d) $x + z = cy.$

6. (a) $x + z = cy^2.$ (c) $4x^4 + 4xy^2z + z^4 = c.$

(b) $z^5 - x^4y = cx^4z^5.$

9. (a) $xy + yz + zt + tx = c.$ (c) $x^3y^2 + 2yz + tz = c.$

10. (a) $(y + xz - t)e^{x^2} = c.$

(b) $\log x + y^2 + z - \dfrac{1}{t} + u + v^2 = c.$

12. $x^4 + x^3y + x^2yz + xyzt = c.$

Section 58, page 191

1. (a) $\begin{cases} xy + y^2z = c_1, \\ x^3y = c_2z. \end{cases}$ (d) $\begin{cases} \dfrac{1}{x^2} - y^4 = c_1, \\ y^4 - z^2 = c_2. \end{cases}$

(b) $\begin{cases} x^6 - y^3 = c_1, \\ x^4 - z^2 = c_2. \end{cases}$ (e) $\begin{cases} x + y + z = c_1, \\ x^2 + y^2 + z^2 = c_2. \end{cases}$

(c) $\begin{cases} (xz - y^2)e^y = c_1, \\ yze^y = c_2. \end{cases}$ (f) $\begin{cases} x^3 - y^3 = c_1, \\ y^3 + 3e^{-z} = c_2. \end{cases}$

2. (a) $\begin{cases} x^2 - y^2 = c_1, \\ x + y = c_2 z. \end{cases}$

(b) $\begin{cases} x^2 y + y^2 z = c_1, \\ xz^2 = c_2. \end{cases}$

(c) $\begin{cases} y^2 z = c_1, \\ x^2 z^2 - 4y^2 z^2 \log z + 1 = c_2 z. \end{cases}$

(d) $\begin{cases} x^2 + y^2 = c_1, \\ yz + x \sqrt{1 - z^2} = c_2. \end{cases}$

(e) $\begin{cases} uv = c_1, \\ 4u - z^2 = c_2. \end{cases}$

(f) $\begin{cases} (z - x)^2(z - 4x) = c_1, \\ (x + y)e^{x-z} = c_2. \end{cases}$

(g) $\begin{cases} z = c_1, \\ \log(x^2 + y^2 - 10x - 10y + 50) - \\ \qquad\qquad 2\tan^{-1}\left(\dfrac{x + y - 10}{x - y}\right) = c_2. \end{cases}$

(h) $\begin{cases} x^2 y^2 = c_1(x + y)^3, \\ xyz^9 = c_2. \end{cases}$

3. (a) $\begin{cases} x + 4y + 9z = c_1, \\ x^2 + 4y^2 + 9z^2 = c_2. \end{cases}$

(b) $\begin{cases} 2x - 3y + z = c_1, \\ z + 2x = (3y - z)[c_2 + \log(3y - z)]. \end{cases}$

(c) $\begin{cases} 2x + 3y + 4z = c_1, \\ xyz = c_2. \end{cases}$

(d) $\begin{cases} x^2 + y^2 = c_1, \\ x^2 - 3z^2 = c_2. \end{cases}$

(e) $\begin{cases} 9x^2 + 4y^2 + z^2 = c_1, \\ x = c_2 yz. \end{cases}$

(f) $\begin{cases} xyz = c_1, \\ x^3 + y^3 + z^3 = c_2. \end{cases}$

5. (b) $\begin{cases} y = c_1 e^{4x} + 2c_2 xe^{4x}, \\ z = c_1 e^{4x} - c_2 e^{4x} + 2c_2 xe^{4x}. \end{cases}$

(c) $\begin{cases} y = 2c_1 e^{-x} + c_2 e^{-7x}, \\ z = -3c_1 e^{-x} + 3c_2 e^{-7x}. \end{cases}$

(d) $\begin{cases} y = c_1 e^{-4x} + c_2 e^{-7x} + \dfrac{7}{40} e^x + \dfrac{1}{27} e^{2x}, \\ z = c_1 e^{-4x} - 2c_2 e^{-7x} + \dfrac{1}{20} e^x + \dfrac{7}{27} e^{2x}. \end{cases}$

(e)
$$\begin{cases} y = 4c_1 + c_2 e^{5x} - \dfrac{(25 \cos x + 21 \sin x)}{26}, \\[2mm] z = -c_1 + c_2 e^{5x} + \dfrac{\cos x + 5 \sin x}{26}. \end{cases}$$

(f)
$$\begin{cases} y = e^{2x}(c_1 + c_2 x + 6x^2 + x^3), \\[1mm] z = e^{2x}(c_2 - c_1 - 12 - c_2 x + 12x - 3x^2 - x^3). \end{cases}$$

(g)
$$\begin{cases} y = \dfrac{e^{\alpha x}}{\beta} \Big\{ c_1 \cosh \beta x + c_2 \sinh \beta x + \sinh \beta x. \\[2mm] \quad \displaystyle\int e^{-\alpha x} h(x) \cosh \beta x \, dx - \cosh \beta x \int e^{-\alpha x} h(x) \sinh \beta x \, dx \Big\}, \\[3mm] z = \dfrac{y' - ay - f(x)}{b}, \text{ where} \\[3mm] \alpha = \dfrac{a+g}{2}, \ \beta = \dfrac{1}{2} \sqrt{(a-g)^2 + 4bc}, \ h(x) \equiv f'(x) \\[3mm] \qquad\qquad\qquad\qquad\qquad\qquad\qquad + b\varphi(x) - gf(x). \end{cases}$$

7. (a)
$$\begin{cases} e^{x^3}(y - z) = -\dfrac{1}{2} e^{2x^3} + \displaystyle\int e^{2x^3} \, dx + c_1, \\[3mm] e^{2x^3}(y + 2z) = \dfrac{2}{3} e^{3x^3} + \displaystyle\int e^{3x^3} \, dx + c_2. \end{cases}$$

(b)
$$\begin{cases} 5x^5(y - z) + 2x^5 = c_1, \\[1mm] 3x^3(y - 3z) + x^6 = c_2. \end{cases}$$

(c)
$$\begin{cases} e^{\frac{(-1+\sqrt{33})x}{2}} \left(y + \dfrac{3 + \sqrt{33}}{2} z \right) \\[3mm] \quad = \displaystyle\int e^{\frac{(-1+\sqrt{33})x}{2}} \left[\sinh x + \dfrac{3 + \sqrt{33}}{2} \cosh x \right] dx + c_1, \\[4mm] e^{\frac{(-1-\sqrt{33})x}{2}} \left(y + \dfrac{3 - \sqrt{33}}{2} z \right) \\[3mm] \quad = \displaystyle\int e^{\frac{(-1-\sqrt{33})x}{2}} \left[\sinh x + \dfrac{3 - \sqrt{33}}{2} \cosh x \right] dx + c_2. \end{cases}$$

(d)
$$\begin{cases} (\cos x)^{\frac{-1-\sqrt{33}}{2}} \left(y + \dfrac{1 + \sqrt{33}}{2} z \right) \\[3mm] \quad = \displaystyle\int \left\{ (\cos x)^{\frac{-3-\sqrt{33}}{2}} + \dfrac{1 + \sqrt{33}}{2} (\cos x)^{\frac{-5-\sqrt{33}}{2}} \right\} dx + c_1, \\[4mm] (\cos x)^{\frac{-1+\sqrt{33}}{2}} \left(y + \dfrac{1 - \sqrt{33}}{2} z \right) \\[3mm] \quad = \displaystyle\int \left\{ (\cos x)^{\frac{-3+\sqrt{33}}{2}} + \dfrac{1 - \sqrt{33}}{2} (\cos x)^{\frac{-5+\sqrt{33}}{2}} \right\} dx + c_2. \end{cases}$$

Section 59, page 196

1. $\begin{cases} x^2 + y^2 + z^2 = c, \\ \log(x^2 + xy + y^2) + \dfrac{10}{\sqrt{3}}\tan^{-1}\left(\dfrac{2y + x}{x\sqrt{3}}\right) = c_1. \end{cases}$

2. $\begin{cases} ax + by + cz = d, \\ a^2 x^2 + b^2 y^2 + 3abxy + acxz + bcyz = c_1. \end{cases}$

3. $\begin{cases} x^2 + z^2 = 1, \\ x^2(a\cos^2 y + b\sin^2 y - 1)^{a+b} = c_1. \end{cases}$

4. $\begin{cases} x = c, \\ xy + \dfrac{z^2}{2} = c_1. \end{cases}$

5. $\begin{cases} 2z^2 = x^2 y^2, \\ 2x + y = cxy. \end{cases}$

6. $\begin{cases} z = f(y), \\ x - z - \displaystyle\int f(y)\, dy = c. \end{cases}$

Section 64, page 207

2. (a) $\dfrac{dz}{0} = \dfrac{dx_1}{x_2 - x_3} = \dfrac{dx_2}{x_3 - x_1} = \dfrac{dx_3}{x_1 - x_2}.$

(b) $\dfrac{dz}{0} = \dfrac{dx_1}{0} = \dfrac{dx_2}{0} = \dfrac{dx_3}{x_3} = \dfrac{dx_4}{-x_4}.$

(c) $dz = dx_1 = dx_2 = 0.$

3. $u' \equiv -\sqrt[4]{\dfrac{2}{3}}\, z^{3/2},\ u'' \equiv -\sqrt[4]{\dfrac{2}{3}}\, z^{1/2}(x_1 + x_2),$

$$u''' \equiv -\sqrt[4]{\dfrac{2}{3}}\, z^{1/2}(x_1 + x_3),\ u^{iv} \equiv -\sqrt[4]{\dfrac{2}{3}}\, z^{1/2}(x_1 - x_4).$$

4. $x_1 x_2^2 = c_1,\ z = c_2 x_2,\ x_3 = c_3.$

5. $\begin{cases} x_1^2 = c_1(x_2 + x_3 + x_4), \\ x_1 x_2 - x_1 x_4 = c_2, \\ x_1 x_2 - x_1 x_3 = c_3. \end{cases}$

6. $\begin{cases} u^{1/4}(5x_1 - u) = c_1, \\ u^{1/4}(5x_2 - u) = c_2, \\ u^{1/4}(5x_3 - u) = c_3, \\ u^{1/4}(5x_4 - u) = c_4,\ \text{where } u \equiv x_1 + x_2 + x_3 + x_4 + x_5. \end{cases}$

7. $z = c_1 x_1^a = c_2 x_2^a = c_3 x_3^a.$

8. $x_1 = c_1 x_2 = c_2 x_3, \ (a-1)x_3 x_4 + x_1 x_2 = c_3 x_3^{a+1}.$

9. 1.

10. $(x + y).$

13. $xyzw = c_1, \ x^2 y + y^2 z + z^2 w + w^2 x = c_2, \ w^2 x + yz = c_3.$

14. $x + \log(wy + wz) = c_1, \ x + yz + wz = c_2, \ x^2 yz = c_3.$

Section 66, page 214

1. (a) $\phi(mx - ly, \ nx - lz) = 0.$

(b) $\phi\left(y^2 - z^2, \dfrac{x}{y+z}\right) = 0.$

(c) $\phi\left(y, \dfrac{z}{y} - \log x\right) = 0.$

(d) $\phi\left(x^2 - y^2, \dfrac{z}{5} - \log(x+y)\right) = 0.$

(e) $\phi\Big(x - y - z, \ \{a^2 c x^2 + a(b-a)(by+cz)x - a(by+cz)^2\}$

$\left\{\dfrac{2acx + (b-a-\sqrt{a^2-2ab+b^2+4ac})(by+cz)}{2acx + (b-a+\sqrt{a^2-2ab+b^2+4ac})(by+cz)}\right\}^{\frac{a+b}{\sqrt{a^2-2ab+b^2+4ac}}} \Big) = 0.$

(f) $\phi(x + 2y + 3z, \ 13x^2 + 10y^2 + 5z^2 - 4xy - 12yz - 6zx) = 0.$

(g) $\phi(x + y + z, \ x^2 + y^2 + z^2) = 0.$

(h) $\phi(x^2 - y^2, \ y^2 + 2z^2) = 0.$

(i) $\phi\left(\dfrac{\cos z}{\cos y}, \dfrac{\cos z}{\cos x}\right) = 0.$

(j) $\phi(x^2 + z^2, \ y^3 + z^3) = 0.$

(k) $\phi(y^2 + z^2, \ xz^3) = 0.$

(l) $\phi(x^4 + y^4 + z^4, \ xyz^2) = 0.$

(m) $\phi\left(\dfrac{x}{y}, \ xz\right) = 0.$

(n) $\phi(xy, \ x \sin z) = 0.$

2. $\phi(x^2 - z^2, \ x + y + z) - \phi(-8, 6) = 0.$

3. $\phi\left(x + 2\log y, \dfrac{y}{z}\right) - \phi(0, 1) = 0.$

4. $x + 2\log y - \dfrac{3y}{z} = 0.$

5. $x^3 + y^2 - z = 8.$

6. $y^2 - z^2 - z - x - 4 = 0.$

7. $z = 0.$

8. $(xz^2 - xy^2)z_x + (x^2y - z^2y)z_y = y^2z - x^2z.$

9. $xz_x + 2yz_y + 2 = 0.$

10. $z = a(x + y) + b.$

11. $z = a\left(\dfrac{1}{xz} + \dfrac{\log y}{e^z}\right) + b.$

12. $z_x + az_y = b; \phi(ax - y, bx - z) = 0.$

13. $xz_x + yz_y = z; \phi\left(\dfrac{z}{x}, \dfrac{z}{y}\right) = 0.$

14. $(x - a)z_x + (y - b)z_y = (z - c); \phi\left(\dfrac{z - c}{x - a}, \dfrac{z - c}{y - b}\right) = 0.$

15. $(\gamma y - \beta z)z_x + (\alpha z - \gamma x)z_y = \beta x - \alpha y.$

16. $(\gamma y - \beta z - \gamma b + \beta c)z_x + (\alpha z - \gamma x - \alpha c + \gamma a)z_y =$
$$\beta x - \alpha y - \beta a + \alpha b.$$

17. $xz_x + yz_y = 0; \phi\left(z, \dfrac{x}{y}\right) = 0.$

19. $\phi(\mu x^2, \mu y^2) = 0.$

Section 68, page 219

1. $\phi[x - y + z, (y - z)e^{-t}, (yt - zt - x - t - z - 1)e^{-t}] = 0.$

2. $\phi(z, l^2x_1^2 + m^2x_2^2 + n^2x_3^2, l^2x_1 + m^2x_2 + n^2x_3) = 0.$

3. $\phi\left(\dfrac{4x_2 - x_1 - x_3 - x_4 - z}{4x_1 - x_2 - x_3 - x_4 - z}, \dfrac{4x_3 - x_1 - x_2 - x_4 - z}{4x_1 - x_2 - x_3 - x_4 - z},\right.$
$$\left.\dfrac{4x_4 - x_1 - x_2 - x_3 - z}{4x_1 - x_2 - x_3 - x_4 - z}, \dfrac{4z - x_1 - x_2 - x_3 - x_4}{4x_1 - x_2 - x_3 - x_4 - z}\right) = 0.$$

4. $\phi(z^2 - x_1^2, z^2 - x_2^2, z^2 - x_3^2) = 0.$

5. $\phi\left(z, x_1^2 - x_3^2, \dfrac{x_1 + x_3}{x_2}\right) = 0$

Section 70, page 228

1. $z = 2a^2x + 2ay + b.$

2. $2z = 2ax + (a^2 + 1)y + b.$

3. $z = ax + (1 - a^{2/3})^{3/2}y + b.$

4. $z = 2x \cos a + 2y \sin a + b.$

5. $z = ax + \dfrac{2ay}{a + 1} + b.$

6. $z = a_1 + a_2x_1 + a_3x_2 - (a_2 + a_3)x_3.$

7. $z = ax_1 + bx_2 + \sqrt{1 - a^2 - b^2}\, x_3 + c.$

8. $z = ax_1 + bx_2 + \dfrac{ab}{a - b}\, x_3 + c.$

9. $4(z + a^2)^3 - 4b(z + a^2)^{3/2} + b^2 - 90x^2 - 180axy - 90a^2y^2 = 0.$

10. $2(x + ay) = \log\left(\dfrac{-1 \pm \sqrt{1 + 4az^2}}{2a}\right) + \dfrac{4az^2}{-1 \pm \sqrt{1 + 4az^2}} + b.$

11. Each of the following is a solution:

    i. $a \sqrt{a^2 - 4 + 4z} + a^2 \log(-a + \sqrt{a^2 - 4 + 4z}) - x$
$$- ay - b = 0;$$

    ii. $a \sqrt{a^2 - 4 + 4z} + a^2 \log(-a + \sqrt{a^2 - 4 + 4z}) - x$
$$+ ay - b = 0;$$

    iii. $z = b.$

12. $5x^2 + 10axy + 5a^2y^2 + 10bx + 10aby + 5b^2 - 4(1 + a^2)z = 0,$
$z = 0.$

13. $2 \sqrt{1 - z} + \log\left(\dfrac{\sqrt{1 - z} - 1}{\sqrt{1 - z} + 1}\right) \pm \dfrac{x + ay}{\sqrt{a}} = b.$

14. $(z - b)(z - ax - a^2y - b)(z^2 - 6x - 6ay - b) = 0.$

15. $z = b(xy^a)^{\frac{-1 \pm \sqrt{1 + 4a^2}}{2a^2}}$

16. $(z - b)(\log z - x - ay - b)(a^2 \log z + x + ay + b) = 0.$

17. $ab^4z^2 - 2a^3b^2z + (a^5 - ab^2) \log(b^2z^2 + a^2z + 1)$
$$+ \dfrac{3a^3b^2 - a^7}{\sqrt{a^4 - 4b^2}} \log \dfrac{2b^2z + a^2 - \sqrt{a^4 - 4b^2}}{2b^2z + a^2 + \sqrt{a^4 - 4b^2}}$$
$$- bx_1 - abx_2 - b^2x_3 = c.$$

18. $\pm \sqrt{1 + 4az} + \log(-1 \pm \sqrt{1 + 4az}) - x - ay - b = 0,$
$z = 0.$

19. $z = be^{\pm a(x + ay)}.$

20. $z = be^{\pm 2a(x + a^2y)}.$

21. $ax + y + b = \displaystyle\int \dfrac{(1 - a^2)\, dz}{z \pm \sqrt{a^2z^2 + 1 - a^2}},$
$z = 1.$

22. $3z = x^3 + y^3 + ax + ay + b.$

23. $4z = 3(a + x)^{4/3} + 4ay + b.$

24. $z = \pm \dfrac{2\sqrt{a}}{3}\, x^{3/2} + \dfrac{y^2}{2} + ay + b,$
$z = 0.$

25. $z = \dfrac{ax^2}{2} + \dfrac{y^2}{2a^2} + b.$

26. $z = -a \cos x - \cos y + \dfrac{y}{a} + b.$

28. $z = ax + by + 2a + 3b^2,$
$$z = -\frac{y^2}{12}.$$

29. $z = ax + by + a^2 + b^2 + 1,$
$$z = -\frac{x^2}{4} - \frac{y^2}{4} + 1.$$

30. $z = ax + by + 5a^3 - 2a - b.$

31. $(z - ax - by)^2 = ab.$

32. $z = ax_1 + bx_2 + cx_3 + abc.$

33. $z = a_1x_1 + a_2x_2 + a_3x_3 + a_4x_4 + a_1a_2 + a_3a_4.$
$z = -x_1x_2 - x_3x_4.$

34. $(x - a)^2 + (y - b)^2 - z^2 = 1.$

35. $\dfrac{x^2}{a^2} + \dfrac{y^2}{b^2} + \dfrac{z^2}{a^2b^2} = 1.$

36. $\dfrac{x}{a} + \dfrac{y}{b} + \dfrac{z}{1 - a - b} = 1.$

37. $(x - a)^2 - (y - b)^2 - z^2 = 1.$

38. $(x - a)^2 + \dfrac{(y - b)^2}{5} - z^2 = 0; z = 0.$

39. $z = ax + by + \log ab, z = -2 - \log xy.$

40. $x^2(y - a)^2 + \dfrac{3}{4} x^4 + xz = b.$

41. $z = ax + b + a^2y - b^2x.$

42. $z^2 = x^2 + ax + \dfrac{2}{3} (y + a)^{3/2} + b.$

43. $z^2 = a_1x_1 + a_2x_2 + (1 - a_1^2 - a_2^3)x_3 + a_3.$

44. $(1 - a_1a_2) \log z = (a_1 + a_2)(x_1 + a_1x_2 + a_2x_3 + a_3); z = 0.$

45. $z^2 = a_1e^{x_1} + a_2e^{x_2} + (a_1 + a_2)^2e^{x_3} + a_3.$

46. $e^z = a_1x_1^3 + a_2x_2^2 + a_3x_3.$

47. $z = \dfrac{\frac{3}{4} (x_1 + c_1x_2 + c_2x_3 + c_3x_4)^{4/3}}{(c_1c_2c_3)^{1/3}} + c_4; z = c.$

48. $z = \dfrac{7c_1^2c_2^2c_3^2}{8} \left(\dfrac{x_1 + c_1x_2 + c_2x_3 + c_3x_4}{c_1^2c_2^2c_3^2} \right)^{3/2} + c_4.$

Section 73, page 236

1. $z = F_1(y + 2x) + F_2(y + 5x).$

2. $z = F_1(y - x) + F_2(y + 3x).$

3. $z = F_1(y + x) + F_2(y + 2x) + F_3(y + 3x).$

4. $z = F_1(y - x) + F_2(y + x) + F_3(y - 2x).$

5. $z = F_1(y + x) + F_2(y - x) + F_3(y + 2x) + F_4(y - 2x).$

6. $z = F_1(y) + F_2(y - x) + F_3(y - 3x) + F_4(y + 2x).$

7. $z = F_1(y + x + x\sqrt{3}) + F_2(y + x - x\sqrt{3}).$

8. $z = F_1(y - 2x + x\sqrt{10}) + F_2(y - 2x - x\sqrt{10}).$

9. $z = F_1(y + 3x) + F_2(y - 2x + x\sqrt{2}) + F_3(y - 2x - x\sqrt{2}).$

10. $z = F_1(y - 2x) + F_2(y + 3x + x\sqrt{2}) + F_3(y + 3x - x\sqrt{2}).$

11. $z = F_1(y + x + x\sqrt{5}) + F_2(y + x - x\sqrt{5})$
$\qquad + F_3(y - 2x + x\sqrt{2}) + F_4(y - 2x - x\sqrt{2}).$

12. $z = F_1(y - 3x + 2x\sqrt{2}) + F_2(y - 3x - 2x\sqrt{2})$
$\qquad + F_3(y + 3x + x\sqrt{14}) + F_4(y + 3x - x\sqrt{14}).$

13. $z = F_1(y - 2x) + xF_2(y - 2x).$

14. $z = F_1(2y + 3x) + xF_2(2y + 3x).$

15. $z = F_1(y - x) + xF_2(y - x) + x^2F_3(y - x).$

16. $z = F_1(2y + x) + xF_2(2y + x) + x^2F_3(2y + x).$

17. $z = F_1(y + 3x) + F_2(2y - x) + F_3(y + 2x) + xF_4(y + 2x).$

18. $z = F_1(2y + x) + xF_2(2y + x) + F_3(2y + 3x) + xF_4(2y + 3x).$

19. $z = \sum_i \{c_i e^{(y+x)g_i} \cos(g_ix) + d_i e^{(y+x)h_i} \sin(h_ix)\}.$

20. $z = \sum_i \{c_i e^{(3y+x)g_i} \cos(2g_ix) + d_i e^{(3y+x)h_i} \sin(2h_ix)\}.$

21. $z = F_1(3y + x) + \sum_i \{c_i e^{(y-2x)g_i} \cos(2g_ix) + d_i e^{(y-2x)h_i} \sin(2h_ix)\}.$

22. $z = F_1(2y + x) + \sum_i \{c_i e^{(y-x)g_i} \cos(3g_ix) + d_i e^{(y-x)h_i} \sin(3h_ix)\}.$

23. $z = \sum_i \{(a_i + b_ix)e^{(y-x)g_i} \cos(g_ix) + (c_i + d_ix)e^{(y-x)h_i} \sin(h_ix)\}.$

24. $z = \sum_i \{(a_i + b_ix)e^{(2y+3x)g_i} \cos(g_ix) + (c_i + d_ix)e^{(2y+3x)h_i} \sin(h_ix)\}.$

Section 75, page 238

1. $z = F_1(y + 2x) + F_2(y + 5x) + \dfrac{231}{20}\, x^5 + \dfrac{43}{4}\, x^4 y + \dfrac{7}{2}\, x^3 y^2 + \dfrac{1}{2}\, x^2 y^3.$

2. $z = F_1(y + x + x\sqrt{3}) + F_2(y + x - x\sqrt{3})$
$$+ \dfrac{11x^9}{630} + \dfrac{2x^8 y}{35} + \dfrac{3x^7 y^2}{35} + \dfrac{x^6 y^3}{15} + \dfrac{x^5 y^4}{20}.$$

3. $z = F_1(y + 3x) + F_2(y - 2x + x\sqrt{2}) + F_3(y - 2x - x\sqrt{2})$
$$+ \dfrac{x^4}{24} - \dfrac{y^5}{360}.$$

4. $z = F_1(y - 2x + x\sqrt{2}) + F_2(y - 2x - x\sqrt{2})$
$$+ F_3(y + x + x\sqrt{5}) + F_4(y + x - x\sqrt{5}) + \dfrac{x^8}{720}$$
$$- \dfrac{x^7 y}{630} + \dfrac{x^6 y^2}{360} + \dfrac{x^6}{360}.$$

5. $z = F_1(y + 3x) + F_2(y - x) + \dfrac{20}{3}\cos{(y + 2x)}.$

6. $z = F_1(y) + F_2(y - x) + F_3(y - 3x) + F_4(y + 2x)$
$$- \dfrac{1}{27}\cos{(2y + 3x)} + \dfrac{1}{135}\sin{(2y + 3x)}.$$

7. $z = F_1(2y + 3x) + xF_2(2y + 3x) - \cos{(x + y)} - \dfrac{1}{49}\cos{(2x - y)}.$

8. $z = F_1(y + 2x) + F_2(y + 3x) - x\sin{(y + 2x)}.$

9. $z = F_1(y + 2x) + xF_2(y + 2x) + \dfrac{x^2}{2}\cos{(y + 2x)}.$

10. $z = F_1(y + 3x) + F_2(y + 2x) + x\cos{(y + 2x)}.$

11. $z = F_1(y + 2x) + F_2(y + 3x) + 3x\cos{(y + 2x)} + x\sin{(y + 3x)}.$

12. $z = F_1(y - 2x) + xF_2(y - 2x) + x^2 F_3(y - 2x) - \sin x$
$$+ \dfrac{x^3}{6}\sin{(y - 2x)}.$$

13. $z = F_1(y - 2x) + xF_2(y - 2x) + \dfrac{5}{64}\, e^{2x + 3y}.$

14. $z = F_1(2y + x + x\sqrt{33}) + F_2(2y + x - x\sqrt{33})$
$$+ F_3(y + 3x) + \dfrac{1}{24}\, e^{3x - y}.$$

15. $z = F_1(y + 2x) + F_2(y + 5x) - \dfrac{1}{3}\, xe^{y + 2x}.$

16. $z = F_1(y - 2x) + xF_2(y - 2x) + x^2 F_3(y - 2x) + \dfrac{1}{6}\, x^3 e^{y - 2x}.$

17. $z = F_1(y + 2x) + F_2(y + x) + xF_3(y + x) - \dfrac{1}{2}\, x^2 e^{y+x}$

$$+ xe^{y+2x} + \frac{1}{4}\, e^{y+3x}.$$

Section 78, page 244

1. (a) $z = F_1(y + 2x) + F_2(y + 5x) + \dfrac{1}{2x}.$

(b) $z = F_1(y + x) + xF_2(y + x) + \dfrac{1}{4}\,(1 + x)e^{3x+5y}.$

(c) $z = F_1(y + x) + F_2(y - x) + F_3(y - 2x) - \dfrac{8}{525}\,(3x - 2y)^{\frac{7}{2}}.$

(d) $z = F_1(y - x) + xF_2(y - x) + x^2 F_3(y - x) + \dfrac{y^3}{6}\,\phi(y - x).$

(e) $z = F_1(2y + x) + xF_2(2y + x) + x^2 F_3(2y + x)$
$$+ \frac{x^3}{48}\,f(2y + x) + \frac{3x^7}{13440} + \frac{x^6 y}{960}.$$

(f) $z = F_1(y - 3x + 2x\,\sqrt{2}) + F_2(y - 3x - 2x\,\sqrt{2})$
$+ F_3(y + 3x + x\,\sqrt{14}) + F_4(y + 3x - x\,\sqrt{14})$
$$- \frac{1}{176}\,x\cos\,(y - 3x) - \frac{3}{968}\,\sin\,(y - 3x).$$

(g) $z = F_1(y + 3x) + F_2(y - 2x) + \dfrac{2x^4}{3} + \dfrac{x^3 y}{3} + \dfrac{x^2 y^2}{2}.$

(h) $z = F_1(y + x) + F_2(y + 2x) + F_3(y + 3x)$
$$- \frac{x\sin\,(y + x)}{2} + x\cos\,(y + 2x) + \frac{xe^{y+3x}}{2}.$$

(i) $z = F_1(y + x) + F_2(y - x) + F_3(y - 2x) +$
$\dfrac{x^2}{20}\cos\,(2x - 3y) + \dfrac{21x}{200}\sin\,(2x - 3y) - \dfrac{441}{4000}\cos\,(2x - 3y)$

$$+ \frac{3x}{80}\,(x + y)^{\frac{5}{3}}.$$

(j) $z = F_1(y - 2x + x\,\sqrt{10}) + F_2(y - 2x - x\,\sqrt{10})$
$$- (x - 5y + 46)e^{x+y}.$$

(k) $z = F_1(y + x) + F_2(y - x) + F_3(y + 2x) + F_4(y - 2x)$
$$- \frac{x^7}{360} + \frac{x^5 y^2}{120} - (x^2 - y^2 - 8x + 10)e^x$$

(l) $z = \displaystyle\sum_i \{c_i e^{(3y+x)g_i}\cos\,(2g_i x) + d_i e^{(3y+x)h_i}\sin\,(2h_i x)\} + e^x\cos y.$

3. (a) $z = -\dfrac{16}{17955}\,(2x + y)^{\frac{5}{2}}.$

(b) $z = \dfrac{1}{6283}\cdot\dfrac{3!}{9!}\,(4x + 3y)^9 + \dfrac{1}{4}\,e^{x-y}.$

(c) $z = -\dfrac{1}{8} \sin 2x + \dfrac{1}{7} \cos (x - y)$.

5. (a) $z = \dfrac{x^4}{4!} (3x + y)e^{3x+y}$

(b) $z = \dfrac{x^3}{3!} \cosh (y - x)$.

(c) $z = \dfrac{x^2}{2!} \sqrt{y - 2x}$.

7. $z = \Phi_1(x_3 - b_1x_1, x_2 - a_1x_1) + \Phi_2(x_3 - b_2x_1, x_2 - a_2x_1)$.

8. $z = \Phi_1(x_3 - 3x_1, x_2 + 2x_1) + \Phi_2(x_3 + 2x_1, x_2 - x_1) - \dfrac{1}{12} e^{3x_1+x_2-x_3}$.

9. $z = \Phi_1(x_3 - x_1, x_2 + x_1) + \Phi_2(x_3 - 2x_1, x_2 - 2x_1)$

$$- \sin x_1 - \frac{x_1}{2} \sin (x_2 - x_3).$$

Section 81, page 248

1. $z = f_1(x) + e^{3x}f_2(y - 2x) + e^x f_3(y - x)$.

2. $z = f_1(x) + e^{3x}f_2(y - 2x) + e^x f_3(y - x)$

$$+ \frac{x^2 y}{3} - \frac{xy^2}{3} - \frac{4y^2}{9} - \frac{2xy}{9} - \frac{4y}{3}.$$

3. $z = f_1(y) + xf_2(y) + e^{-5x}f_3(y + 4x)$.

4. $z = f_1(y) + xf_2(y) + e^{-5x}f_3(y + 4x) + e^{2x+y}\left(\dfrac{x}{12} - \dfrac{y}{12} - \dfrac{2}{9}\right)$.

5. $z = e^x f_1(y - 2x) + f_2(x) + f_3(y) + xf_4(y)$.

6. $z = e^x f_1(y - 2x) + f_2(x) + f_3(y) + xf_4(y)$

$$+ \frac{13 \sin (x - 7y) + \cos (x - 7y)}{1190}.$$

7. $z = e^{-x}f_1(y - x) + e^{-2x}f_2(y - x) + f_3(y - x)$.

8. $z = e^{-x}f_1(y - x) + e^{-2x}f_2(y - x) + f_3(y - x) + \dfrac{e^{5x-y} \sinh (x - y)}{120}$.

9. $z = f_1(y - 2x) + e^{-x}f_2(y + 2x)$.

10. $z = f_1(y - 2x) + e^{-x}f_2(y + 2x) + \dfrac{y^4}{8} - x^2 + 6y^2 + 25y$

$$+ y^3 + \frac{x^3}{3} - \frac{1}{70} e^{x-4y}.$$

11. $z = e^x f_1(y - 2x) + e^{3x}f_2(y + x) + e^{5x}f_3(y - x)$.

12. $z = e^x f_1(y - 2x) + e^{3x}f_2(y + x) + e^{5x}f_3(y - x)$

$$- \frac{1}{9240} [31 \cosh (x + 5y + 6) + 101 \sinh (x + 5y + 6)].$$

13. $z = e^{-x}f_1(y) + e^x f_2(y - x).$

14. $z = e^{-x}f_1(y) + e^x f_2(y - x) + \frac{1}{4} e^{3x-y+1}.$

Section 83, page 250

1. (a) $z = \frac{1}{19} e^{2x-y} + \sum_i c_i e^{a_i x + b_i y}$ where $a_i^3 - 2a_i b_i$
$$+ b_i^2 - a_i + 8 = 0.$$

(b) $z = \frac{1}{5} \sin (x - y) - \frac{2}{5} \cos (x - y) + \frac{3}{34} \sin (x - 2y) +$

$\frac{5}{34} \cos (x - 2y) + \sum_i c_i e^{a_i x + b_i y}$ where $a_i^2 + a_i b_i - b_i^2 + a_i - b_i = 0.$

(c) $z = \frac{1}{4155} e^{4x-5y+6}\{37 \cos (x + 2y) - 4 \sin (x + 2y)\}$
$$+ \sum_i c_i e^{a_i x + b_i y}$$ where $a_i^3 + 3b_i^2 + a_i - 8 = 0.$

(d) $z = \frac{1}{625} (125y^3 + 125x^2 + 225y^2 + 270y + 112)$
$$+ \sum_i c_i e^{a_i x + b_i y}$$ where $a_i^2 + 2a_i b_i^2 - 3b_i + 5 = 0.$

(e) $z = \frac{1}{32} \{\sinh (3x - y) + \cosh (3x - y)\}$
$$+ \sum_i c_i e^{a_i x + b_i y}$$ where $a_i^3 + 3b_i^3 + a_i - 5b_i = 0.$

(f) $z = \frac{e^{2x}}{2401} \{343x^2 - 1029xy^2 + 294xy + 735y^2 - 532x - 126y$
$$+ 258\} + \sum_i c_i e^{a_i x + b_i y}$$ where $a_i^2 + a_i b_i + a_i - b_i + 1 = 0.$

(g) $z = \frac{1}{6} e^{3x-2y} + \sum_i c_i e^{a_i x + b_i y}$ where $a_i^3 + 3b_i^3 + 3 = 0.$

(h) $z = -\frac{1}{10} \sin (3x + 2y) + \sum_i c_i e^{a_i x + b_i y}$ where $a_i^2 + a_i b_i + b_i^2$
$$+ 2a_i - 3b_i + 9 = 0.$$

(i) $z = -\frac{7x}{6} + \frac{5y}{4} + \sum_i c_i x^{a_i} y^{b_i}$ where $a_i^2 - 2a_i b_i - b_i^2 - 2a_i$
$$+ 2b_i - 5 = 0.$$

Section 84, page 254

3. (a) 0.449, (b) 0.123.

4. (a) $\rho^2 v_{\rho\rho} + v_{\varphi\varphi} + \csc^2 \varphi v_{\theta\theta} + 2\rho v_\rho + \cot \varphi v_\varphi = 0.$

5. (b) $v = \dfrac{240}{\pi}\left(\sin\dfrac{\pi x}{30}\cdot e^{-\frac{\pi y}{30}} - \dfrac{1}{2}\sin\dfrac{2\pi x}{30}\cdot e^{-\frac{2\pi y}{30}} + \dfrac{1}{3}\sin\dfrac{3\pi x}{30}\cdot e^{-\frac{3\pi y}{30}}\right.$

$$\left. - \cdots\right).$$

6. $v = \dfrac{8}{\pi}\left(r\sin\theta + \dfrac{r^3\sin 3\theta}{3\cdot 5^2} + \dfrac{r^5\sin 5\theta}{5\cdot 5^4} + \cdots\right).$

7. $\pi/4$.

Section 89, page 274

1. $z = f_1(y + ax) + f_2(y - ax)$.

2. $y = f_1(z) + f_2(x)$.

3. $z = xf_1(y - x) + f_2(y - x)$.

4. $z = (x + y)\log y + f_1(x) + f_2(x + y)$.

5. $z = f(x + \cos y) + g(x - \cos y)$.

6. $p\operatorname{sech} x + q\operatorname{sech} y = f_1(\sinh x + \sinh y)$

or

$p\operatorname{sech} x - q\operatorname{sech} y = f_2(\sinh x - \sinh y)$,

$\therefore z = F_1(\sinh x + \sinh y) + F_2(\sinh x - \sinh y)$.

7. $z = xf_1\left(\dfrac{y}{x}\right) + f_2\left(\dfrac{y}{x}\right)$.

8. $z = e^{\frac{2y}{x+y}}\left[f_1(x + y) + \dfrac{1}{x + y}\displaystyle\int e^{\frac{-2y}{a}} f_2(2y - a)\, dy\right]$

with a replaced by $x + y$ after the integration.

9. $y + xf_1(x + 2y + 3z) + f_2(x + 2y + 3z) = 0$.

10. $\dfrac{2p - q}{x - 2y} = f(xy)$ or $\dfrac{px - qy}{x - 2y} = f(x + 2y)$,

$\therefore z = f_1(x + 2y) + f_2(xy)$.

11. $p - 4x - 3y = f(q - 3x - 3y)$, whence

$$z = 2x^2 + 3xy - ax - by + \dfrac{3}{2}y^2 + c$$

or

$$z = 2x^2 + 3xy + nx + \dfrac{3}{2}y^2 + \phi(y + mx).$$

12. $4p + y - 5x = f(4q + x - 5y)$, whence

$$8z = 5x^2 - 2xy + 5y^2 + 2ax + 2by + c$$

or

$$8z = 5x^2 - 2xy + 5y^2 + 2nx + \phi(y + mx).$$

13. $2p - 3x + 4y = f(2q - x + 4y)$, whence
$$4z = 3x^2 - 8xy - 4y^2 + ax + by + c$$
or
$$4z = 3x^2 - 8xy - 4y^2 + nx - 5mx^2 + \phi(y + mx);$$
$2p - 3x - y = f(q + 2x + 2y)$, whence
$$4z = 3x^2 + 2xy - 4y^2 + ax + by + c$$
or
$$4z = 3x^2 + 2xy - 4y^2 + nx + 5mx^2 + \phi(y + mx).$$

14. $2p + x - y = f(3q - x + y)$, whence
$$12z = -3x^2 + 6xy - 2y^2 + ax + by + c$$
or
$$12z = -3x^2 + 6xy - 2y^2 + ax + mx^2 + \phi(y + mx);$$
$6p + 3x - 2y = f(6q - 3x + 2y)$, whence
$$12z = -3x^2 + 4xy - 2y^2 + ax + by + c$$
or
$$12z = -3x^2 + 4xy - 2y^2 + ax - mx^2 + \phi(y + mx).$$

15. $px + y = f(qy + x)$, whence
$$z = n \log x + mx + \frac{y}{m} + \phi(x^m y).$$

16. $px^2 + q = f(qy^2 + p)$, whence
$$z = \frac{n}{2m} \log \frac{x - m}{x + m} + \phi\left(\frac{(x - m)(1 - my)}{(x + m)(1 + my)}\right).$$

17. $px^2 + qy = f(qy^2 + px)$, whence
$$z = n \log \frac{my}{my - 1} + \phi\left(\frac{(x - m)(my - 1)^m}{xy^m}\right).$$

Section 90, page 279

1. $z = \dfrac{x}{3} + \dfrac{y}{3} - \dfrac{1}{6} + e^{-3(x+2y)} f_1(x + y) + e^{-2(x+y)} f_2(x + 2y).$

2. $15(2y - x)^2(2x - 3y)z = 5(2y - x)^3(2x - 3y)^4$
$$+ 3(2y - x)^5(2x - 3y)^2 + f_1(2y - x) + f_2(2x - 3y).$$

3. $z = -\dfrac{1}{4}\left(x - \dfrac{1}{y}\right) - \dfrac{1}{8} + e^{2\left(x - \frac{1}{y}\right)} f_1(y) + e^{-\frac{2}{y}} f_2\left(x - \dfrac{1}{y}\right).$

4. $z = f_1(y - \sinh x) + f_2(y + \sinh x).$

5. $z = f_1(x - y) + f_2(xy).$

6. $z = xy + f_1(x^2 + y^2) + f_2\left(\dfrac{y}{x}\right).$

7. $z = e^{2(x-2y)} f_1(x - y) + e^{3(x-2y)} f_2(x - y) + 1.$

8. $z = 2(x + y)^2 + e^{-10xy-5y^2}f(x + y) + e^{-2xy-y^2}g(x + y).$

9. $z = 2x - 10y - y^{-5}f_1(x - 5y) + y^{-1}f_2(x - 5y).$

10. $z = \dfrac{y^3}{6} + \dfrac{y^2\phi(x + y)}{2} + yf_1(x + y) + f_2(x + y).$

11. $z = y^3f_1\left(\dfrac{x}{y}\right) + y^{-3}f_2\left(\dfrac{x}{y}\right) - \dfrac{1}{9}\log\dfrac{x}{y}.$

12. $z = (4 + y)f_1\left(\dfrac{x + y}{x}\right) + (4 + y)^2f_2\left(\dfrac{x + y}{x}\right)$
$$+ (4 + y)^3\left(\dfrac{x + y}{x}\right).$$

Index

A

Adjoint equation, 99
Approximation, numerical, 124ff.
Arbitrary constants, 7, 14, 70, 105
Arbitrary functions, 211

B

Bernoulli, 38
Bernoulli's equation, 38
Bessel, 166
Bessel's equation, 166
Bessel's function, 167

C

Capacity, 45
Catenary, 49
Cauchy, 94
Cauchy's linear equation, 94
Characteristic equation, 70, 107
Characteristics, 199, 222
Charpit's method, 219
Clairaut, 63
Clairaut's equation, 63
Complementary function, 80
Complete solution, 11
Complex roots, 75
Conditions:
  for exactness, 23, 97, 181
  for functional dependence, 197
  for integrability, 10, 19, 183, 187
  for linear dependence, 73
Constants, arbitrary, 7, 14, 70, 105
Cross ratio, 42
Curvature, radius of, 16
Curve, integral, 3

D

Damped, harmonic motion, 77
Degree, 1
Dependence:
  functional, 197
  linear, 72
Determinants:
  functional, 55, 197

Determinants (*cont.*):
  Wronskian, 73
Determinate system, 198

E

Elementary functions, 40
Euler, 32
Euler equation, 94
Euler's theorem on homogeneous
  functions, 33
Exact equations, 23, 96
Exactness, conditions for, 23, 97
Exactness, generalized, 202
Existence theorems, 10, 19

F

Factor, integrating, 26, 99
Factorization of operators, 86
Fractions, partial, method by, 241
Functional dependence, 197
Functional determinant, 55
Functions:
  arbitrary, 211
  Bessel's, 167
  complementary, 80
  elementary, 40
  homogeneous, 31
  orthogonal, 162

G

Gauss, 173
Gauss equation, 173
General solution, 10, 212, 222, 233
Generalized exactness, 202

H

Homogeneous equation, 30, 185
Homogeneous function, 31, 185
  Euler's theorem on, 33
Homogeneous linear equation, 69
Hypergeometric series, 174, 175

I

Impedance, 48
Independence, linear, 72

Indeterminate system, 206
Indicial equation, 148
Inductance, 45
Infinite series, solution by, 16, 124, 143
Infinite solution, 66
Inspection, integrating factor by, 27
Integrability, conditions for, 10, 19, 183, 187
Integral:
  curve, 3
  intermediate, 259, 260
  particular, 11, 80, 156
Integrating factor, 26, 99
Inverse operators, 87

J

Jacobi, 197
Jacobian, 55, 197
Jacobi's method, 225
Jacobi's multipliers, 201, 206

L

Lagrange, 90, 200
Lagrange's method, variation of parameters, 90
Lagrange's system, 213, 218
Laplace, 251
Laplace's equation, 251
Laplace's transformation, 275
Legendre, 160
Legendre polynomial, 161
Legendre's equation, 159
Legendre's transformation, 67
Lineal element, 3
Linear dependence, 72
Linear differential equation, 36, 69, 147, 212
Linear independence, 72

M

Matrix, rank of, 198
Method:
  by partial fractions, 241
  Charpit's, 219
  Jacobi's, 225
  Lagrange's variation of parameters, 90
  Milne's, 129
  Monge's, 261, 266
  Picard's, 125
Milne, 129
Monge, 261, 266
Monge's method, 261, 266

Multiple roots, 77
Multipliers, Jacobi's, 201, 206

N

Non-integrable equations, 195
Number of arbitrary constants, 7, 14, 70, 105

O

Operators, 86
  factorization of, 86
  inverse, 87
Order:
  of differential equation, 1, 14
  reduction of, 74, 111, 153, 155
Ordinary differential equation, 2
Orthogonal functions, 162
Orthogonal trajectories, 44

P

Parameters, variation of, 90
Partial differential equation, 2
Partial fractions, method by, 241
Particular integral, 11, 80, 156, 246
Particular solution, 11, 212, 218
Picard, 125
Picard's method, 125
Polynomial, of Legendre, 161
Primitive, of a differential equation, 6

Q

Quotient:
  of two integrating factors, 56
  of two Jacobi multipliers, 208

R

Radius of curvature, 16
Rank of matrix, 198
Ratio, cross, 42
Recurrence relation, 148
Reduction of order, 74, 111, 153, 155
Resistance, 45
Riccati equation, 40, 113, 114
Roots:
  case of complex, 75, 233
  case of multiple, 77, 234

S

Separation of variables, 21
Series:
  hypergeometric, 174, 175
  infinite, solution by, 16, 124, 143ff.
  Taylor's, 16, 124

Simple harmonic motion, 76
Simultaneous equations, system of, 101, 187
Singular solution, 12, 57, 221
Solutions:
  complete, 11, 212
  definition of, 5, 259
  general, 10, 212, 222, 233
  infinite, 66
  in series, 16, 124, 143ff.
  particular, 11, 212, 218
  singular, 12, 57, 221
Steady state, 48, 120
Systems:
  determinate, 198
  indeterminate, 206
  of simultaneous equations, 101, 187

T

Taylor's series, 16, 124
Total differential equation, 180
Trajectory, orthogonal, 44
Transformation:
  of Laplace, 275
  of Legendre, 67
Transient terms, 48, 120

V

Variables separable, 21
Variation of parameters, 90

W

Wronskian, 73